A FOOT IN FRONT

Chad

Phototype set, Made and printed in Great Britain by
N.T.A. Printers Limited, Hyde, Cheshire.

ISBN   0   9511048   0   2

Published by The Old Rectory Hotel and Diner's Club
(Denton) Ltd.

Foreword

Fifty years or so ago, it was only the fortunate members of the upper classes who used restaurants and ate out regularly.

A number of us ate in restaurants only once or twice a year and then only when impelled by the need to celebrate some special occasion, a birthday or perhaps an anniversary or some other high day or holiday.

The majority, many of whom ate little enough in their own homes, never ate outside their own homes at all except for a boiled ham and plates of 'fancy' cakes do at the Co-op to mark the occasion of the hatched, matched or dispatched.

Today's is a different scene.

It is the majority now who eat out several times a year, if not even weekly, not to celebrate some major event but just because they enjoy the experience and can afford it. And in the hotel and catering business, more than two hundred and fifty thousand people are occupied in seeing to the needs of that majority.

Eating out is a big business sector.

Eating out is a big social experience.

The following pages are one restaurateur's light hearted look at both the bright and the darker side of that experience.

******

There were four of us having a Sunday lunchtime drink together in my house. Ken has a restaurant only, but it is a good one and is given honourable mention in the Good Food Guide. John has a hotel but caters only for his residents mostly on a bed breakfast and dinner basis. Brian and myself both have a hotel and restaurant open to the public.

"I don't have your daily experience with the public at large," John said. "My trade is largely seasonal and most of my people have been coming to us for years. Mine is essentially the role of the 'how-nice-to-see-you-again-it's-been-a-year-now-hasn't-it?' host. I've got to make them feel that although they're paying for it, they are coming to spend a week or a fortnight as guests in the house of old friends."

"It's rather like that at my place," Ken said, "except that they are not staying with me, just having dinner. Still, as you say, they must feel that they're dining out with friends."

"I go along with all that," Brian put in, "the only difference being that Chad and I have to deal with the general public, even the casual passer-by."

"Anyone at all," I added, "anyone who wants a drink, some nosh and or a bed for the night."

There was a long, reflective pause whilst we sipped at our drinks. Ken spoke first.

"I hate the bastards," he said, bitterly.

"Don't we all," Brian said.

"Can't stand them," John said. "Especially the regulars."

"Take you over, the regulars do," I said. "Insufferable."

"Hate the bastards," Ken said again, morosely.

*****

Now from my experience, whenever hoteliers and restaurateurs get together, that just about sums up how they feel. We know a lot of our customers are well mannered, courteous and above all, appreciative of the food, drink and services that they have come out to enjoy and that we have supplied. Perversely, it is not of them we think. It is of the rest, who for reasons known only to their sorry selves, have come out, not to enjoy themselves, but to make everyone else thoroughly miserable.

that unholy throng, I hope that in future, you will have the decency to stay at home, preferably sitting in that cupboard under your stairs, and post your money in.

Whatever or however, anyone coming into the hotel and catering industry soon comes to realise is that the only thing wrong with the business is the behaviour of far too many of the customers. Not all of them, thank God, but enough to put you daily in fear of passing through the madhouse gates. In attempting to please these customers, strong men have been made bald and impotent and have either lost their power of speech altogether or have been driven to telling the customer that really what he wants is ....ing. Customers come in all shapes and sizes, of varied sex and from every income group. "When they are good, they are very, very good, but when they are bad, they are horrid," as the phrase goes.

There are arrogant men, accompanied by haughty womenfolk weighed down by jewellery, furs and fat. These women do not recognise the existence of the restaurant staff. They will neither look nor speak directly to them but speak only to their menfolk who will, in turn, address the staff in tones once used by particularly boorish squires to suitably submissive serfs but nowadays heard only when white South African police threaten the barefoot Bantu.

Then there is the aggressive customer blustering his way through yet one more interlude of 'aggro', his only enjoyment being in refusing all the reasonable requests and defying all the reasonable rules of the house. He suffers from the Hemingway complex of seeking at all times to prove what a hairy-chested, natural-born bastard he is.

Let any notice ask him not to park his car in a certain place and that is just the place where he'll park it, after having driven in through the opening marked 'No Entry — Exit Only'. Once having parked, he will wind down the car windows and start

5

to clear his car of the week's detritus. First he empties the ashtrays through the windows and then the cigarette and crisp packets, half-eaten Chinese take-aways and used and part-used condoms.

I watched a fellow doing all this one evening and was prepared to overlook the rest of it but not the selfish way he had parked. The bonnet of his car was stuck out across the access road making it difficult for others to get into the car park.

I stood outside my door and called across to him.

"You're a foot in front," I shouted. He went purple. "You're not so bloody clever yourself," he shouted back. Now what was all that about? Just sheer bad temper, I would say.

******

Some years ago, a plain brown envelope came through my letterbox and in it was a 'leaked' document more revealing than anything to come out of Whitehall. Titled 'A Plain Man's Guide to Users of Hotel and Restaurant Guides' and subtitled 'How to gain the upper hand by being an absolute pain in the arse', it made grim reading for all restaurateurs.

"On first entering a recommended restaurant, you must brandish your copy of the guide which lists it and thus make it clear from the outset that you are not there primarily to enjoy yourself but to check their guide entry and that they had all better watch their peas and stews. Under no circumstances should you book a table in advance. If you are to win the bout, you must destabilise the restaurateur as soon as possible and there is no better way of doing that than to turn up unannounced with a party of eight people, especially if the party includes two Vegans, a devout Muslim, the Chief Rabbi and at least one person on a salt and fat free diet. You can, however, reserve a table if (a) you have no intention whatsoever of turning up or (b) and this

6

is especially applicable to busy Saturday nights, you reserve a table for eight and turn up with three, or even better, book for three and turn up with eight. If you do reserve a table and actually go to the restaurant, see to it that you and your party arrive an hour earlier or an hour later than the time that you gave them and, as the mood takes you and according to how busy they are, explain that you are in a desperate hurry and must eat right away, or that you don't want to sit at a table before eleven p.m.

When the menus are handed to your party, you must all lay them down unread and carry on talking. When someone comes to take your order, ignore them and still carry on talking, they are bound to go away eventually. As soon as they do, call them back by snapping your fingers and say petulantly "We are waiting to order. If you don't mind." Ordering is an art in itself. The management will have put together a menu of say twelve starters and ten main courses. This will all be on one page. Read through it registering slow but definite disbelief then turn it over as if you can't believe that these paltry offerings are all that there is. There must be some more somewhere. Turn the page backwards and forwards a few times, then say to a companion, "Well, it seems this is it. We'd better try to find something here that we can eat." You now have the advantage and now is the time to start with the irritating questions such as, "Which vegetables are in the vegetable soup?" or "Are the Mushrooms a la Greque, cultivated or field mushrooms?"

It is likely that there will be a brief description of the composition of made-up dishes, especially if they have foreign names. Read the whole thing out aloud slowly, for instance, *"Fegato alla Venezianne.* Paper thin slices of calves liver marinaded in red wine with oreganum, lightly fried in butter and served with onions cooked in the wine marinade." Pause reflectively then ask the waiter "Tell me, just what is that?" Or having sonorously read aloud the description of *Boeuf a la*

7

Bourguignonne, "Cubed beefsteak cooked in a red wine sauce with diced bacon, button onions, button mushroms, mixed sweet herbs and a little garlic," give the waiter a let's-have-the-truth-old-boy look and say "Tell me. Would *I* like that?" or just simply "Is it nice?"

The patron chef was down at the fish market early that morning hand-picking the best of the turbot. Ask him what he recommends and, if he says "The turbot is superb, sir," say "It sounds as if you've got a lot of it left on your hands," or give him a knowing wink and say "Trying to get rid of the fish eh? No thanks old boy, I don't want to come out in purple spots." Whatever he recommends, under no circumstances accept his recommendation. Make sure you order something else and that way show him you won't stand for any bullying.

At this stage you should be given the wine list. Bring out your nasty, little plastic vintage chart and waffle on to your companions, using all the buzz words you picked up last week from the wine writers in the Sunday colour supplements. "Crisp with a pleasing finish. Well balanced. A fruity nose. A flowery nose. A bit empty. Thin. Short on grape. Plenty of acidity. Bottle tired." Don't let it bother you that what you are saying is a meaningless load of cock or that you always drink La Flora Blanche with everything. The wine waiter will be very impressed! *He* only drinks Guinness. In fact the only reason he's been made wine waiter is that he can't serve soup without spilling it and at least the wine is in a bottle.

When you are told that your table is ready say, "And about time too. We were just going to ask for a plate of sandwiches to keep us going." When you are escorted to your table, refuse to sit at it complaining that it is too near the wall, too near the centre of the room, too near the radiator, the window, the bar, the kitchens, that it is too brightly or too dimly lit, that it is the wrong shape and facing the wrong way. Keep saying to your companions "Of course, I blame the Guide for this. They're certainly going to hear from me. This chappie won't be in there next year. I'll see to that."

When you are finally seated to your satisfaction, lay the guide book conspicuously by your plate, get out the gold propelling pencil that Mumsie gave you for your twenty-first and start your report to the guide. Bear in mind that your asinine and puerile comments, no matter how ill informed or inaccurate, are much more likely to be published if they are malicious. You must say that the food is crap or damn it with faint praise like "Surprisingly, in a culinary desert like Lancashire (or whichever county you happen to be in) the mushroom soup was of the correct graphite colour even although, regrettably, it tasted of damp dish cloths." Slide in one or two snide remarks about the decor or, better still, about the proprietor and his wife. Publication in the guide is thus assured and you need have no fear of reprisal because your poison pen is wielded from the shadows of anonymity.

The wine waiter will now bring the wine to the table. Do the whole damn thing. Sniff the cork, trying not to let your nose drip on to it. Lift up the measure poured for your approval. Swirl it around the glass, not too sharply or it will come out at the top all over your wrist. Sniff the bouquet, again being very careful not to drip, even the merest falling drop of snot quite spoils the impression you are trying to create. Now take a little into your mouth, wobble it about, under and over the tongue. Blow heavily down your nose like a boxer coming out of his corner or coma, you see once again how important that dry nose is. By now your wine waiter will be at your mercy and you can let the wine down your throat. Another pause whilst you wait for the after-taste which, like the before-taste, should taste of wine. Then a brief comment such as "Adequate." "Acceptable." Never, even if you think it, describe the wine as "Like cat piss" or its bouquet "Like a scrum half's jock-strap." Both phrases, whilst often accurate, are thought to be indelicate.

******

The food you ordered earlier on should now have started arriving on the table. You will have seen to it that you have ordered only those starters you do not like and never eat. This is important to remember because you must now deny that you ordered two vegetable soups, one rillettes of pork and one smoked mackerel and insist that your actual order was for one pate maison, one avocado and two Ogen melon. The waiter will go back to the kitchen and accuse them of having given him the wrong order and a great deal of bad feeling will be caused.

Remember that it is not considered soigné to eat any food that tastes only of itself. The true gourmet always masks or confuses the taste of one thing by the addition of another. Now is the time to send the waiter back to the kitchens for wedges of lemon to drench the chicken liver pate, ground ginger to murder the melon and prawns to screw up the taste of the avocado. You will see to it that you are served with malt vinegar mint sauce with all lamb dishes, bitter sage and onion with turkey and pork, and H.P., Lee and Perrins or Soya sauce with everything else.

When the trout arrives, head on and white eyeball blindly staring, one of the women should faint and, coming round, should continue to whimper until the head of the trout has been removed. If half a pheasant is ordered, only the breast should be eaten, the rest being sent back as too tough or too rare with a demand that it must be kept off the bill.

There are six glasses of wine to the bottle. Having drunk the fourth glass, pour the fifth and drop into it a little cigarette ash or even a little fluff from your pocket. The wine can now be sent back as 'contaminated', and substituted with a full bottle at the expense of the restaurateur.

Smoke pipes and cigars at the end of your meal and cigarettes during it. Cigarettes should be extinguished in coffee cups or on the lemon souffle and cigars by treading them out on the carpet. Before you leave, tell the host that his food is quite tasty and very filling and then threaten him by saying he'll see you again. Don't however, try to gild the lily by telling him that you'll bring your friends as well. Even a clown like your host will know that you couldn't possibly have any.

"Smoke pipes and cigars at the end of your meal and cigarettes during it."

Finally, when leaving at 2.0am, an hour after everyone else, slam all your car doors, shout goodnights to your friends and drive off over the flower beds and out of the gates marked 'No Exit. Entrance Only' tooting merrily on your car horn.

******

That was it then, a diabolic document if ever there was one. The product of a fiendish mind or minds and obviously widely read and acted upon.

I will come back to the vexatious behaviour of customers in later pages and in depth but first I must tell you how my own personal tribulation began.

******

PART ONE
Nuts, crisps and acorns

I had been in cinema advertising for some years when commercial television started. At the time, there were two big companies competing with each other and more or less splitting the national cinema advertising cake between them. Theatre Publicity was the Rank Organisation and had its power base in the Odeon and Gaumont cinema circuits. My company, Pearl and Dean, had the rights of the A.B.C. cinema circuit plus a host of independents.

For the first year or so, commercial T.V. showed a loss running into millions and in cinema advertising we all fell about laughing, especially people like Bob Dean and the brothers Pearl who had had an opportunity to buy in on the ground floor and were now congratulating themselves on their perspicacity in staying out.

We were still laughing — but not for long — when things began to change. There was a tremendous spread in the number of television sets being bought and as more and more people stayed at home glued to the box, cinema admissions began to fall. This itself was serious enough because, just as a newspaper bases its advertising rates upon the number of copies it sells — its circulation figures — so did we in the cinema business base our rates on the number of bottoms on seats, the Board of Trade figures for cinema admissions.

Bad enough then that the value of our advertising was going steadily down week by week. Much worse, that the big spenders on advertising, Thomas Hedley, Unilevers, the tobacco companies, any major organisation producing short life, quick consumption goods, were now being advised by their advertising agents to come out of the cinemas and put their colourful, forceful advertising films right in the heart of the homes where their jars and packets were on the shelves.

Commercial T.V. had taken off and as people said — some most ruefully — had become a licence to print money.

I'd been in advertising for years, coasting happily along with a company car, a good salary and a 'smoked salmon' expense account. To be honest, I'd never really been dedicated as, deep down inside, I didn't give a monkey's whether Mrs Smith used Blobbo or Schmobbo to get rid of those down-under stains. Now, it seemed, it really did matter and especially to the cinema advertising heavy mob. If a cinema campaign could be shown to be successful, then we had a chance of staying in business. But first we had to secure the cinema advertising campaigns.

I was Manchester manager for Pearl and Dean and just when I was getting to be an old man approaching forty, it was all going wrong. "The client had decided to withdraw from the cinemas this year, old boy," some nattily-dressed, smooth-talking, agency git would say between downing the oysters Pearl and Dean were paying for, "but don't let it bother you. I'm sure we'll be back next year. You know, this really is a remarkably fine Chablis."

Don't let it bother you? *Merde alors.* I tried to even things up a bit with Head Office by cutting back on my expenses, not tipping the hall porter at the Midland, the maitre d' at the Adelphi, starting with the soup instead of the Strasbourg paté, toying with an omelette in place of the Tournedos Rossini, cutting out the cheese and one of the brandies with the coffee. To no avail.

The day came when, on one of my regular trips down to our Dover Street offices, I noticed that the sergeant commissionaire at number 33 had dropped the "Hello Mr Chadwick, down from the frozen North again," and the old "Jolly nice to see you,"

14

bit. The Sales Director found that he no longer wanted me to join him at his table in Brown's Hotel for a perceptive breakdown of our forward looking prospects in the North. Even the Chairman, who had always been happy to feed and water me as a bit of a comic, eventually dropped me from his Vendome luncheon list.

It became obvious that if my goose was not yet actually cooked, it had been in the oven for some time and was beginning to crisp up more than somewhat.

What to do? I was not the first middle-aged executive to ask that question as the clouds gathered and the workhouse gates yawned open just ahead.

A good question, what to do. And the obvious answer? Get yourself into the pub game lad, while there's yet time.

A pub, that was what to do! A pub, that time-honoured lifeboat that has carried so many otherwise shipwrecked and drowning executives to the sheltered, calm waters of a boozy harbour for life. A roof over your head, a fire in the grate, a cheering glass (at trade prices) to hand and someone to talk to. A pub it must be.

I had my secretary write twenty copies of the same letter to twenty different breweries. In the letter, I explained that I was a natural born tenant of a pub and that the brewery would be very foolish if it didn't at once find me a tenancy, to the immediate financial advantage of us both. The letter was couched in lucid, confident tones with just a touch of impertinence which I knew could not fail to appeal. I was wrong. Lucidity, confidence and touches of impertinence proved singularly unappealing.

Fifteen of the brewers were deaf to my seductive whispers and four put me on their tenancy waiting lists. Over twenty years later, I'm still waiting to hear from any one of those four that my name has moved up to the top.

Happily, however, one brewery, Robinson's of Stockport, responded and within a couple of weeks had offered me the tenancy of one of their small, country pubs.

I took it. With alacrity and a deep feeling of relief. Formalities concluded, one dull October day, the uprooted Challenor-Chadwicks, ma, pa and teenage son and daughter followed the removal van up to the rain-soaked Derbyshire hills and took over the pub. We had taken our seats in the lifeboat. It was now time to take up the oars and row for the distant, sunlit shore.

We paid four hundred and odd pounds to the outgoing tenant for fixtures, fittings, furniture and stock at valuation, which was a pitiful low figure and about twice what the ingoing was worth.

The fixtures were pretty loosely fixed and kept falling down or off. The fittings were very ill-fitting and often stuck out more than a bit. The furniture was mostly stuff that had been too damp to burn on the last November the 5th bonfire and still smelled of paraffin and smoke. There were some antiquated old-fashioned, iron-framed Britannia tables which I immediately threw out. Years later, the change in fickle public taste sent me out hunting to buy them back at forty pounds a time.

The glasses had been stoutly constructed by Britsh craftsmen and, if dropped on concrete, would bounce at least a foot high without breaking. The liquid stock consisted of one third of a bottle of Scotch, half a bottle of Gin, two thirds of a bottle of dark Rum, six bottles of something called Green Goddess and eight bottles, unbroached, of Cherry Flip. There was a cardboard shoe box full of tiny plastic umbrellas and other assorted clip-on drinking glass impedimenta — fish, gnomes, replica pineapples — for the more soigné customers who like their drinks to have a touch of theatre and far-flung places.

My children were less than delighted to have been uprooted from the residential, cosily integrated suburb in which they had been born. None-the-less, on take-over day, they set-to washing down shelves, cleaning years of nicotine goo off the now ochre but once cream-painted ceilings, beating dust out of and sponging down what little upholstery there was, changing the forty watt light bulbs for seventy-fives, polishing bottles and glasses and sweeping out little hidden clusters of dried orange peel, old bus tickets, empty crisp and cigarette packets and balls of sticky grey fluff.

When my pals had heard that I was taking a pub, they had all given me the same advice. "Don't be a big city slicker. Look after your locals. It's a country pub. Okay, in the summer you can rely on the carriage trade, but come the winter, and snow drifts eight feet high, it's the locals who will climb over, to dig their way into you. Look after your locals. And they'll look after you."

Well, that first night out, we did just that. We'd not only polished the whole place up, unblocked the gents lavatory and fixed the seat back on it and put real, unused toilet paper in there, we'd also put crisps and nuts and olives on the bar.

We had to damp the fire down pretty quickly because we hadn't realised the previous tenant had never lit a fire and had kept the down-draught out of his unwarmed bar by blocking the chimney with newspapers.

First the bar filled with dense smoke, four feet thick and then, at last, the paper burst into flames and created a fire storm and we lost one ashtray and a lot of beer mats up the chimney. Standing near the roaring updraught, I was glad I was no longer a stripling and was heavy enough to stay earthbound.

Although by then we'd been open for two hours, no one had come in. As it turned out, what had at first seemed to be a commercial disappointment was actually a temporary blessing in disguise.

An hour later, we had washed, dried and repolished everything and we were ready to cope with come what may. Or even whomever might come.

Outside our front door, we had repaired the light fitting and now a powerful light bulb shone invitingly down onto the wet but untrodden doorstep. How warm and inviting looked the two red table lamps we had put on the window sills, "Come in, come in, wherever you are" they cajoled and wheedled.

Flo and I stood in our bar. We smiled encouragement at each other and, every now and then we nodded. After a while the nodding seemed a bit daft and the smiles began to ache, but, at last, those warm and inviting lamps brought them in.

Nine-fifty pm, four of them. Four of them, together. All at once. The lamps did it. The red lamps. They thought we'd opened a knocking shop!

"Evening," I said, the very essence of the genial English host; pushing a tray of peanuts forward.

They stared at me with a degree of mixed, witless astonishment and absolute contempt.

Their spokesman — he had only one and a half ears and a I later learned that there were rats, or at least one rat, in his bedroom — cut through my bourgeois posturing.

"Four pints," he said, baldly, but to the point.

I thought to engage him on my side with a show of wit. "Four pints," I said, "Certainly. Pints of blood? Of Milk? Mild? Bitter?"

"Four pints of mild,"

I pulled his four pints, a real treat, not a drop spilled And a head on each that Einstein would have envied.

When I put his change on the bar, he slowly rocked from foot to foot as he thought it all out. Foot rocking helped his brain to keep moist and active in its container pan. Sort of stirred it up.

"Tha's fourpence leet," he said, knotting his skull with the effort of speech.

"Four pints at one and fivepence is five and eightpence. Change from the six bob you gave me is fourpence." I said. "There's your fourpence. Four separate big, round, brown pennies. Fourpence. Your change."

"We're locals. We pay one and four a pint, not one and five."

"One and four? One and four a pint? A pint of mild?"

"Tap room price. One and four." "But you're not in the tap room!" I said triumphantly.

"Nor would you be on a neet like this without a fire."

I took his point.

"Well alright then. It's one and four in there, without a fire and it's one and four in here, plus a penny for the fire," and pointing to the nuts and crisps and olives, I said, "and have those on me." The nuts and crisps I think they had seen before but the stuffed olives baffled them. "What's them?" one said, "Acorns?"

"What's them? Acorns?"

Look after your locals! "It's a country pub? Don't be a city slicker?"

Ten minutes with that fearsome foursome and on that very first night, I abandoned my plans for potato pie and red cabbage on those winter nights in the tap room when I was looking after my locals with fresh straw on the floor, a pigs' bristle dart-board on the wall, with in-house, true-flite darts, packs of playing cards, boxed dominoes, a pegging out board, Devil amongst the Tailors, clay Churchwarden pipes and a baccy-jar and brass spittoons, emptied each day. The locals?

Bollocks to the locals, I decided.

******

Sherry and Green Lime Juice

Many years ago, when I first went out on the road renting films for Columbia Pictures, my sales manager at the time was a large and bony Scot with something less than a romantic view of his fellow men.

"Always remember, laddie, that people are either bastards or berks. If they won't do what you say, they are bastards. If they will do what you say, then they are berks." I soon found out that all the cinema film-booking managers on the East Lancashire territory were bastards and I spent the next six years trying to make berks of them.

Now, history was repeating itself in the pub.

******

The locals and I had met each other and sized each other up. Neither side was happy with what they had encountered.

At the end of that first evening, I had burned half a bag of coal and my takings were under three pounds including cigarette sales. There was no ash in the ashtrays but plenty on the carpet. The cigarette butts were in the urinals. We'd had eleven in, all of them locals. None of them seemed partial to stuffed olives but the new tablets of soap had gone from the toilets as had the toilet rolls from the Ladies and two ash trays from the bar.

"Look after your locals. They're all you have in the winter." Well, my locals could look after themselves and if necessary we would winter abroad or, if we couldn't afford that, we could hibernate.

In that first dismal week, we realised that we must attract a new clientele or both go mad and skint as well.

A few new faces turned up in the bar, not all of them pretty, but at least they all had a whole ear on each side of their heads. They liked the log-fire that we now kept burning and they commented on the shine on the bottles and the glasses. We told them about the buckets of malodorous sludge we had scoured from the beer pipes and pumps and they said they could quite believe it, because the beer was now clear and without crut and the mild and the bitter now tasted like mild and bitter, whereas before, they had both tasted the same, like camel piss and not even fresh at that, but vintage, crusted camel piss.

We started to serve simple food, mainly on Friday and Saturday nights, well-filled chicken and beef muffins, oven bottom muffins bought locally.

On one occasion, I got carried away by something I'd read in one of the Sunday supplements and I rubbed the chicken with garlic before roasting it. One chap said the chicken tasted of salami and that it must have got 'contaminated' in the fridge. I turned in the haute cuisine and put the H.P. and tomato ketchup back on the bar.

I knew nothing about costings but, by keeping the food cash separately, it was easy to see that not only did food bring people in but also made a healthy profit. This was in the days, you must remember, when to ask a publican if he could find you something to eat was to invite a hurt and bewildered look and an offer of nuts, crisps or a packet of those dreadful, damp biscuits stuck together with cheese paste.

The pub was slowly taking on a new character. Softer, warmer lighting, new curtains and covers, pictures on the walls, the log fires, Flo's endless waxing and polishing and my own regular cleaning of the pumps, all were showing results. We still got fag-ends in the urinals but they were beginning to become a better-class of fag.

I had the G.P.O. move the public telephone box off my forecourt to a more central spot in the village. People no longer rang my bell out of opening hours to ask for pennies for the 'phone. I had the local bus company take its battered, enamelled-tin, time-tables off my walls and move the stop to the new telephone site. The locals no longer blocked my doorway while waiting for the bus down to the next pub.

To the locals, I was a first class bastard but if one has to be one or the other, then and now, I prefer to be a first class bastard rather than a first class berk. All the very opposite of received knowledge on how to run a country pub, but received knowledge is often a load of codswallop and our methods were working. We were now able to embellish the front with sunblinds, flower boxes at the windows, clematis and climbing nasturtiums on trellis. We built stone-walled flower beds and put out white tables, settle seats and bright umbrellas. The conservationists who would rather keep village pubs 'natural', 'honest', 'untouched', even when ugly, dull and squalid, will shudder at our cultural vandalism but at least the flowers weren't plastic and the local night air was scented with the smell of our burning applewood logs, as well as the local garden-privies. Gentle floodlighting and the place was, as pubs, hotels and restaurants should be, slightly larger than life, warmly theatrical and on the map.

******

I went on a licensed victualler's course and got an honours certificate. I learned two important things on that course, the first being that the average man, supping beer from the cradle to the grave, holding his glass up to the light and giving out learned discourse in the bar about Tetleys, Whitbreads, Youngers and so on, in actual fact, knows sweet f.a. about it. Until then,

I had been the average man but, not any more. Now, when some hop-head began to sound off in my bar, I would cock my thumb at my framed certificate and give him the works, Fuggles and Goldings, malted barley with particular reference to the acrospire, sweet wort, mash tuns, original gravity, the lot. You didn't need taped music in my bar, not with my fine, rotund, sonorous voice twittering on about bittering.

The second thing I learned was how to keep a perfect beer cellar. Fortunately Flo is a quick learner so I was able to pass on the technical details. Always ready to cosset her and see to her every need, I bought her a tool for scraping the old whitewash off the walls and a brush for putting new whitewash on. I gave her another brush, a wire one, so that she could keep the pipes and the brass beer taps burnished and she got so good at it that I was proud to take people around my beer cellar and show them what could be done if you had an honours certificate and knew about original gravity, sweet wort and all that. And what sort of brushes your wife needed to keep the beer cellar up to your very high standards.

******

The months went by and I steadily developed my prejudices.

I couldn't tolerate men who stood or sat in my bar with hats on their heads. "May I take your hat, sir, and hang it on one of them there 'at pegs?" "No I'm alright for the minute." "Well I'm not. You are a guest in my house and whilst you're here I'd like you to take your hat off." I used to get proper worked up I did! Very sniffy with it. "And you." I would shout as he pushed off to the George and Dragon up the road.

Couldn't stand their bloody dogs either, nose goosing the customers, shagging the varnish off the table legs, peeing in your boot and constantly farting. Dogs on Lassie are just about bearable but dogs on the other one, fart killer-farts, infinitely more dangerous than killer-bees, believe me.

I cured the table leg rapists. I just glued sandpaper to the legs instead of re-varnishing them. There's many a dog has whimpered his way out of the bar with both his legs and his eyes crossed.

On the subject of dogs, I once fell for the advertising slogan 'Dogs love Vims' and bought some for my Alsatian-Labrador cross, Robbie. It's a lie. Dogs don't love Vims. Or at least, Robbie didn't. As I fed them to him he would simulate eating them but somehow pouch them in his cheeks and then, when he thought I wasn't looking, he'd spit them out like grape seeds, behind the settee.

What, I reasoned, will make dogs love dog biscuits? What wonderful ingredient will make dogs salivate with anticipation? What do dogs find most attractive, most compelling. Eureka! Dogs can not resist some subtle, probably musk-like, odour that emanates from other dogs' private parts. Fired with enthusiasm and anxious to test out my theory, to isolate and identify and eventually to sythesise this magnetic odour, I lost no time in dropping onto all fours and stealthily moving up, nose a twitch, behind the nearest dog, a rather large Old English Sheepdog, I remember. I was not stealthy enough. Through its curtain of hair, it had observed me and, probably misunderstanding my approach and out of pique, it turned around and before I could escape, cocked its nearside leg against my head and pissed copiously in my ear. I never did find the answer but one day, wearing a frogman's wetsuit and ear plugs, I intend to take up my research again.

******

In those early days we were still getting people in who had the most revolting taste in drinks. Whether they thought it rather smart and way-out to mix drinks, who knows, but they would ask for Guinness and orange squash, rum and peppermint or rum and blackcurrant, and even, incredibly, sherry and lime.

I said to one such nutter, "Sherry, sir, certainly, sir. We have Amoroso, Oloroso, Fino, Amontillado and Manzanilla but I'm afraid that we only have Rose's Lime."

"Nowt wrong with Rose's Lime," he reassured me. "One of the best is Rose's."

I tried again. "As you feel like that about Rose's Lime — and I must say, I share your opinion of that renowned elixir — I beg you, sir, to look again at the situation and then perhaps reconsider the choice you have made. It is not widely known that Rose's is a local Derbyshire product. Deep in the limestone caverns there is an ancient race of stunted, troglodyte limestone miners, their faces as white, their skins as pitted as the limestone itself. Deep down in the bowels of the earth, far below the woods and sunlit fields above them, for hours on end, day after day these poor wretches beat the hell out of the limestone with great heavy hammers and then catch the juice in stainless steel vessels as it drips slowly from the crushed stone. Father takes over from grandfather and then as he in turn succumbs to the passage of time, his own son takes the family hammer from his weakening hands and so on down the decades."

"Gerraway."

"But that's not all. At this stage, the lime juice is perfectly clear and colourless as tap water. Who, one must ask, wants colourless lime juice? God knows, life itself is colourless enough. And in any event, how would you ever know if the barmaid had put it in your gin, or in your case, in your sherry?"

"That's right," he said. "Wouldn't be able to tell if it was in but you'd still be paying for it. What a bloody racket. Colourless lime juice! Bloody hell."

"Exactly," I said. "So, for your protection, if nothing else, it has to be coloured. Extensive market research and field trials indicated that whereas nobody seemed to want blue or red or turquoise lime juice, everybody likes it green."

He nodded. "Quite right," he said. "*I* like it green. My better half likes it green. Our Madge and her Henry, they always have green lime juice."

"So if it has to be tinted green, what better, what more healthy colouring agent could there be than pressure-strained juice of young and tender spinach leaves, grown on the Southern slopes of the Appallachian mountains, dawn picked by comely and winsome country maidens and flown daily to the spinach leaf presses of Wirksworth and Brassington."

"Bugger me," he breathed.

"Behind locked doors, using a formula kept locked in Rose's company safe and known only to the head blender and Hymie Rose himself, the delicately balanced blend is made, this much Derbyshire lime juice to that much Appallachian spinach juice, thus producing the lime juice known for its excellence throughout the civilised world and not only for its excellence but for the delicacy of its colour."

"Who would have thought it?"

"And you, sir, would you really have me destroy three pennorth of that superb juice by adding it to two bob's worth of sherry? Brownish sherry. Sherry made from *grapes?* Out of respect for that uncomplaining body of men, living out their lives in those damp and dismal caves, respect for those green-fingered spinach pickers, up before dawn each day and those spinach pressers who turn up for work regardless of whether their piles are or are not giving them gyp, we should not do it, sir." I could see that I had him, I'd won him over.

"Never thought of it that way before," he said, "but you're right, by God you are. It would be a crime. Forget the sherry and lime. I'll have sherry and peppermint instead."

******

One thing about a pub, there's always something going on. I was down in the 'Gents' one day just checking things out.

A chap came in, positioned himself for action, took a last pull at his cigarette-end then threw it into the urinal. He reached in his pocket, brought out his cigarette packet, found it empty, crumpled it up and threw that down the urinal. From the way he settled his feet, and set his shoulders, like a golfer making ready to drive, I guessed what he intended to do next.

I tapped him on the shoulder. "Don't waste that in here," I told him. "Go back in the bar and pee in one of the ashtrays."

******

Stuck away on a bleak hillside on the road from nowhere to nowhere, the only weekday lunchtime trade we got was the occasional commercial traveller wanting to use the bog.

In an effort to drum up week-day, lunch-time trade, we started using our old tap room, now dignified by the title 'snug', to put on a serve-yourself buffet lunch for eight and sixpence. (If younger readers find these references to an archaic monetary system confusing they should ask their Dad or Grandad, or read it up in the local reference library. Twelve pence, one shilling; two shillings, one florin; two shillings and sixpence, half a crown; twenty shillings, ten florins or eight half crowns, one pound. It's all on record).

Home made soup was brought to you by a waitress. You helped yourself to cold meats, salads, cheeses and fruit. Finally, the waitress served you with coffee.

You know the joke about the woman with the appetite of a bird — a vulture. We got them all, vultures, gannets and plain carrion crows. They homed in from miles around, people whose doctors had told them they must put on some weight, people who had won cups at Eat-your-own-weight-in-suet-pudding competitions, German weightlifters, Japanese wrestlers and people harbouring twin, twenty-foot long, ravenous tape worms with jaws at both ends.

For the first time, the catering was not making money, or at least not enough to make it worthwhile. The event which finally decided us to abandon it was when, just after half past two one day, a vintage Bentley pulled on to our car park and a smartly dressed, middle-aged foursome came into the bar. They knew it was awfully late and a bit of a cheek to ask but could we possibly let them have something to eat, anything at all would do. We had finished serving and the other customers had left

"Remarkable figure that woman's got!"

but we hadn't yet cleared the table in the snug. "Sure," we said and we served them with their soup and left them to it.

Eventually the two men came into the bar, paid their bill and fulsomely praised the food they had eaten. They went out to their car and I went into the snug to get some food for Flo and myself, our waitress already having signed off and gone home.

The two women were at the table, one pushing a hand of bananas up her jumper, the other filling a paper sanitary bag from the Ladies with Stilton and biscuits. I don't know whether they saw me. I think they did. I went back into the bar and stood there sweating with embarrassment until they had left and driven away.

That was it, no more unsupervised self-service. We would offer a three course lunch served in the bar itself. For years in the advertising business, I'd enjoyed a liberal expense account to cover those vinous lunches and dinners that are alleged to lubricate the wheels of big business. In one expensive restaurant after another, my guests and myself had flinched as the maitre unfolded and handed to each of us a menu as big as the table top, Hors D'Oeuvres, Potages, Poissons, Entrees, Farinaces, Legumes, Fromages, Desserts, acres of print for our glazed eyes to slide over whilst our numbed minds desperately tried to make a decision. Often we took the coward's way out, and asked "What do you recommend today Pierre?" or when truly desperate, gabbled "Just bring me something to eat. You know what I like, Georgio. I leave it all to you."

We would make decision making easier.

No more than four starters, four main courses, three British cheeses and three desserts, that would be our formula. I bought Robert Carrier and Elizabeth David paperbacks, scales, plastic measures, a Kenwood mixer, more pans, mixed herbs and a sack of garlic. I bought in meat and vegetables, fresh fish, cheeses, fruit and that first day, wearing my striped apron and running my index finger along the line of print, I read "Take four large green peppers and with a sharp knife ......" We were off, taking the first steps along the road that was to lead eventually to the Old Rectory.

In those first few weeks and for the first time in my life, I cooked Moussaka a la Greque, Hungarian Pork Gulyas, Carbonnade de Boeuf, Spiced Ox Tongue in Burgundy, and, of course, Coq au Vin. I also made Steak and Kidney Pie and I roasted Ribs of Beef and Legs of Pork.

We sold a lot of Steak and Kidney Pie and Roast Rib of Beef and Roasted Leg of Pork and we, the staff, lived off warmed up leftover Moussaka, Gulyas, Carbonnade, Ox Tongue and Coq au Vin.

Throughout it all, our waitress, a tall and bony local widow with social aspirations, was a gem. Someone asked if the roast beef was rare. "Oh no," she told him proudly, "we have it on every day." Someone else asked if he could have some Melba toast. She said she was sorry but it was all Mother's Pride. I used to enjoy buying leeks so that later on I could watch my clients' convulsions when she asked them "Would you like a little leek, sir," and her repeated bewilderment when they said No, they'd already been or they were alright for the minute but they *would* like some of that vegetable, whatever it was.

As the first catering year went by, the word got round and we became full every lunchtime. We could only accommodate about twenty-five people but they learned that they must book a table. We even started to get people in who actually liked Moussaka, Gulyas and Carbonnade and eventually, we and the staff were able to get a belated crack at the Steak and Kidney Pie, the Roast Beef and the Roast Pork and a nice change it was too, after all that mucked about, foreign stuff we'd been eating up for twelve months.

By now, I had come to realise that serving just one plate of smoked salmon as a starter made me more profit than did a chap drinking three pints of ale four nights a week, and without all that cellar work for Flo and my pump cleaning. There was no room at the pub to make a proper restaurant and, at night, both the bar and snug were needed for drinkers so I was never able to serve dinners, only lunches.

The brewery owned the adjoining row of terraced cottages, all let at peppercorn rents, most to extremely aged tenants. I begged the brewery to let me take over the cottages as they came empty and at my own expense make a restaurant, but the brewery, like most others in those days, couldn't see that food was an essential concomitant with drink and that selling food helped to sell beer. They weren't interested.

I started to look round for a place of my own and eventually, the local estate agent, who occasionally lunched at the pub, put me on to a nearby Victorian rectory that had been empty for three years and stood in all but an acre of overgrown garden. The building had been slightly vandalised and there were tramps sleeping rough in what had been the rector's pine-panelled dining room. The old, grass tennis court had saplings growing out of it. Rampant rhododendrons and laurel bushes leaned against the windows but the glass was plate glass and the Rectory had been built to last as long as Christianity itself. It was late in the Spring of 1967 when I first saw it. I stood thigh deep in nettles and I listened to the birds quarrelling in the elms, the beeches and the ash trees, the sycamores and the oaks, that had been planted a hundred and more years ago to mark the church land off from the open country that then surrounded it. I knew that this was what I wanted.

The Church Commissioners wanted £5,000, yes, that's right! Nineteen sixty seven, five thousand pounds freehold! They accepted my offer of four thousand. I had paid some four hundred pounds to go into the pub, but the incoming tenant paid me three and a half thousand to take it over. We had come out of it pretty well.

Thirty of the most eminent local businessmen who had eaten

at the pub, signed a statement that they needed the facilities of a diner's club in Denton.

Whatever anyone wants to do in this business, no matter how much it would satisfy a local need, no matter how well planned or conducted, there is always a body of obstructionists yelping about the slamming of car doors, and the lowering of the high tone of the area by the introduction of people who want to eat or have a drink or do both. All of whom, the protestors try to convince the magistrates, will ignore the restaurant's immaculate and well equipped toilet facilities and stagger out into the night to piss all over the protestor's prize dahlias and fart on the fuschia.

Our case was no exception, so it was in face of the vociferous opposition of the Licensed Victuallers Association and the near hysterical snivelling of one's neighbours for half a mile's radius, that the local Bench granted us a licence for a Private Member's Club, two of the magistrates having to sit back and declare an interest, one being a devotee of our pub's Rare Roast Beef, the other besotted with our Stroganoff.

******

The builders moved in and started to rip the place apart. We must have started with some sort of plans, if only to get them past the Planning Officer, but soon the plans were lost sight of and daily on-site decisions were made on an ad-hoc basis. "Let's open it all up by cutting through those two chimney breasts and if we brick up this doorway and open up an arch off this corridor, we could pull that small room into the bar complex." The builder was very patient. "Right," he said. "Right." Knowing that every time he said Right, every time he agreed, I was sticking another five hundred on my final bill.

He only said No once.

"I think we could get a big effect, a big result if we took this entire wall out," I told him. "You certainly would," he said, "the

33

whole ...... place would fall down." I'm always ready to be guided by experts in their field. Never argue with the man who knows. "In that case," I said, reasonably. "We won't do it."

******

My son was then the youngest manager in Britain for a leading chain store and was all set for a high flying career with a possible board room finish. He resigned his office and with his wife he joined Flo and me. We registered the partnership The Old Rectory Diner's Club, Denton, and before we actually opened we had raked in a hundred or so members at three guineas a year (three pounds fifteen pence. I told you, ask your Dad!) We anounced an opening date. By the operation of Sod's Law we opened in dense fog and literally on the same day that saw the introduction of the breathalyser.

Under these circumstances, our opening, even with a hundred members, made about as much initial impact as a mouse fart in a thunderstorm. It was just as well that, in order to brave myself for that opening and in order to recover from the stresses and strains of daily contact with the builders, I had decided on a two week break, by myself, to get away from it all.

Friends said "Scotland, that's the place. You've never been? Fantastic place. West coast. Washed by the warm Gulf Stream. Golden beaches, coconut palms, peaches and pineapples growing wild, lochs, haggis, salmon, heather, mountains. Scotland! That's the place to heal a bruised mind."

I believed them. I went.

It was a salutary experience. So much so that even now, nearly twenty years later, I go pale and a nerve in my cheek starts to twitch whenever I hear a Scots voice. It doesn't have to be loud or harsh. It only has to say 'och' or 'wee' or 'd'ye no ken' and I'm into my trauma.

******

Scotland, and the Colonel's Lady

It was September 1967.

I bought some sun cream and Hugo's English/Scottish Phrase Book and waving goodbye to my family and the last of the builder's men who were still clearing up, throwing plaster and broken brick into the flower beds, I set off in glorious sunshine. I seem to remember singing "You take the high road and I'll take the low road" but those halcyon days were all too long ago and I couldn't actually swear to it.

The sky went dark and it started to squirt at Kendal. It went on squirting. At Penrith, I found a sports outfitters and bought a fisherman's waterproof jacket and trousers. At Carlisle, I added a Sou-wester and wellingtons. Except for going to bed and just for an odd couple of dry days, I never took them off for the next two weeks. And don't believe that stuff about the coconut palms, the peaches and pineapples, it's just not true. What I thought was a giant ant-hill turned out to be a pillar-box crusted with rust. At one stage, it was a fish caught in my windscreen wiper that made me realise that I had inadvertently left the road and was driving along the bed of Loch Lomond. It rained! It rained and it rained! I'm telling you. Man, it rained. I was pissed off with being pissed on.

******

Diana Petrie in the Observer Colour Magazine or somewhere or other, had recommended a small hotel somewhere on the wind swept marshes of the West coast. I booked a room by telephone.

It was about four in the afternoon when I found it, a long, low, white building with a stone-clad roof.

Alone in the bar, the middle-aged chef, his face afire with an incendiary strawberry nose, stared briefly at me with incredible malignancy and then went back to contemplating his half-pint or so of straight malt. The rain hammered down.

The Colonel's lady was a huge woman in a collar and tie, a tweed jacket and skirt, knitted stockings and heavy brogues. She rocked violently backwards and forwards, feet apart, reminding me inevitably of that old joke, "Are you being served, madam." "Don't be stupid. I always do this."

"The Colonel's out at the moment," she barked at me, "but you'll meet him at dinner. Are you a curry man? Vindaloo, Beef Madras, what?"

"Are you a curry man? Vindaloo. Beef Madras. What?"

36

"Not really, I'm afraid."

"Pity," she said. "Colonel's ex-India. Bowler-hatted. Do a good vindaloo. Still! Better leave you to chef then. He'll do you proud."

Chef said nothing but gave me a baleful look that said he'd rather do me in than do me proud, and belched his contempt for the whey-faced Sassenach.

At the dreadfully early hour of 6.30, a bell was tinkled up and down the corridors by an infirm and aged crone who seemed not likely to finish the course. We — that is myself and the only two other residents, who both looked old enough to be the bell-ringer's mother — were summoned to table.

As we took our seats, there came the most blood-chilling caterwauling that I had ever heard. It was blowing a force 9 gale outside and there, just outside the window, in full regimental mess flummery was the gallant Colonel, purple-faced, piping us in to dinner with his left hand and elbow, his right hand being mainly concerned with protecting, against the violence of the storm, the timeless secret of what a Scot wears beneath his kilt. His duty done, his bagpipe deflated and detumescent, the Colonel, like Banquo's ghost, quitted the scene. Subdued and silent, we three slowly ate our way through the mandatory grapefruit segments, breaded plaice fillets and trifle in a paper case.

Now and then, a sliding panel in the wall slammed back to permit the chef to pass his nose and plates through, and to threaten us with his demonic eye.

******

I reached the pass of Glencoe and the sun came briefly out. I enjoyed a pleasant lunch at the Kingshouse Hotel and then, taking advantage of the brief break in the weather and wielding my shooting stick, I set off to walk for a while up the pass. I was joined by an amiable pointer dog which, I imagined, lived at the hotel. Together, we went up the pass, I panting, the dog snuffing the air and circling the heather. Suddenly, he put up a brace of raucous grouse. He pointed and froze. My shooting stick jammed and wouldn't fire. He couldn't believe it. No shot. The grouse had got clean away. We went on, me still panting but now his snuffing and circling seemed less happy, less a part of a good day. He was wrestling with a problem. It happened again. Up went the grouse, up and away. "There," he said, "You bloody great useless berk, there they are," his nose extended, leaning forward, tail erect. No death dealing fusillade shattered the air.

There comes a time with all of us when we suddenly say "Right. That's enough. No more. Finish." We pack it up, we jack it in. That's just what the dog did. "Sod this for a lark," he said. "I'm wasting my time with this grockle." To be honest, I didn't actually hear him say it because after all, dogs can't talk, can they? But he certainly thought it. He gave me one of his looks and then he turned back and loped disconsolately back home with never a backward look, not even in anger.

I'd grown to like him. I was sorry when he went.

******

On my way to Skye and finally, as far as this tale goes, I got to Mallaig, which apart from being the jumping off place for Skye, is also one of the centres of the kippering business. Mallaig, Loch Fyne and Manx kippers are the best kippers in the world.

It was the end of the season. Everything — not that everything means a lot in Mallaig — was closed down. Everything but the kippering. The herring were still being landed on the quay and the great smoking sheds were full of gutted and split herring, open and spitted in the endless ranks above the smouldering oak chips. Vast numbers of shrieking gulls wheeled and circled in the gloomy sky.

Late in the afternoon, I checked into the only one of Mallaig's two or maybe three hotels which was just about still open.

"We stop serrrving dinner on September the fourrrrteenth," the hotel proprietress told me, "so if tomorrow, you'rre wanting hot soup with yourr high tea, will you please tell the waitrress at brreakfast." When you read that in your mind's ear, read it the way you would hear it, rolling those r's and stretching out those vowels and getting the proper cadences and the lilt of it. "We stop serrrrving dinnairrrr ......"

"If I may," I said, "I'd like a brace of your world famous kippers for my breakfast." That was just in ordinary English, the way I speak it, wherever I am.

"Ah, no," she said, "we neverr serrve kipperrrs, it's the smell y'know. Ye can have a boiled egg. Or two, if that's your fancy."

******

I'd taken a bath and before high tea, was relaxing in my dressing gown on my bed when, again at that hour of six-thirty, so peculiar to the Scots, there was a tap on my bedroom door. "Come in," I called. Another tap, but louder. "Come in," I called again, also louder. A third tapping this time, becoming more of a sustained knocking.

I got up and opened the door.

As the waitress saw my dressing gown, she rapidly stepped back a couple of feet and protectively put her arms up in front of her chest. It was obvious she had been had, or nearly had, like this before.

"Are ye no coming doon forr yourr high tea?" she asked. "It's afterr the time, noo, and we'rre all waiting to gang away hame."

******

In search of Mallaig kippers, I went down to a kiosk on the quayside. 'Kippers by Post'. It was closed.

But at last I finally got my Mallaig kippers.

It must have been six months later when I was making one of my first calls on the old Manchester Smithfield fish market.

"I'd like a box of large Manx kippers please."

"No Manx, guv. Only Mallaig kippers. From Scotland. Very nice too."

I went overboard. "I'll take a box then, and the wee bridie and myself will have them for oorrr high tea, so we will. The noo. Yee ken och aye."

He thought I was balmy. Perhaps you think the same.

Och, away with ye then. Bejabers. Or is that the other lot?

******

The man from the
big bank

I came back to England, pale of face and suffering from fibrositis and xenophobia. As I've already noted, we opened at a disastrous time.

To make matters worse, many of our good friends from the pub had complained that although we were only moving a few miles away, they wouldn't be able to visit us for a drink unless they were having a meal. I was really touched, and, as a rather late second thought, spent a couple of thousand I didn't really have, converting the stone flagged cellars into an attractive cellar bar. The breathalyser broke upon us and my old pub pals, terrified of being nabbed, stayed where they could walk to their pub if necessary. The cellar bar was a disaster.

Not only did no one turn up but, with a perfectly dry cellar until now, the making of the car park had somehow altered the water table and water started to pour through the walls whenever it rained.

We had only just put that right — needless to say at great expense — when the main sewer was blocked with so-called disposable napkins crapped in by our grandson and flushed away by our daughter-in-law. They got hooked on tree roots in the ancient drains. Where we had once had water in the cellar bar, we now had sewage. Not nice sewage either, quite nasty sewage in fact. It set us back a further £2,000, half the original price of the house and land, to put that right and it almost broke us. I was scared witless and when I wasn't shaking all over I was wet with cold and clammy sweat.

We were having appalling difficulty in finding the right staff and the money wasn't coming in as we had hoped. We went to bed too late and utterly exhausted. We got up too early and scarcely less beaten. With every new set-back, I ranted and raved like a madman. We hated each other's guts and if Flo, Lee and daughter-in-law Margaret had had anywhere to go, they would surely have walked out on me and left me. But they didn't. We survived. Slowly, we learned our trade. Slowly our membership increased and with it, our turnover and local reputation. I knew we had turned the corner when, on a visit to our bank, the manager saw me come in and for the first time, instead of bolting into his office he came forward, greeted me with a smile and inquired after my health. "And how's business?" he asked, as if he didn't know down to the last penny.

Eventually we had not one hundred but eight hundred members. Some of them started to natter. "Bedrooms, why don't you build some bedrooms? We have all these clients and business visitors. We bring them here to eat and then we have to put them up somewhere else. Build bedrooms."

I wanted bedrooms like I wanted another hole in my head but they were very persuasive and I had my son and our grandchildren to consider.

The matter was finally clinched when Lee applied for and was given a Government grant of £12,000 against our projected hotel at a total cost of some £80,000.

We'd already gone through all the nitty gritty. Our architect had drawn up the plans and once again the Licensed Victuallers and the local residents had set up a hullaballoo but had failed to block our planning permission for twenty-four bedrooms with en suite facilities.

We had the plans and the planning permission and a promise of £12,000 from the Government. All we were short of was about £50,000, not a lot really.

"No bother at all," said one of our club members, "My best

pal is head man at — " and he named the biggest merchant bankers. "He'll fix you up."

A couple of silver-haired chaps, wearing cravat ties and dark pin-stripe suits turned up and the boss man, after lunch and over a brandy, said "Now then, Mr Chadwick, we're here to discuss your need for a little investment capital. Just how much are you looking for?" I swallowed deeply and over paralysed tonsils grated out "£50,000." There was a shocked and embarrassed silence. "Fifty thousands?" the man queried once he had recovered. "Fifty thousand pounds is it?"

"Forty thousand would help," I stammered. "Thirty five thousand?"

"You misunderstand us," the other chap put in. "I'm afraid that sort of loan is not on the scale we deal in. You're not asking for too much. You're asking for too little."

"You're not asking for too much. You're asking for too little."

"I'm afraid," said the boss man. "Far too little. With great respect to your plans, we understood you wanted to build a hotel."

"I do. Twenty-four bedrooms."

"No Mr Chadwick, I mean a *proper* hotel. Six or seven storeys, perhaps. One hundred, one hundred and fifty bedrooms perhaps."

"Twenty-six bedrooms," his colleague repeated, disbelievingly.

"They'd be very nice bedrooms," I said. "Fully furnished. Fitted carpets, bathrooms and thingies and that. Nothing cheap and nasty."

"I'm terribly sorry," said the silver-haired man.

"Awfully sorry," said his silver-haired colleague. They sounded as if they almost meant it.

******

Eventually, Robinson's Brewery came up trumps and the late Sir John loaned us what we needed at straight base rate in return for a twenty year trade tie. We were away.

Our builder moved in with his bulldozers, J.C.B's and a corps of ditch diggers and drain layers. Hod carriers ran up and down ladders, lithe as ballet dancers. Brickies moved relentlessly along wooden staging, lifting a brick in their left hand, stooping for a trowel of mortar, coating the brick, placing the brick, tapping it into exact place, sweeping off the squeezed out mortar, flicking it back, lifting a brick in their left hand, stooping for a trowel of mortar, rythmically creating walls where once there had been only air and space. Walls built in weeks that, with any luck at all, could stand, cloaked in ivy, for a century or more.

Joiners, plasterers, plumbers, electricians, painters, all came and went, each craftsman accompanied by his apprentice, there to pass a hammer or a paint brush then stand with arms folded watching his mate earn wages for the two of them.

One day, they had all gone and we had a bedroom block, a

new restaurant and kitchens and a signwriter putting up boards that read 'The Old Rectory Hotel'. The day we opened up for business, we owed £60,000, we were charging £5.00 a night for room and full English breakfast and virtually no one wanted to know. One or two eggs with their bacon, sausage and tomato and still no one wanted to know. Two eggs!

The self-same people who had talked me into the expansion — 'Why don't you build bedrooms. You need bedrooms. Build bedrooms' — were turning up for lunch or dinner with Japanese guests who weren't booked into my rooms.

"These chaps aren't going back to Tokyo tonight," I'd say "Why aren't they staying here?"

"They're in the Midland."

"But you are the chap that got me to put a £60,000 noose around my neck."

"Well actually, old chap, it's not really up to me. I'm the M.D. but it's Miss Blenkinsop in the Travel Section who handles visitors. Have a word with her. Tell her I said so. I'm sure it'll be alright."

We phoned Miss Blenkinsop and still got nowhere. Until Lee, who doesn't share his father's high moral standards, invited Miss Blenkinsop, her boy friend and any other couple they knew, to dinner as our guests so that Miss Blenkinsop could 'check out for herself' what services and facilities we were offering. It sometimes took Miss Blenkinsop two or three such visits to check things out but eventually, one or two and then three or four Miss Blenkinsops were convinced and we started to get a few in.

In India they call it baksheese. In Britain we call it sales promotion.

Still, in retrospect, the fact that our hotel was two thirds empty for nearly a year wasn't quite so bad as it might have been. In those days, the room rate was £5.00 a night. At the time of writing, it's £32.00 a night. If we were two thirds empty now, instead of then, I'd be losing money six times as fast.

Housekeeper
and Receptionists

While all this was going on — in fact before we could even kick off — we'd had to find extra staff.

For the Old Rectory Diner's Club we already had bar staff, waiting staff, kitchen and cleaning staff. Now we needed chambermaids and receptionists.

Perhaps more than any other business a hotel is only as good as its staff.

The building itself can be an architectural triumph, superbly sited and magnificently kitted out but if the staff are no good, the hotel is no good and residents would be better off in a Salvation Army hostel.

We found two receptionists, two chambermaids and a night porter about all of whom, more later, but in my ignorance I appointed a housekeeper. She was a small, sparse and leathery woman, very rigid and straight-backed from years of service as an Army hospital matron. Foreign suns had dried her skin to a yellow parchment stretched tightly across the ivory bones of her face.

She started with us on the very day which saw the delivery of thirty six mattresses and divan-bed bases. For a day or two all hands were put to unwrapping beds, screwing on feet and headboards and manhandling them into place.

Under the beady eye of our militant housekeeper, the chambermaids made up the beds and, at last, they were ready to receive the weary carcases of our first residents. I went into a bedroom and pressed down on a mattress, testing its firmness. The mattress seemed particularly resistant and there was an odd crackling noise. Under the pristine sheets, the mattresses were still encased in thick, plastic, protective covers.

Never one to beat about the bush, I said to the housekeeper, "You have just observed me testing a mattress for firmness and like me, you will have heard an odd crackling sound. I find, madam, that under these pristine sheets, the mattress is still encased in a thick plastic, protective cover. Please tell me why."

"No draw sheets," she said. "You've forgotten to get draw sheets." As some of you will know, a hospital draw sheet is that sheet that, doubled, is stretched midways across the bed to absorb any this or that leaking out of the patient.

"Draw sheets?" I said, "this is a hotel not a hospital. You don't

"Draw sheets perhaps, Miss McTavish ...... Nappies, No!"

47

need draw sheets." "Oh yes, you do." she snapped. "You've told me that your residents are going to be mostly men and not young men at that. Company directors! I can tell you that men of that age often tinkle in their beds. Especially if they've been in your bar all night. You leave those covers on or you get me some draw sheets." Within a couple of weeks she had moved on and we never found it necessary to replace her. Or to use draw sheets!

Not so, unhappily, with our receptionists, either one or the other of whom we regularly replaced over the next few years. For some reason we have never identified, our only real staff turnover in the twelve or more years we have run the hotel has been in the realm of receptionists. As a comparison, we have kitchen workers, barmaids, waitresses and chambermaids who have been with us for anything up to the twelve years the hotel has been open. The longest any receptionist has stayed has been two and a half years and some, only as many weeks or months.

In the big city-centre hotels, with comings and goings around the twenty-four hour clock, the job of receptionist must be a taxing one, calling upon vast reserves of patience, stamina and plain fortitude. In a small, family hotel like ours, the job is a sinecure.

It follows that anyone wishing to enjoy a reasonable life as a hotel receptionist should avoid like the plague the big hotels and seek out small hotels, like the Old Rectory where, once the resident businessmen have breakfasted and gone out for the day, returning like dutiful husbands between six and seven pm, there is little to disturb the cloistered quiet of the day. True, the telephone may ring occasionally with someone wishing to reserve a room or a restaurant table but the receptionist, determined not to be disturbed, will probably wear ear-plugs, or leave the phone off the hook. Leaving the phone off the hook is probably the fairest to the proprietors as the constant engaged tone gives callers the impression that the hotel is always tremendously busy and therefore must be a very fine place indeed. The fact that they can't get through to reception is not, actually, very good for business but excellent for the hotel's reputation and will undoubtedly cause great speculation as to causes when the hotel finally goes bankrupt.

Receptionists taking up posts in any small hotel, should ensure that the reception office is properly equipped with colour television and a video recorder so that, once the guests have left for the day, the receptionist can either play video games or perhaps take an Open University course. A really shrewd and ambitious receptionist will use the hotel's otherwise idle and wasted facilities for running a small but profitable private

"And I have runners and starting prices for Doncaster, York and Cheltenham ..."

business, the operating of which can be helped by a Government Small Business's grant.

For instance, most ordinary small businesses do not have a telex. If the hotel does have telex, then the receptionist can rent a most useful service to local businessmen allowing them the use of the hotel telex number and relaying telex messages to them through the hotel's telephone switchboard. Or, using that same telephone switchboard and instant race results from the television set, the receptionist can run a small telephone betting shop.

Apart from an hour or so from 7.30am and a couple of hours around six in the evening when residents are checking in or out with credits cards, cheques and occasionally money, or asking for the bill to be forwarded, asking the exchange rate for yen, piastres and dinar, or complaining that their room is too small and stuffy, too small and draughty, too large, too noisy, too far from the lift or fire escape and yes, they know the hotel is absolutely full but you had better give them a different room or they'll have those A.A. stars off your signboard, there will be very little to do.

There will probably be a stream of requests for incoming or outgoing phone calls, stamps, stationery, aspirins, sticking plaster, brown paper, lengths of string, sealing wax, sellotape, sewing kits, electric irons, a tie press, trouser press, the address of the nearest vet, doctor, dentist, lawyer, massage parlour, whorehouse, branch of Alcoholics Anonymous or Weight Watchers. There will be requests for hot water, cold water, ice, iced water, water ices, tea, coffee, hot-chocolate, drinking-chocolate, sandwiches, salads, peanuts and crisps, a dictionary, foreign-language phrase book, black or brown shoelaces, black or brown shoe polish and brushes, and shampoos for dry hair, normal hair, greasy hair or bald heads. But all in all, there will be very little to do.

Receptionists bored with watching Dallas, reading a Joan Collins' paperback or just dozing on the office chaise-longue, might well try logging a telephone reservation for two single rooms for four nights as four single rooms for two nights. Or transpose the next day's lunch and dinner bookings. The results can often be hilarious and well worth it, later on, just for the look on the boss's face.

******

A last word on the subject of reception. At one time, having a particular unfortunate run with incredibly inefficient and equally unfortunate short-stay receptionists, we reasoned that we were probably short on induction training, so we composed a list of guidance lines to be handed to each new receptionist on arrival.

"The two fleshy lumps at the bottom of your legs are called *'feet'.* The two fleshy lumps at the top of your legs are called *'bottom'.* The *'bottom'* at the top is what you sit about on all day. How and where we will now explain.

It is quite possible, with a little practice, to place one of your feet — *'a foot'* — a couple of feet in front of the other foot, it doesn't matter which, both will be right, even the left. If you haven't fallen over, repeat the process, bringing whichever foot is left, past the other foot, even if it's right, and place it firmly down two feet in front. This process, known as *'walking',* will enable you, when it is your tour of duty, to move from your centrally-heated, fitted-carpeted, luxuriously furnished staff flat to the *'office'.* The *'office'* is that room housing various equipment, including lights and buzzers, all of which will be flashing and buzzing when you get there. They are merely a distraction and not physically dangerous. Ignore them.

In front of you, you will find a chair. Lower the bottom at the top of your legs onto the horizontal padded surface of the chair and when sufficient surface contact has been made, take the weight off your feet. You are now *'sitting'.* On the desk in front of you is an object like a bent plastic banana, flattened at both ends. This is a telephone or more popularly and in the vernacular, a *'phone*. Try to remember that name, *'phone,* and the object it represents. You will hear it a lot in the course of your duties, *''phone''. ''phone''.* Instructions, in your tooled moroccan staff-training kit, will explain how this *''phone'* can be picked up and placed to your ear. The earpiece has been covered in swansdown to protect your ear against unduly prolonged pressure when you are 'phoning your friends and relatives in Australia.

You will also find instructions on how and when to open or close your eyes, how to move your eyelids up and down to prevent them from sticking, how to keep on breathing, what to do when you go to the lavatory and the telephone number and address of the local Industrial Tribunal ......"

******

Oh Mr Porter

Night porters are a rum lot. I suppose they've got to be, in order to get through a day in reverse, as it were. They go to bed when everyone else is just starting a day's work. They sleep most of the day behind drawn curtains. If they like a drink, they join their mates in the pub and then, when their mates go home and sleep it off, sober or drunk, they go off to work.

It's little wonder that night porters tend to be withdrawn, manic depressives and quite often are alcoholics. In our early days, we had a run of odd-bods, mostly men of retiring age, twitching, grey-haired, grey-faced men with a 'frozen' shoulder or a stiff leg, halitosis and hallucinations. Then came along Ernie. Ernie was a real card.

A bald, middle-aged batchelor, prematurely stooped and painfully thin, he wore a bizarre, ginger wig that looked as though some failed wig-maker had taken a pair of rusting garden shears and hacked it out of a rotting old hearthrug. Ernie tried to drown whatever problems he had in draught bitter, large quantities of which he sank in the nearby local. Unfortunately, his troubles had learned to swim and Ernie found that while his troubles were doing the breast-stroke, it was his brain that was sinking nightly without trace.

In all, he was with me for three years and during that time, I must have fired him half a dozen times, never, it must be said, for any heinous offence other than that of coming on duty tanked-up to the eyeballs. The day after each sacking, a penitent, bleary-eyed Ernie would come in, ask to see me and swear future, total temperance. I, being one well aware of the lure of demon drink, subject to frequent tankings-up on my own part, mostly off duty, but occasionally on, would reflect that, as I was the boss, no one could fire me for the very offence for which I had just fired Ernie, and I would take him back again. "Alright Ernie, but I warn you! This is definitely your last chance. You turn in the drinking or you turn in the job. I'm telling you, this is your very last chance." Ernie would look grave and resolute. "You're a white man guvnor."

Well, I suppose it couldn't go on for ever. It was only a matter of time.

It finally happened in August. We'd had a very busy week with half the staff away on holiday. To cap it all, we had a new, not very bright receptionist struggling to cope with an influx of Sunday night arrivals, up for the Manchester Furniture Exhibition. Totally knackered, I was in bed at 12.30am Monday morning and was instantly asleep. At ten past one, my bedside 'phone rang and Ernie, stoned out of his head, blurred — believe it or not — "Hey Chaddie, that new office bint's not left mi list fer't morning calls and tea and that ......" I cut him short with a few admonitory comments during which his mother's marital state at the time of his birth was called into question and I fell back on the bed and into instant oblivion. At one thirty am the phone rang again and an even more incoherent Ernie said "I've had enough of this Chaddie, I'm buggering off."

Without waiting to put on a dressing gown or my slippers, I raced barefoot from my bedroom, down the stairs, through the bar-lounge and across the darkened restaurant where I ran into a chair, knocking back a toe but much more painfully, savaging my courting tackle on the wooden chair-arm. Bent double, I hopped into reception, whimpering and tenderly cupping my injured parts. Ernie was just leaving.

"Give me your keys," I snarled. I'm quite good at shouting and bawling but I'm not so hot at snarling and not used to it, I bit a piece out of the inside of my cheek.

"I'll give you more than the bloody keys," eight and a half stone Ernie shouted, taking a wildly ineffectual swing at me.

I lost my temper completely and, taking hold of him by his tie and the front of his shirt, I roughly bundled him backwards through the hotel door. I thought I'd give him some slight idea of how I felt.

"For Christ's sake sod off before I bloody well murder you," I inferred. A startled owl fell heavily out of a tree, dogs started to bark, wetting themselves the while, sleeping babies woke and cried with terror and bedroom lights came on all over Haughton Green.

Despite my hints and my very persuasive tone, Ernie ignored my suggestion that he should remove himself from my vicinity and he came back to throw yet another haymaker, this time falling flat on his back on the tarmac. He lay still.

"Oh my God, he must have killed himself," I thought with a degree of morbid satisfaction. I closed the hotel door and went into the office and phoned the police. With a body on my doorstep, it seemed the proper thing to do. Then I switched on the car park floodlights and went back outside to drag in the corpse but, like Lazarus, the corpse was risen from the dead and gone away. As I wandered about in my pyjamas, plaintively calling his name, "Ernie, where are you Ernie?" the hotel door clicked to behind me and I was locked out. I could not help but notice that by now, it was raining heavily. Barefoot and in my pyjamas, I found this turn in the weather to be for the worse.

I circled the building but all the ground floor doors and windows were securely locked. On my way to the boiler room to get the long ladders, in the hope of gaining entry through an upper window, I fell into a rosebed and again, my lower appendages took the brunt of it. The boiler room door was securely locked.

Through the rain, I saw that, despite the late hour, the light was still on in bedroom one and I knocked persuasively on the window pane. In a light, almost jocular tone intended to give confidence to the person so addressed, I called out "Mr McNee.

Mr McNee, are you there? This is Mr Chadwick. I'm sorry to disturb you at this hour, Mr McNee, but I have been inadvertently locked out of the hotel. Could you please go to the hotel door and let me in? Mr McNee?"

The man answered in a quavery voice. "If you were Mr Chadwick ye'd know that I'm no McNee but McNab. I'm McNab and I'm away to my wee bed the nu. Och, it's sleeping I am." There followed some instant, simulated snoring in a heavy Glaswegian accent. I persisted. "You may well be awa t'yer wee bed," I said, talking man to man, "and ah'm nay dooting yer worrd on that but it's nay likely that you're asleep the nu" The effort of continuing in this strain was too much after all that had gone before. Rolling my r's was loosening the caps on my teeth and I reverted to my mother tongue.

"Come at you, sir," I cried, losing patience with the foolish fellow, "allay your fears. It is I, Challenor-Chadwick who stands without your portal and without umbrella withal. Challenor-Chadwick, traveller, writer, entrepreneur, chef, your genial host — need I go on thus. I am standing here barefoot in my pyjamas and to exacerbate my unhappy position, I am being pissed on from a great height. Now for Christ's sake get your finger out and get me in."

The more direct approach paid off and had an immediate effect. The bedroom curtian was pulled aside and McNab — for indeed t'was he and not McNee — peered out at me.

"Och," he said, or it may have been 'Havers', or some other witless word from what I have always thought of as the wrong side of Hadrian's Wall. "If it's no Mr Chadwick, locked oot of doorrs and not drressed for the inclement weather we're having the nu. Bide there a wee while until I can open the doorr."

As he was letting me in through the hotel door, a Panda car drew up and a young policeman, quite new to the district, jumped out, took me firmly by my soaked shoulder and pushed me into the hotel. "Had too much again, have you Ernie? Brahms and

Liszt are we?" he said, shaking me about and then to McNab, "I've heard about our inebriated Ernie, Mr Chadwick. A master booze-hound from all accounts and I must say, he looks it. That's a real purple hooter on him, a right old bottle nose, that is. High time you gave this clapped out old soak his marching orders." How the policeman could have thought McNab to be me baffles me. He should have known that no one bearing the name of Challoner-Chadwick would be seen dead, let alone alive, in tartan pyjams and carrying a plaid golf umbrella, as was McNab.

"That's a real purple hooter on him, a right old bottle nose, that is."

How he could mistake me for a drunken lush is also beyond belief!

We sorted that one out, then while McNab folded up his umbrella and gang back awa to his wee bed and the policeman went off into the night to look for Ernie or his body, I got into some dry clothes and went back to wait in reception.

In very little time, the policeman was back with Ernie. "Found him wandering up the middle of Two Trees Lane," he said. "Are you going to lay any charges?" Ernie's wig was on sideways. Or it could have been on sideways, it was difficult to say with that particular wig.

"No charges," I said. "Just bring him in please." Ernie stood there grinning vacantly, weaving backwards and forwards and licking his dehydrated lips.

"Get up to the store room, drink some black coffee and get your head down," I said.

"Am I fired guvnor?" he asked.

"Just do as I tell you and get out of my sight, Ernie, get going while the going's good."

"You're a gent," he said and tried to salute me. He fell down again.

"Jesus," said the policeman. "You get off to bed, Mr Chadwick, you look knackered."

"I was knackered two hours ago," I told him.

"You get off to bed and leave this one to me. I've nothing else to do, I'll see him safely tucked up." As I went off, the policeman was lifting Ernie up. He shouldn't have bothered. Ernie coughed twice and honked on the policeman.

At 3.50 my bedside phone rang. "Ernie here," he said. "Just thought I'd tell you, I've got rid of that copper and everything's locked up. Anything you want me to do before you turn in?"

******

I didn't see Ernie the next morning, he was away before I was up and down to work. I spent the day wondering what to do about him. I decided that if he even smelled of beer when he came on duty that night, he was for the chop.

He didn't come on duty that night. He was due in at 10pm. At ten to ten, one of his mates phoned and asked for me. He said Ernie wouldn't be in to work because he'd hurt his back when I'd knocked him down. I could hear the glasses clinking in the background and all the noise of a busy pub. The phone must have been near the fruit machine. Someone got three crowns or cherries or lemons up and the machine hammered out ten times.

I hope it was Ernie because, I fired him and this time it was for real.

******

There is a minor footnote to this sad story.

We did away with the position of night porter and we kitted out the rooms with alarm and hot drinks facilities. To give residents access late at night, we installed call-phone and electronic lock release system on the hotel door with response phones and lock-opening buttons up in our flats.

On the first night after installation, I checked the working action at about 10.30pm. Flo had gone up to our flat. It seemed humorous to press the doofer and when she answered, to say throatily into the microphone on the wall "Is that the Special-Services Sauna? Can I speak to Yvette?"

"Very funny," Flo said, "Now that's enough childishness. I'm going to bed." The chaps had done a good job. It worked perfectly.

At about quarter to midnight I was explaining the installation to two of our regular residents. We'd gone outside to check it all out and one of them pressed the call button.

I panicked.

"Did you just press that?" I yammered.

"You mean this call button?" he said, and he did it again.

There was an electronic crackle and then, loud and clear, an enraged and venomous female voice rasped "Why don't you piss off and let me sleep. Stop playing silly buggers."

He seemed to recognise the style. "Good God," he gasped, white-faced and trembling with shock. "That's my wife."

"No sir," I said sadly. "It's mine."

******

That was all some years ago but perhaps once or twice a year, Ernie, boozed out of his head, comes down the lane and presses the doofer and wakes me up. I sit on the edge of the bed and hear him say, "It's me guvnor, can you let me in?" I don't ever reply. Perhaps I should but I don't. I just hang up. The telephone buzzes again then it stops.

I don't speak to Ernie and I don't let Ernie in and he gives up and goes back up the lane. All the pubs have long been shut. I feel guilty. Perhaps I should have let him in. We could have had a jar or two and a bit of a natter ......

When I wake up in the morning, I'm glad that I didn't.

******

The bonfire on a base

It's not only night porters who are funny lads.

Tim is another funny lad, one of the funniest in fact. Tim is our general dogsbody, our knockabout, general purposes handyman. Tim is five feet four inches short and four feet round the middle. If Tim fell over, you wouldn't have to help him up, he would have rolled away.

We have a clutch of those big garden umbrellas in emerald green, deep orange and royal blue, all with natty white fringes, tatty white bird droppings and inspiring advertising slogans such as 'Schweppes', 'Martini', 'Robinsons'.

Rain or shine, come Whit we put them out with tables and chairs around our garden patio.

I found four of these umbrellas behind the high fence which screens our dustbins from the public gaze.

"Tim," I said. "There are four umbrellas leaning up against the dustbins. Only you, Tim, and I say this advisedly, could have put them there. Why, Tim, why did you so place them?"

Tim believes that on the ball, efficient go-getters speak in brief, staccato, clipped phrases. No wasted bits and pieces of verbal bric a brac.

"Gone," he said, "Gone, them are."

"Gone? I questioned. "They're not gone. I've just seen them there. Leaning against the dustbins. They're not gone."

"Not that sort of gone," Tim said, patiently. "Not gone, gone. They're gone, knackered gone, kaput gone. Buggert. Gone they are. Broke. That's what they are, broke. Broke off near the top. Metal fatigue. Buggert." he said again, allowing his lips the very merest horizontal and vertical movement. He sometimes clips his speech so short that the words have no real time to get out and they bounce off the back of his teeth and fall down his throat.

"Gone," Tim said. "Gone, them brollies. Shot. Won't stay up straight. Metal's broke. Brollie tips over."

We went together to look at them.

I pointed to the hinged joint designed so that the umbrella head can be angled against the sun. "They're made like that," I said. "They do that bit on purpose," and I explained the principle to him. "Now, if you pull this little metal collar here over that hinged joint, the tube becomes rigid and the umbrella stays up straight. If you want to tilt the umbrella when the sun has dropped down a bit, you push this collar up out of the way and the whole top tilts over. It's made to do just that," and I slid the thing up and down a few times to show him how it worked. He had a go for himself.

"I'll be damned," he said. "Bloody clever. Bit of thinking gone into that. Now't they can't do if they think on," and still marvelling, he took the umbrellas back to the garden. Once or twice during that day, I caught Tim tilting and straightening the umbrellas. Checking out the scientific principle. Making sure they still worked and weren't buggert.

******

I was deeply into growing vegetables from seed. I used to bring them on early in cold frames at the Old Rectory and then take them over to our house in Betwys y Coed for planting out. I grew petit pois, sugar and mange tout peas, dwarf and climbing beans, courgettes, parsley, lettuce — you name it, I grew it.

We had suffered about six weeks without any rain at all, an official declaration of drought and in some areas, standpipes in the streets. Tim watched while, every other day, I took the covers off the cold frames and watered the plants with a can, the hose pipe being forbidden.

"Green fingers," Tim said. "That's what you've got is green fingers. Couldn't grow grass, me. Great watching you, though.

Green fingers, that's what you've got with them veg."

Then, after all that drought, it started to rain. It was only just after dawn but as I heard the rain, I got up straight away. I was due to get up early for the market but hearing the rain, I got up even an hour before usual, got dressed and went out to take the covers off the cold frames.

Down in Manchester market I listened to the rain drumming on the high roof.

"Lay the dust, this will," said Len, on Cheshire Produce. "Good for the garden," said Dave on Sykes Fish. "Not half," I said. "You bet."

Tim's part-time. He works from nine until two. Tim's pretty hot on the right going home time. He's so anxious to get it right that he spends the last three ¡quarters of an hour or so of each work session, outside if dry, walking briskly backwards and forwards with a great show of purpose or, inside if wet, carrying an empty plastic bucket from room to room and, in both circumstances, making calls every five minutes in the kitchen to check the clock. Just before 2pm, on this particular day, he stuck his head around the kitchen door and by working his eyebrows up and down and I think, waggling his ears — although he may not have been waggling them, perhaps they were just being pulled up and down by his eyebrows — anyway, he gave me silently to understand that he wanted a word with me outside, before he signed off. Tim doesn't think that his close man-to-man relationship with the boss has any place in it for the female staff.

I went outside.

Tim looked over both his shoulders, not of course, at the same time but first over one and then over the other.

"Getting absent minded," he squeezed out.

"You are?" I asked.

"Not me ...... You. Not thinking proper."

"Oh!"

"You watered them plants yesterday. Forgot put covers back. Spotted it as soon as I come on. S'alreet. Purrem back."

"Put them back? The covers?"

"Purrem back. Them plants was getting soaked. Drowning they was. Covered 'em up, put them lids back on. Wet through they were, them veg." Tim clipped out at me, waiting for a pat on the head. If I'd have had a brick handy I would have given him one but I didn't, so I didn't.

"Thanks Tim," I said.

"Look after you, I do," said Tim and he went off to find an empty bucket to carry about for a bit.

*****

A few days later, Tim was washing down my car outside the kitchen door. I opened the kitchen door to ask him not to forget to vacuum the interior just as Tim, on the far side from me, sluiced the car down with a bucket of cold water chucked onto the roof. I can tell whichever aero-dynamic design engineers were responsible for the shape of the Citroen CX2400 that their lines work as well with water as they do with air. Dynamically, I got the lot straight through the air.

What was really interesting about this little contretemps was how clearly it isolated those with a sense of humour, those who can enjoy a joke, from the rest. I was glad to see that my kitchen staff to a woman all had a great sense of humour. They fell about laughing hysterically and eventually had to sit down and drink a cup or two of tea and eat butter with some toast before they stopped giggling and felt fit enough to lean back on the bain-marie — it's warmest there — chatting about Dallas and Dynasty and all that. Real lively sense of humour they had. I thought the way the water came off the roof of the car all over me was pretty funny too but I didn't bother laughing, not just then. A bit earlier, one of the girls had dropped half a dozen Denby ten inch dinner plates and I'd had a good belly laugh at the really dry way Betty had said "Less for the washer-up" and Joan had chipped in with "They're not good bouncers, are they?" "Not a patch on yours," I had quipped merrily and we had really enjoyed ourselves for a minute or two, well you have to laugh, haven't you? Any road up, it seemed that I'd used up all my laughs for that day, so when the water hit me, I just stood there in my wet clothes and I looked at Tim. He just stood there in his dry clothes and looked back at me. He didn't have any sense of humour at all, evidently, not a flicker of a smile. Just a look of frozen terror. I think someone had just walked over his grave, as we say.

******

Only last week, I asked Flo, "Where's Tim? What's he doing?" "He's outside making a bonfire of all the wood the gales brought down," she said. "A bonfire," I cried. "Oh no. Not a bonfire. Not Tim."

He really had been busy. He must have scoured the grounds for dead wood and he'd made a huge roaring bonfire, as big as a haystack. Right in the middle of our tarmac car park. I raced towards him. Well, raced is possibly a bit too strong. Let me say that I **would** have raced towards him if I could, but at my age and weight I suppose I lumbered towards him making what speed I could, waving my arms about and shrieking with mental anguish.

"S'alright guvnor. Plenty of room for cars to get round. In the middle, this is. Room all round." Tim prodded the blaze with the garden rake. The rake handle burned through and the rake head was lost in the flames.

"The car park you .....," I shouted. "You're burning a hole in the tarmac, melting the bloody car park."

Tim gave me a pitying look.

"Not that daft, guv," he said. "Thought of that. It's on a base."
It was. He'd built his bonfire on an old, eight by four sheet of
hardboard.

"Not that daft, guv, it's on a base."

******

Well. that's Tim. Before he came to work for us he worked
for a big local firm. I'll bet that when the board had one of those
godawful days when every single damn thing goes horribly
wrong and the sales director, the managing director and the

Chairman were all deciding whether to resign or just take a runing jump off Beachy Head, one of them, probably bent over a hari-kari knife, would pause and think for a moment and then look up and say "Just before I go, chaps, I must tell you what Tim did today down in the stores." They would all listen and then laugh and then another one would say "That's nothing, why only last week Tim was on the coggling bander and ......" They'd dig each other in the ribs and laugh a lot more and the first chap would wipe his eyes and put the big knife back into its leather case. They'd feel a whole lot better just thinking about Tim and the things that Tim does. So much better that they'd say "Let's have another look at this can of worms," and after chatting it over again, and kicking it around, one of them would suddenly say "Bollocks to it. I don't give a ......" and they'd all stand up straight again and say "Hear-hear, hear-hear, you're so right, old boy" and then they'd take a slug or two from the Chairman's special reserve before going off home to take their wives out for a drink with perhaps a bit of on the side leg-over later on.

That's the sort of effect Tim has on people. Every company should have a Tim. Every company but this one.

If you want our Tim, give us a ring. You can transfer the charge.

******

Chambermaids and Kitchen Staff

Whatever job we do in life, we all love our perks and thank heaven, every job has them. The humblest office worker need never go short of pens, paper clips or stationery and what a blessing is the company stamping machine when it comes time to post that bundle of Christmas cards or the annual report to the members of the Rugby Club. At much higher levels, the bill for a family dinner at a fashionable restaurant may well find itself in the business-entertainment expense file, the family having driven to and from the restaurant in the company car running on company petrol.

It's much the same in the hotel and catering business. The boss slides a bottle or two out of stock into his private quarters and lower down the ladder of opportunity the staff have to make what arrangements they can.

To be either a kitchen worker or a chambermaid is somewhat akin to having a pass key to a supermarket storeroom.

The chambermaid handles tea bags, sachets of coffee and drinking chocolate, creamers and U.H.T. milk, small packets of sugar or sugar cubes, paper tissues, toilet rolls, shampoos, soaps, and stationery. With a little sensible forward planning it is possible to acquire the more durable items such as bath mats and bath towels, bed sheets, blankets and pillows. Even the disappearance from the bedrooms of the odd trouser-press, colour TV set, divan bed or fitted carpet can always be blamed on the departed guest, especially if the guest is by now safely back in Tokyo or Houston.

I mentioned sensible forward planning. Although nothing to

do with the hotel business, I always remember the case of the nine-year-old boy who set out to swim the English Channel. Walking bravely into the sea he struck out for France. On and on he went, his head bobbing like a cork, now on the crest of a great rolling wave, now all but lost in the surging green trough and always followed closely by the motor boat carrying his trainer and helpers. A mere three miles from the French coast, the lad signalled that he was abandoning his attempt and needed urgently to be brought aboard. "Get him in lads," the trainer shouted. "He's got the cramps."

They laid the lad flat on the boat bottom, ready to massage his knotted muscles. "Where's the cramp, boy?" the trainer asked. "Cramp?" the lad said, "Cramp? Who said anything about cramp?" "Well, why did you give up lad?" "Stop messing about and help me up," the boy said, "I had to come out, I'm bursting for a pee." Too many bottles of Coke with his butties at lunchtime; complete lack of forward planning.

******

The link between the chambermaid and the kitchen worker exists in the need to barter goods. For instance, no matter how hard a chambermaid tries, or how many in her family at home, she can only usefully use so many toilet rolls, so many shampoos or pieces of soap a week, so it makes sense for her to trade those goodies surplus to her requirements with the similar surpluses of butter-portions, eggs, bacon, sausages, paté, pork chops, steaks, chicken pieces, asparagus spears, Brillo pads, heavy aluminium pans and copper fish kettles that the kitchen worker often finds such an *'embarassment de richesses'.* I think the proper name for this state of tandem operation is symbiosis and if it isn't, then it ought to be.

******

Astonished to discover the quantities of tea, coffee, soap, toilet rolls, etcetera used in the bedrooms every week, I decided that, although our residents were businessmen up here on business trips, they could hardly have left their bedrooms each day except to eat a truly enormous breakfast. After the porridge, the kippers and the haddock, and the bacon, sausage, egg and tomato, they immediately returned to their rooms where they must have spent the rest of the day either drinking — complimentary tonics, ginger ales, soda waters, tea, coffee and chocolate — or, as the consumption of toilet rolls and soap tablets indicated, they locked themselves in their bathroom for hours, alternately squitting and washing their hands.

*****

Experienced chambermaids and kitchen hands remember that it is politic to limit themselves to the daily use of a large carrier bag, never of the see-through plastic or the string-bag variety but, for obvious reasons, quite opaque. They tell management that they need the carrier bag for their lipstick and a clean handkerchief. They also bear in mind that walking away from work with a heavy list to one side, the bottom of the bag dragging on the floor or being pulled along on strap-on wheels, could arouse suspicion. As indeed, could anyone turning up for work pushing an empty supermarket trolley or driving a fork-lift truck.

When I was in my teens, I never needed an alarm clock to get me off to school on time. I was woken each morning by my lifelong companion and friend, Percy, tapping me gently on the chest. Well, I have to rely on my alarm clock nowadays and I haven't actually seen Percy for a year or two although I know he still hangs about somewhere nearby.

However, there are still plenty of other chaps about who don't need alarm clocks, and chambermaids, delivering early morning tea, occasionally come across 'homo erectus' in the person of the flasher. An experienced chambermaid knows that it is most injudicious to encourage the poor fellow, by rolling her eyes and flattering him with comments such as "Cor blimey sir, you don't get many of those to the kilo." Much wiser, whatever the actual facts of the case, to reduce his fervour with a pitying smile. "Never mind, sir. We all have to do the best we can with what God sends us. Nobody's perfect."

******

I mentioned that when Tim tossed a bucket of water over me, my kitchen staff proved they had a keen sense of humour by falling about laughing.

They know I like a good laugh too, so they are always giving me something to laugh about like using several times the amount of expensive dish-washing detergent necessary, then standing there embedded in a mountain of suds and bubbles, washing up in their wellies and snorkel masks.

When they are glazing vegetables with butter and sugar, they like to put them on full heat and leave them on until they begin to smoke. They know that the smell of burnt butter, sugar and carrot or cauliflower always brings me rushing into the kitchen as it does when they drop Denby plates, cups and saucers, French casserole dishes and so on. I had the kitchen floor covered in quarry tiles instead of thick foam rubber on a spring base. The girls love to remind me of what a fool I was.

They don't like the round heavy aluminium pans either. Buying round ones was another mistake on my part, so whenever they have a slack moment, they set about bashing the pans until they are square instead of round or even triangular instead of round. They are quite right though, it's amazing how many more pans you can get on the gas if they've got straight sides. The lids don't fit anymore, but I've managed to sell them to a local rock group as cymbals.

One of my kitchen staff specialises in tricks and comic turns with the vegetables. Using only an ordinary swing blade vegetable peeler, she is able to reduce a whole bag of potatoes into a single pan full of irregularly shaped potato balls or turn a net of carrots into Julienne matchsticks, one matchstick per carrot taken right down the centre. She decapitates broccoli or asparagus slap up against the head and chucks the stems away or dumps a whole net of mange tout peas on the compost heap because there "is nothing in them" and they aren't worth shelling. A laugh a minute she is.

Another lady has found out that if you always leave the fridge doors slightly ajar, you don't have that tiresome chore of defrosting the fridges because no ice has formed. She was also the first to discover that if you mix warm portions of a dish containing onions with cold portions of the same dish and put them in a frostless fridge, the next time you bring them out, they'll be fizzing away like a pot full of sherbert and frothing up all over. They have a lot of fun with that one.

But of them all, I think their best joke was the time we had a wedding reception and the menu started with consomme.

We had a huge pan of consomme on the stove and another of black coffee. They sent out bowls of coffee instead of consomme but just for once the laugh was on them. The sort of coffee and consomme we make, no one could tell the difference, even when of necessity, we had to follow the whole thing through and send the consomme out in the coffee pots. Well, when you think of it, with demerara sugar in it and double cream on top, I don't suppose there's a lot of people about, certainly not in Haughton Green, who *could* tell the difference.

******

Beatrice and Gertrude work in my kitchen on the day shift from 9.0am until 3.0pm. Practically every day starts the same way.

They are supposed to start at nine am but it's actually 9.15
G.M.T when they come into the kitchen. The clock on the wall
reads 9.30.

"Just look at that," Beatrice says, "still set by the night staff
fifteen minutes fast for going home time. Just a minute love,
we'll soon have that right." And she sets the clock back to just
after nine, fifteen minutes slow, just right for signing on time.

"Put kettle on love," she says to Gertrude. "I must just nip
into the toilet. I can't wait any longer."

"It's silly to be uncomfortable," Gertrude replies. "You should
have gone before you left your house."

"What, in my time! Eeh, never."

They both draw on their full tar fags and lean on the wall to
enjoy some real, in-depth, coughing and hawking.

While Beatie is out of the kitchen, Gert takes half a pound
of butter from out of the fridge and puts the kettle, filled to
overflowing, on to boil. She puts six slices of bread into the
toaster and switches it on.

Beatie and Gert only have four slices between them, but the
toaster holds six slices and neither of them have ever worked
out the selector switch's confusing markings 2- 4- 6.

Beatie comes back and they start on their butter with toast
and wash it down with tea and the cream from the top of two
previously unopened bottles of milk.

They start their day with a good chat.

"What was it last night then, the bingo or the telly?"

"It were telly. There was a new one on last night. First of
a series, the TV Times said, called 'Hang About, Hang About'."

"Eeh, I watched that too. Weren't it good. All about that Irish
Catholic girl as wanted to turn Jewish so she could marry that
rabbi's son."

"The rabbi's son, him what were working in the rag trade for
that Packy Indian boss that stuttered. That Indian what stuttered

and was complaining to the Race Relations Board because the B.B.C. wouldn't give him a job as a Newsreader. He said it were because he were coloured but they said if he were't newsreader, the news would be stale before he'd read it all out."

"And that bit where the rabbi goes on a visit to the Irish girl's home and without him knowing what's in it, they give him a ham sandwich and as soon as he bites into it his trousers fall down. Talk about laugh!"

"Eeh, it were so true to life, you just had to laugh."

"Eh, and what about that 85-year-old lady, in 'Grab What You Can'? Did you see her, that old lady that won all them presents?"

"She won a set of golf clubs and a rowing machine, twelve free lessons at Karate and twelve free lessons at break-dancing **and** a heart and kidney transplant, whichever she needs first. Lucky old bugger."

As they talk, rivulets of melted butter spill off their sodden toast and run down their chins. They finish their tea-break. It was all of half an hour to the next. Just as they are reluctantly about to start peeling potatoes, Lily, the cleaner, comes into the kitchen.

"Eeh, I don't know," Lily complains, "I just don't seem to be able to get started this morning. My heart's not in it. Make us a cuppa ducks. My back's killing me."

Gert takes half a pound of butter from the 'fridge and puts the re-filled kettle on to boil. She throws the two cold slices of toast into the bin then she puts six fresh slices of bread into the toaster and switches on.

"Were you watching telly last night, or did you go Bingo?" Lily asks, "There were this Catholic girl and her boy was a Jew working in the rag trade for a darkie who stuttered."

"Don't forget the boy's father were a rabbi, can you imagine them giving a rabbi a ham sandwich. Mark you I don't think they meant any harm. They weren't just thinking."

"Well you wouldn't, would you? I mean, our lot wear their

collars back to front. You can always see who's a priest. I wouldn't know a rabbi if I fell over one. But it were funny when his trousers fell down. And the look on his face, what you could see of it behind that nose on him."

The lunchtime waitresses come in at about 11.30, so they fill the kettle up to the top, put it on to boil and get some butter out of the 'fridge. The waitresses had watched 'Hang About, Hang About' and they both thought it was right funny the way the black chap had taken it the wrong way when he couldn't get a job with the B.B.C. as a newsreader. "He should have known it was nothing to do with him being coloured," says Mildred. "It were the radio he wanted a job with not TV. They wouldn't have known he was coloured. You can't tell on the wireless."

"Eeh," says Gert. "And I'd never even cottoned on to that."

They all agree that when it came to putting on comedies that were true to life, you couldn't beat I.T.V., Granada especially.

And weren't that old biddy a right lucky bugger, winning all them prizes just for rearranging the words 'And-Chips-Fish' to make a wellknown phrase or saying. As Beatie says, if that old trout had fell down the lav she'd have come up with a gold watch in her hand.

******

A New Approach
to Staff

"You know," I said, to my wife, "I've come to the conclusion that when the staff — God bless them — do something wrong, instead of me keeping my cool and talking things over with them quietly and constructively, I'm inclined to blow my top. I think I rant and rave too much."

"Rant and rave? Never. Not you," Flo said. I was touched by her loyalty. "No, let's be honest. Let's face it. I do tend to rant and rave too much. I'm going to try a new approach, a conciliatory approach, an appeal to reason, a real effort to get them to understand that I also have problems."

"Like growing old, being overweight and drinking too much?"

"Not exactly," I said, a shade huffily. "I mean the problems of management."

"Well, you **do** that. Feel free. Have a go. Tell them about your problems."

"I will," I said. "I will. Starting today."

******

I found Betty in the kitchen.

"Betty, if you don't mind, if it's convenient, that is, I'd like a quick word. Got a minute then have you? If you don't mind?"

"Fat lot you care what I mind, Mr Chadwick. Well let's out with it then, what have I done wrong now, I don't know what's come over you lately, but for the last seven years you've done nothing but find fault with everything I do and speaking frankly, while we're about it, I don't mind telling you that I'm just about up to here with your arm waving and shouting and finger jabbing and while I'm getting a load off my chest, I'd like to remind you that some of the language you use is very unpleasant, most offensive it is, I'm not one to take offence at language, I mean we get language on the pictures and the telly all the time don't we but it's not alright down here, no it's not and if my hubby knew how you spoke to me he'd be down here in a flash, just look at that time I dropped a tray and broke six plates and two advocat dishes, it's not even as if I did it on purpose, so it was just an accident and we couldn't help laughing, Ann and me but not you, oh no, you couldn't join in with us, could you, you standing there all white-faced and trembling, that's just the trouble, you see, you can never see the funny side of things, you have no sense of humour you don't, always fidgeting about nothing, fussing like you do about switching lights or gas rings off when they're not being used and stirring things so that they don't stick to the pan and burn and all that carrying on about the vegetables have to be cooked half raw, Al Denton, whoever he is when he's at home, I'll tell you this, you wouldn't catch me biting into those carrots and all that, *I'd* be afraid for my top set I would, and look at the fuss you made when something went wrong with the microwave and you tried to make it out it was because we'd put a baking tray of Yorkshire's in to freshen them up, as if it was the metal tray that did it and not that it was just a duff machine, bought second-hand and dirt cheap if I'm any judge."

"And another thing," she said. "While we're about it I'm sick of you snatching the veg peeler off me when I'm peeling carrots and then wagging your hand about as fast as you can just to show me that when you do it so fast, your hand stays on your arm and doesn't come off at the wrist, it's nothing but rules and regulations here, no smoking in the kitchen, don't lick the serving spoons, don't stick your fingers in the soup to taste it or see whether it's hot enough, don't pull rollmops out of the jar with your fingers, don't blow your nose on your apron, don't, don't, don't, that's all we ever hear from you, never a do, it's all don'ts and don't you think for a minute that I'd be slaving away here if I didn't need every penny of the money, if you think I'm here because I like the place, you're wrong you are, not that you'd ever admit it, to being wrong about anything, and no, if you don't mind, I'd be obliged if you'd stop lecturing me and let me just get on with the job, such as it is, me being always on the last minute and you wanting me to do the work of two, so just leave me alone will you and let me get on, the sooner I'm finished the sooner I can get back to where people have a bit of understanding."

"Right Betty, I'm glad we had this little talk," I said, "that's fine then. Carry on love."

*****

I tried again, this time with our waitress, Maureen.

"Maureen .....," I started, but Maureen butted in.

"It's never any different, it's always the same here, isn't it, just see how the breakfast staff have left the restaurant, just look at the state of it, the dirty buggers and that's swearing but it's not fair what with Doreen not being in today and I've got the place to clean up, there's half the tables without clean napkins, all them butters and the Melba toast to do and I told you last week that there's no more redcurrant jelly and Andrew says there's roast lamb on for lunch, they'll all want the lamb and they'll blame me that there's no redcurrant jelly, not that we've been all that busy lately what with you and young Mr Chadwick, if you don't mind me saying so, upsetting all our customers, him with his C.I.D. Ban-The-Bomb stuff all over the place and the Evening News publishing your letters saying everyone else is balmy and we're being run by a bunch of lunatics and that God is either dead or mad and if all that wasn't enough to empty the place, all your carry on about they're not to do no smoking in the restaurant and they've got to wear a jacket and tie and socks, and they mustn't turn up without booking, and no standing at the bar, just you stop and think for a moment Mr Chadwick and you can see that not all the fault's on one side, like when you're going on about we must never go back to the kitchen empty-handed or there's fish knives and horseradish and all that still on the table when they're sitting there eating their sweets or having their coffee, as if it mattered, they're not in the way or anything, those fish knives and condiments there's still plenty of room for their sweets it's only you that carries on not the customers."

"I mean you wouldn't believe the fuss you make every day if you can't see the table numbers from the restaurant desk because I've put them on the tables sideways and behind the flower bowls. Like I've said there are faults on your side a lot worse than table numbers, just look at the way you go on at us about the cheese board, because we've forgot to trim the cheese and that we must always cut the cheese through the rind so that they all get a bit and we must only *offer* the celery and the biscuits to them and then we must take them away because if we don't and we leave them on the table, they'll all have some celery and biscuits even when they're not having the cheese, as if you couldn't afford the celery and biscuits, it's none of my business but you always seem to have enough money for holidays two or three times a year, it's a bit too much sometimes, I do my best even when I have a cold like all last week, I'm still a housewife and you know when I've finished here, I can't put my feet up and look at my travel brochures, I'm off back home cleaning up and getting my Eric's tea ready, a bit of kindness would help, I don't have an easy life like you do with people working for *me* but I don't suppose we can expect a kind word from you except at Christmas time when you know you're coining it and you've had a few drinks and given us a bottle of Golden

Guinea between the ten of us, I could weep sometimes, I really could ......" and she started to.

******

"Well?" Flo asked, "how did it go?"
"How did what go?"
"Your heart to heart. Your new approach to staff?"
"Oh, that! It went very well, actually. I had a long talk with Betty and then later on with Maureen and I explained what problems we have and they both agreed with me that the faults are not all on one side, and it's not easy for me, being the boss."

******

Mark you, it's not always as clear cut as that.
Mavis is one of our chambermaids. A treasure, Mavis is.
She stopped me in the restaurant.
"Excuse me, Mr Chadwick," she said, "but I'd like a word with Mr Chadwick Junior. Do you know where he is?"
"Yes, Mavis, he's down in London for the weekend. Can I be of any help?"
"Well he's got me down on next week's rota to do the bedrooms each day including Tuesday but Maureen's on holiday next week so on Tuesday Doreen will have to stand in for Betty in the kitchen because Betty's got to go to the clinic. With Maureen on holiday, it's Doreen."
"What's all that about Betty and the kitchens got to do with you and the bedrooms and Doreen is a waitress so what's she doing in the kitchen? For God's sake?"
"I've just told you Mr Chadwick, your son would understand. It's obvious isn't it? With Maureen on holiday and Doreen standing in for Betty then Jean won't be in on Wednesday because she'll be in on Tuesday doing Doreen's shift and you've got the

80

rooms full and Doreen and Colleen can't do twenty-six breakfasts unless Ethel gives them a hand, now can they?"

"Ethel?" I said. *"Ethel?"*

"She'll have to give Doreen and Colleen a hand."

"I'm sure you're right," I said feebly.

"It's not as easy as that," Mavis said. "Oh dear me no."

"It's not?" I asked.

"No, it's not. Who's going to stand in for Ethel while she's helping Maureen and Colleen with the breakfasts?"

"You tell me, Mavis"

"I am standing in for Ethel so if I'm doing for Ethel, I won't be in the bedrooms, will I? Now do you see?"

"I think so Mavis. You won't be on the bedrooms on Tuesday. So what do you want me to do?"

"That's up to you Mr Chadwick."

"It is? It's up to me, is it? Oh. Well. There we are then."

"It is if you want those bedrooms doing and I can't do them because I'm standing in for Ethel. You'll have to get someone else."

"Whom do you suggest?"

"It's not up to me to make the suggestions, I just have to do the bedrooms. It's you that's a director and the chairman and all that how-do-you-do but I know what I'd do if I was the boss. I do indeed."

"You do. Thank God for that. So tell me, Mavis, what would you do, if you were the boss?"

"Well, Denton Wakes holidays don't start till next week, so Colleen could stand in for Doreen if Doreen would do for Maureen on the Monday. Then on the Tuesday, Maureen could do the same for Doreen which would allow Colleen to stand in for Ethel in the kitchen. Then Jean and Edith could come across to the bedrooms, that is until twelve o'clock, then Edith could go back in the kitchen so that Edna could do the bar instead of Joyce."

"Edna? Edna?" I cried. "How long have we had an Edna? Which one is Edna?"

"Edna's the dark-haired one, Mr Chadwick, the one that has a Persian cat and fishes."

"Edna has fishes? What sort of fishes, for God's sake?"

"Not that sort of fishes. Not *fishes*. *She* fishes with her husband Len. That's why Joyce always does the bar on Saturdays, except this Saturday because it's her twins' birthday. Not *her* twins' birthday, Joyce hasn't got a twin. It's her twins' birthday, her little twin girls' birthday. Then when Edna came out of the bar, she could help me with the linen. That should fix it."

"It should? Right, Mavis. I don't know what I'd do without you. Just go through all that again and I'll write it down."

"Really Mr Chadwick, you've got a mind like a sieve."

"It comes to all of us Mavis," I said. "It's old age."

"More likely it's that and the drink." Mavis said.

******

The Chef ...... and the roast kid

It is a strange phenomenon that as we learn more of the Third World starvation the more we are interested in food and its preparation. We turn from eye witness descriptions of whole communities of men, women and children starving to death to scan books of recipes. We turn our eyes from scarifying pictures of pot-bellied children with match-stick legs to colour photographs of the Great Dishes of the World.

Along with this new obsession with food, the chief engineer of the finished product has become something of a cult figure. There is even a glossy, quarterly magazine, baldly entitled 'Chef', dedicated to chefs and all their works. Its front cover usually shows one of the 'greats', Albert Mosiman, one or both of the Roux Brothers or some other legendary luminary clad in immaculate whites, never a gravy stain nor splash of egg yolk to be seen, whites whiter than those a surgeon wears in the operating theatre. Unlike a surgeon who, in a similar picture, could well be holding out a gory transplant liver to the camera eye; the chef, smirking with smug, self-satisfaction is displaying for your astonished approval, a 'painting on a plate', a dish made up of rare and expensive ingredients even more expensively boiled, grilled, steamed or fried and carefully arranged by colour, shape and texture to seduce the eye and activate the salivary glands.

A supreme of chicken, stuffed with caviare, wrapped in a thin slice of truffled parma ham, served on a triangle of Strasbourg paté de foie gras, coated with a lobster sauce, and garnished with sliced kiwi fruit, radichio leaf and a light peppering of

Maltesers. This, or some such other arty-tarty, time and money-wasting creation is presented — with no mention, of course, of what the privileged diner is asked to pay for it — as the very epitome of the chef's art and bears about as much relationship to reality as would the magazine 'Motorcar', if it only published articles about, and pictures of, Rolls Royce's, Mercedes and Cadillacs.

The same trade press which prints the glossy paen to perfection, the 'Chef' quarterly, meantime in the parent weekly magazine draws most of its revenue from equally colourful, full-page advertisements of chemical convenience foods never to be seen in the kitchens of the exalted but, of necessity, heavily relied upon by the majority of working chefs.

Catering colleges all over the country labour long and hard turning out chefs who may well dream of one day replacing Albert Roux on 'Chef's' front cover. Sadly they will, in fact, spend their entire working lives in undermanned and ill-equipped kitchens struggling to produce edible three-course meals that can be profitably sold for a little less than you would pay for an Albert Roux first course. Not for them, recourse to the fresh truffles, the Strasbourg paté, the Beluga caviare. No, theirs is the genuine Mozzarella-type cheese substitute, the boil-in-the-bag chemical formulae, the miracle add hot-water-and-watch-it-swell dehydrates.

Rather than teach the arts of Larousse, Caréme or Escoffier, the catering colleges would serve their aspirant chefs better by putting them through a Beginner's Course on Practical Chemistry.

The practically minded young chefs as opposed to the dreamer of idylls will abandon all notions of one day being backed by a dedicated brigade and producing delectable dishes of Olympic grandeur to delight the palates of Texan oil tycoons and Arab sheiks and settle for the nitty gritty. There just aren't enough well-breeched gourmets to go around and, for the rest, the average British diner prised out of his most favourite place, the bar, and persuaded to put out his pipe or cigar before weaving his way to his table, will already have smoked and boozed to the point where his palate couldn't distinguish between a *'Pot au Feu'* or a tin of Chunky Pedigree Chum. The chef's carefully crafted pastry boats and savoury contents will be sunk and lost, without trace, in an icy sea of 'gee and tee' or the foaming surf of a sea of best bitter.

Second only to his stinking dog and jokes about the Irish, mothers-in-law and genital activity, the average Brit enjoys nothing more than a meal starting with a prawn cocktail or a slice of melon splattered with ground ginger, a slab of beefsteak eight inches long by four across by two deep, cooked, of course, to his most intricate and detailed but totally meaningless instructions such as 'rare to medium' or 'medium to well done' and a final, grand slam topper-out of a block of Black Forest gateau afloat on a bed of double cream.

******

We serve Black Forest gateau — well you have to, don't you? — and on one occasion it had been brought out of the freezer a little too late in the day.

I was sent for.

"This gateau is frozen on the inside," the punter snivelled.

"As it should be, sir." I said. "You have been served with a slice of our speciality 'Winter in the Black Forest' which, unforgiveably, is slightly thawed on the outside. Just leave those nasty, soggy bits and the waitress will chip you another piece from the middle."

******

After years of cooking for the Brits a majority of chefs are either active drunks or members of Alcoholics Anonymous (failed). Many are on ticket of leave from Rampton or Broadmoor or just about to go back inside. They develop a deformity of the right arm operating the Bonzer can-opener and from beating gooey lumps of monosodium glutinous out of made-up packet sauces and soups. They usually have a good pair of welder's goggles and use tube after tube of high density, U.V. barrier sun cream during prolonged spells at the microwave oven. The best of them also develop enough skin sense, tactile awareness, that is, to realise that their three-day old, gungy, green finger-dressing has just dropped off into the minestrone and have heat-immune chef's hands that they can then plunge into the minestrone and rootle about with until they find the poxy thing again before it goes out to a table and is scooped up by the diner.

Good chefs always wear suede shoes in the kitchen because they absorb drops of hot fat better than leather or plastic. They also have those checked trousers, down the back buttock bit of which they like to wipe their hands. They wear a thick white jacket to stop their chest hair from bursting into flames when leaning over the gas burners and a tall white hat under which they can conceal, when needs be, the odd nicked pheasant or fillet steak piece until going home time.

Really sound, steady, reliable chefs must be capable of working long and arduous hours, sustained only by Ceserani and Kinton, fat beef sandwiches, gallons of ale and a salary slightly less than double that of the company chairman.

******

I've had one or two trainee chefs myself.

One sixteen-year-old lad joined us straight from catering college. He'd been with us only a couple of weeks when I came back from the market with a young roe deer, about sixty pounds in weight, as nature made her, all there, head, legs, hooves, pelt, but now very dead and without all her messy inside bits. I lifted her out of the trailer and got her across my shoulders, shepherd and sick sheep wise. I staggered into the kitchen and pitched the beast onto the floor. Young Albert went white. "Oh Mr Chadwick," he bleated. "Whatever's that?" "It's a bloody great Alsatian," I told him. "Just hit it with the car. It's dead."

"Oooh," he whimpered, clutching at the benching. "Whatever are you going to do with it?"

"Skin it, cut it up and cook the bugger. Serve it with a wine sauce as venison."

Young Albert fainted. Just like that, bang. On the deck, he was.

That reminds me of another time. I had a chef called Dai Griffiths. Dai was about six foot two tall, one foot in diameter and nine stone in weight. Dai's engine ran on pure 4 star adrenalin. He was a workaholic and the only man I knew who was likely one day to tear himself down the middle because of his habit of moving violently in two opposite directions at the same time. He modelled his kitchen performance on those one-man-band street musicians, those buskers we used to see, clashing cymbals between their knees, squeezing an accordion with bells on their wrists, working a tap drum with strings from their elbows whilst blowing desperate, false notes on a mouth organ suspended before their lips from a six-inch nail driven into their forehead, just above their bulging, bloodshot eyes.

Dai chopped with one hand, nudged a pan over with his elbow, stirred a sauce with his other hand, using a whisk, of course, not his actual hand, and opened the oven door with his left foot whilst his right leg and foot were resolutely setting off for the cold room.

This time it wasn't a roe deer but half a dozen large hares I'd brought back from the market. "While I'm upstairs having my breakfast, Dai," I said "You can start on skinning, gutting and jointing those hares. I'll be down in a minute or two." Dai took a deep breath, whirled his arms about a bit to wind himself up and then ferociously attacked the first hare. Chop.... chop....

off with the feet.... chop.... now the head. Knife into the belly-pelt, off with the pelt, rip-cut-open it up...., out with the entrails..... glop.... reserve the drained blood from behind the slit diaphragm. Chop.... chop.... chop...., rib-cage gone...., chop.... legs.... saddle.... haunches....

When I came down in my whites from my flat, Betty was looking quite upset. "Dai's had a bit of an accident," she said. I was very cross. With staff, accidents are like going to the lavatory. They never think of having accidents or going to the lavatory in their own time. It's always in the boss's time.

"Now Dai's either working here as a whole Dai or not at all," I said. "If he's chopped off a hand, he'll have to reply to one of those 'Single Hand Chef Wanted' ads. If he's lost a foot, he'll have to try for a grant to train as a one-legged tap dancer. I'm sick of staff having accidents at work. It's time they showed a bit of consideration for management."

"It's not Dai," Betty said, "It's that little boy from across the road. You know that Dai's very short sighted and too vain to wear glasses. Well, this little boy wandered into the kitchen and he really is very small, not the size of two pennorth of copper and he was wearing this brown hairy coat and — well, Dai must have been miles away, because before he knew it, he'd picked this lad up and...." "Really," I shouted, "this is all too much. I'm going to put my foot down. There's going to be changes. I can only put up with so much. Where is Dai?"

"Now see what you have done." I said severely. "How many times have I said slow down? Take your time and do it properly. Y'know Dai, I sometimes wonder if you know what you are doing. There's going to be trouble about this, you mark my words. Is this the sort of thing they taught you at college? Is it?" Dai really was most upset. "I'm terribly sorry," he said. "I really am terribly sorry. I just wasn't thinking. I mean, it's not very well-lit in that prep room and he **was** wearing that hairy brown coat. And he was very small. Not much bigger than a hare. It's a mistake anyone could have made. Nobody's perfect."

"Maybe so but I shudder to think what people will say when this gets out," I said. "Look Dai, the first thing you had better do is to go and see his mum and dad to explain what has happened and how it happened and then to apologise. You can tell them about the lighting in the prep room and the brown coat and the lad being so small and that and point out that it was a mistake that anyone could have made. Tell them it's no good crying over spilt milk — …. Tell them, if there's anything we can do to compensate them …. Anything reasonable, that is …. nothing silly, and you'd better say 'ex gratia' …. That's the way to put it, we'll do anything reasonable that's 'ex gratia'. As long as it's reasonable. No promises, mark you."

Well as it turned out, the lad's parents were quite reasonable. Under the circumstances. Of course, I think that films and TV have changed people's outlook quite a lot, horror films like Halloween and Texas Chain Saw Massacre, and politicians popping up before their eyes on TV, often without any warning, and talking at them. Well, all that sort of thing has certainly got people more used to the downright nasty side of life.

Dai did a sort of action replay, only this time, filleting whole cod instead of hare. They agreed that, what with the lighting and the way Dai went at it all hell for leather, any little lad bearing the slightest resemblance to a whole cod, say if he had sticking-out-eyes and was cold and slimy to the touch, would have been well advised to stand well away from the chopping block. So they could see how much easier it was to make a mistake with a little lad in a hairy brown overcoat and hares in the hairy brown pelt. They raised the one small point that they had already bought the lad a few Christmas presents that wouldn't be needed now. I reimbursed them and let them keep the presents but, as they were still quite young, it was on the strict understanding that should they have another boy and thus be able to use the presents later, they would return the money in full.

When we'd finished the demonstration in the kitchen and we'd hammered out the financial details, I gave them a free cup of coffee and then showed them round. They liked the place and they booked a table for dinner later in the week. As a goodwill gesture, again I didn't charge them for their coffee even although this time they also had an After Eight mint each, I didn't say anything, I just hoped they would notice and appreciate the gesture. I always reckon that no matter what the cost, gestures like that are worth it if they make people your customers for life.

Incidentally, it's worth mentioning that once again it was management, that is me, and not one of my office staff who noticed early on the day they were eating with us that our menu included Roast Kid. Even though it was the culinary Roast Kid, that is baby goat, the very word might have stirred unpleasant memories so I had it taken off and replaced with the more innocuous Jumbo Beefy Beefburger. People can be very touchy and anyway, there were plenty of other things on the menu including some dishes I do quite well, for instance, breaded plaice fillets or roast leg of pork with sage and onion stuffing and apple sauce. To name just a couple.

******

Bar Staff

Very soon now, the relentless passage of time, 'like an ever rolling stream' will have born away all who knew the great railway hotels in their heyday. Then there will be no one left to mourn their passing.

When I was a working class teenager in Manchester in the hungry thirties, the Midland Hotel seemed to represent a totally different, unattainable world and I would have been as lief to try to enter that imposing pile as I would have been to have been shot from a cannon without a safety net.

Just as Liverpool scousers looked upon the Adelphi, Yorkshire tykes saw the more modern Queens or the Brummies felt about the Albany, these hotels, monuments to the wealth and the power of that class which ruled the British Empire and Britain, were foreign territory to the majority of us. Our nearest approach to them was as passing outsiders, looking in through the tall, velvet-draped windows of the magnificent restaurants, banqueting suites and public rooms and watching men and women from the corridors of power washing down the paté foie gras with the Dom Perignon.

I was twenty six and had just broken through the one thousand pounds a year salary barrier — a laughable figure now when lads straight from school start at three times that sum, but I think if my then employers in 1947 had asked me to sign a contract for life at £1,250 a year, I would have snatched their hand off. I was twenty six, I say, before I summoned up the courage to go through the revolving door at the Midland Hotel and brave the top-hatted, frock-coated, silver-haired head porter. If he had jerked his thumb and said "On your way" I would most likely have turned tail and crept out but, miraculously, he let me pass into that hallowed place. He went on letting me pass for many years afterwards, primarily because he now knew that I spent a great deal of my expense account in there, in the French, the Trafford and the cocktail bar. In time he and I became friendly, so much so that he would permit me to press the odd brace of half crowns, then, with inflation, a ten shilling note and finally, a oncer into his palm, not for doing anything but giving me a smile and the time of day.

In those days, there was a baronial men's room, attended by a charming old fellow who would offer you the use of his nail-brushes, nail-files and combs, and would solicitously run the hot water into the basin for you whilst he carefully hung your jacket on a coat hanger. Then he would help you back into your jacket, lightly brushing its collar and shoulders. All for a tanner, a bob and finally a florin or a tosheroon.

The bars were in the charge of men called Samuel or Albert or Joseph and woe betide you if you shortened their names to Sam, Bert or Joe. They were shining, scrubbed men with full, pink cheeks and bright eyes. Their hair was neatly trimmed, as were their short clean nails. They wore black ties and immaculate starched, white mess-jackets. They were the classic bartenders of yesteryear, now but dim shades in old men's memories.

They have all gone, and all is changed. For the worse.

The top hats and frock coats out in the front hall went at about the same time that they put on a dreadful modern front in place of the old portico.

Then they used an architect I imagine they borrowed from a milk bar chain and he destroyed the old Palm Court. The towering marble columns were wrapped in hardboard tubes. They were decorated with garishly painted climbing vines and the place was refurnished with vulgarly modern chairs and settees in Day-Glo colours.

The Lounge, as they now call it, has been done over several

times since but they have never got it back to the splendidly simply elegance of the Edwardian Palm Court and you would have to strain your imagination to catch, once again, the ghostly echoes of the piano and string quartet and the rattle of the quality china on the trolleys serving cucumber sandwiches and afternoon tea. The countless guests of elegance, wit and charm who once graced its muffled corridors have all gone, together with the head porter's silver hairs and Samuel and Albert and Joseph. Nor, as the cliché has it, shall we see their like again.

Where once was the Grill Room is now the Butty Boat Bar. I went in there one night. At a lunatic decibel level, the juke box was belting out some repetitive, thumping din, over which background noise some mindless, hairy neanderthal was shouting words of frustration and hate and rage. The 'group' was probably called 'The Gungies' or 'Snot' or 'The Sweaty Crotch'. I don't suppose anyone else there that night had ever sung or even heard the song that went 'When I grow too old to dream, I'll have you to remember. And when I grow to old to dream, your love will live in my heart.' I'm not surprised either, it was pretty pukey stuff, that song was. But at least it was less repellant than the shouting of the Sweaty Crotch.

I had to wait to order my drink because the bartender, a young man in tight, greasy jeans and long greasy hair, in an open-necked shirt and rolled-up shirt sleeves, with a cigarette going, was chatting up two meaty young ladies sitting on their bar stools. Eventually, I said "I've worked a bar myself. Can I come round and pull myself a pint? I don't mind."

"Oh, we're feeling like that then are we?" he said. "Got out of the wrong side of the bed this morning, did we? Right, Colonel. What can I do for you?"

I'd suddenly had enough. "What can you do for me? I'll tell you. For me, you can piss off," I told him, then I did just that myself, as sharpish as possible, in case he took it the wrong way. *'Better by far you should forget and smile, than that you should remember and be sad.'* Well maybe so, certainly in the context that Christina Rossetti wrote those lines. But with Richard II, I want to cry 'O call back yesterday, bid time return.'

Well, the *modus vivendi* has altered over the years and nowadays it is a necessary qualification for all bar staff to be incurably heavy smokers, as nothing looks more unreal, more incongruous, less professional than someone serving you without a cigarette dangling from their lips or from the fingers of the hand holding the glass.

It is the fingers of the cigarette-holding hand — that is, the fingers that look like brown chipolatas — that are always used for holding the glass. Only at the point of serving, is the cigarette transferred to the mouth. If, during this transference, some ash falls into the drink, today's bartender will use an index finger to push it below the surface where it will probably dissolve, but, in any event, will scarcely be noticed.

For a long time now, actors in films both for cinema and television and on the stage, have demonstrated most clearly the correct, and certainly the most chic, way to pass a glass. "Can I get you a drink?" they say. Then they pour from a decanter, never a bottle, drop the ice in with their fingers and, suspending a glass from a limp wrist, with thumb and four fingers planted firmly around the rim to which the recipient will shortly apply his or her lips, they advance upon their guest, holding the glass out at arm's length as if it were a dead rat.

Our bar staff are quick learners and throughout the length and breadth of the land, that's just the way it's now done. At least, thick fingerprints and perhaps a coat of lipstick on the rim do stop your lips from slipping off the glass.

Bar persons are generally given to wearing heavy-duty, after-shave lotions or hair lacquer and pungent anti-perspirants and deodorants, under-arm for the ladies and the roll-on-ball type for the fellows. Anyone drinking in this miasma and unable to determine whether he's drinking a full port or a dry sherry will soon push off and thus reduce the work load of the bar staff, which seems to be the whole point. A point also helped by rinsing used glasses in industrial bleach and wiping them, all except the lipsticked bit, with the glass-cloth or the floor-cloth, whichever is marginally the cleaner. Get the buggers in and get 'em out again as fast as possible then we can all go home. That seems to be the principle.

As already said, the fashion in working clothes is radically altered from more formal days and it is now quite proper for a bar person to be on duty with sleeves rolled up or just flappng about, a shirt open to the waist and a swinging gold pendant brushing the hairs on the chest.

The bar men can dress the same way too.

******

Whilst we're on the subject of bars, let me tell you about this American. I came into my bar just as his host, a regular whom I knew well, was asking his guest what he'd have to drink.

"A straight malt whisky, on the rocks, with water," he said and then — as a panicky afterthought and not terribly *sotto voce:* "Is the water here safe, is it drinkable?"

"Of course it is Henry," and the host placed the orders with the barmaid. I went up to them. "Hello Chad," the host said. "I'd like you to meet my friend, Henry Phefferschmeckle. Henry, this is Chad, the patron-chef." We solemnly duked each other. "I'm pleased to make your acquaintance," Henry said. "You sure have a nice place here."

"It's okay," I said, slipping easily into Stateside talk, "but as of now, business is a bit schlekt. You can see how quiet we are. You get more action in a morgue."

"You don't say! How is this then? We've been hearing about your goddam recession. You suffering from the economic shortfall?"

"Recession? It's not the recession. It's the public. Disloyal they are. Fickle they are. Rats leaving the sinking ship. I mean, there we were having a pretty good run. The money was good, man. Then last week, we have this bit of an earth tremor. San Francisco? You can forget it. Nothing. Scarcely enough to rattle a loose window pane, but it still happened. You see, we're on a sort of a split in the earth's crust, like you're on the San Andrean or whatever fault, but ours is not as big. Even so, the ground here is pretty ancient, it goes back a long time. It's pretty old soil round here. People have lived here for centuries. The whole place is full of old cess pits that are full. The water still comes to us through Roman clay pipes and they lie side by side with later Saxon sewers. A bit of a land-slip, a hair-line fracture or two and bingo, crappy water through the taps and eleven cases of Old Rectory typhoid. It was the water. Seven dead and four in intensive care. I suppose that under the circumstances, we should boil all the water but the gas main went at the same time and the electricity main fuse keeps blowing. I'm really fed up. It all gets a bit too much sometimes. I'm not a well man you know. I've not had an easy life. No sir. No way!"

The conversation now took on a religious tone. "Gee-Zus." Henry said. "Sweet Gee-Zus" and white as a sheet he pushed his whisky and water away from him.

"Oh for God's sake, Henry," the host said. "Come on, now. That's just Chad's rotten idea of a joke."

"I'm really grateful to you," I told him, "for trying to brush it under the carpet like that. It's at a time like this that you know who your friends are ...... That really was jolly decent of you."

Henry must have had a heavy breakfast because he ate very little lunch. He sat there alternately taking his own pulse and then the odd American-Travellers-Multiple-Antibiotic Pill, with added vitamin C.

It was only when they'd left that I noticed Henry's whisky was still on the bar and I drank it. I got hepatitis. Henry must have been a carrier, goddamit.

******

Then there was the time that I heard a chap say to our barmaid finishing off his order "......and a Campari please without soda." She was pretty new and looked rather baffled. Always ready to give my staff a helping hand, I butted in "I'm terribly sorry, sir, but there's been a bit of a run on Campari without soda and until the brewery delivery, we haven't got any. We've got Campari without gin, Campari without vermouth and Campari without a slice of orange but with ice. Which would you prefer?"

"I'll take the one with the ice please," he said.

******

97

Stout Serviam

It is an obvious fact that waiters and waitresses are as vital to the smooth running of a restaurant as are an adequate supply of clean cutlery and crockery. We have all, at some time or another, suffered the discomfort and indignity of shuffling along in a queue, sliding our nasty little brown plastic tray along the tubular shelving whilst we try to decide which plastic Pandora's box to open or ask the dusky custodian of the baked beans, jumbo sausage and mash to slurp us out a plateful.

We have all at some time or another enjoyed being served with excellent food by equally excellent and caring waiting staff. The difference between waiting upon oneself and being waited on is so vast that I have never failed to be baffled by the manner in which the average British diner out treats waiting staff.

Whereas most people greatly enjoy playing host or hostess to their friends whenever they can, putting their very best efforts into supplying good food and drink and creating the ambiance which makes for a memorable night, very few people would ever think of taking it up as a career. Serving your friends in your own home is great, you are host and hostess, not waiter and waitress. Serving food to a restaurant's clients is another thing altogether. To the British, a waiter is a lackey and a waitress is a skivvy. Both must be treated as such and their best efforts rewarded, not with the warmth, the friendly appreciation, the gratitude, that they deserve, but with attitudes ranging from the arrogant to the coldly indifferent.

It seems that the British, when nurtured, cossetted and generally looked after by others, feel the same puritanical guilt as they do about all matters sensuously pleasurable, all food other than roast beef or a grilled steak, all alcohol other than whisky, gin, or beer, all sexual intercourse other than a roll-on, roll-off missionary position with the lights off. Just as did the Victorians; they suffer a guilt which they try to exorcise by hurting and humiliating those who make them feel guilty.

From the jaundiced view of the customers, it would seem that all waiters must attend a training course on how to walk like a waiter, that is when moving forwards, they must slide their flat feet, turned slightly outward at ten to two, between the grease patches on the restaurant carpet as if skiing in a slow slalom.

When moving backwards they must be able to do it without bumping into anything whilst bent almost double in a deferential crouch, one hand cupped into the shape of a beggar's bowl and sharply raised, the elbow of that arm pressed in at the waist. The whole while, the waiter must wear a would-be ingratiating simper, the sickliness of which would cause even Peter Pan, Wendy and Tinkerbell to throw up.

His working clothes seem to have been assembled from jumble sales or Oxfam shops or rented from agencies specialising in stocks of gungy, gravy-stained jackets with dandruff appliqué collars. If the waiter works in an ethnic restaurant, particularly Greek or Armenian, he will have been supplied with trousers already streaked and redolent with goat's milk yoghurt, fetta cheese and garlic, with the zip fastener coming away from the cloth and jammed halfway up or down, whichever way you see it.

If the food is served by a waitress, the diner believes that she has received training on dropping loaded trays in the restaurant, knocking glasses of red wine into the laps of women wearing white linen suits, leaving fingerprints on cutlery and thumbprints on plates and in butter and chocolate mousse. North of Birmingham it's 'Luv' for everyone, south of Birmingham, 'dear' or 'dearie' will suffice. It is thought that only when waitresses have passed their trade test in these simple skills, are they allowed to wait on table wearing laddered tights and one of those specially designed waitress black dresses, with the snagged hem trailing on the opposite side from the two inches of exposed, off-white underslip.

Well, I think that's a fair assessment of how the customer views the waiting staff and it may be that view is not altogether inaccurate.

On the other hand, how hoteliers, restaurateurs and staff see their customers will be dealt with in depth in Part Two. It may surprise some readers. I hope, if that is so, it might also educate them.

But before we get on to that, I must tell you about a waiter who was exceptionally talented.

He was serving in a restaurant with a piece of string emerging from somewhere inside his trousers and secured to a braces button. He displayed astonishing dexterity wielding a pair of hinged serving tongs. Fascinated, an observant customer eventually said, "My word, I have observed with some fascination the astonishing dexterity with which you wield that pair of serving tongs." "Ah, sir," the waiter said, "I've been here fifteen years now. The boss of this establishment is an absolute nut on hygiene. We're not allowed to touch anything with our fingers. The skill which you have observed, sir, is a skill which comes with long practice. Fifteen years of it, sir. Fifteen years of wielding these here serving tongs."

"Remarkable," said the customer, "but pray tell me if you will, why do you have that piece of string emerging from somewhere in your trousers and secured to a braces button? If it's not too personal a question, that is." The waiter thought that the question was rather personal and he coloured slightly. "I've told you, sir," he said, a shade sharply, "We are not allowed to handle anything with our fingers. That's for when I go to the gents. That's for getting it out with, that string is. For pulling on it to get it out." The customer was into Do-it-Yourself and had a very practical turn of mind.

"Ah yes," he said. "I can readily understand the mechanics

of getting it out by pulling on a piece of string, but how do you get it back?" "Simple, sir," said the waiter, "I use the serving tongs."

******

Waiters and waitresses alike have long realised that it is a waste of time to serve the British diner with a finger bowl. The chances are that he will drink its contents, and it is to offset that possibility that the cautious restaurateur puts a flower or a piece of lemon or even, if he's excessively cautious, a small, dead frog, in the fingerbowls. The average Briton will use his or her fingers for almost anything but the joys of eating. Fingers are used for de-waxing ears, clearing debris from the nostrils, punishing persistently prurient piles and even for some disgusting and erotic sexual practices which I hope you will join me in condeming out of hand. It may be that it is because the diner is well aware of the other uses to which he puts his fingers that, with the exception of fish and chips and mushy peas eaten from the paper, where lashings of strong malt vinegar will have an antiseptic and sterilising effect, he is wise in being chary of using his fingers in the restaurant other than to snap them to call the staff to heel.

Even so, to watch the jerk ineffectually piddling around half a duck, pheasant or grouse with a knife and fork, giving up and letting the most succulent half of the meat go back to the kitchen on the bone rather than get stuck in with his fingers, is as pathetic a sight as watching him farting about with fish on the bone, with no mummy or nanny there to fillet it for him.

******

There is a recently emerged school of radical thought which holds to the view that when a customer snaps his fingers at waiting staff or gives that sharp, haughty, one-fingered, come-here-immediately gesture there is an equally sharp, haughty, one-fingered reply. In America, it is understood to mean 'Up yours, mac.' A better known gesture in Britain is the good old two-fingered one, generally accepted as suggesting that you should indulge in sex and travel.

******

Waiters and waitresses are quite accustomed to the phenomena of becoming invisible and inaudible to diners. Waiting to take an order from people who have had the menus for fifteen minutes or more, they will stand, order-pad in hand, totally ignored by the yoicks and yahoos sitting at the table. Eventually driven to ask "Is anyone ready to order?" they will receive neither a reply nor any sign of recognition of their presence. Waiting staff are of a lesser breed and for the moment do not exist. They are paid to wait, then wait they shall. But yoick and yahoo out there, be warned. There is a revolution afoot and a new breed of waiting staff coming up, or perhaps, just the old staff coming to its senses.

There are reports of several recent occasions when a member of the waiting staff, driven to desperate measures, has leaned forward, inserted an index finger into the nearest diner's nostril, drawn the nostril with nostril-owner attached sharply forward and snarled in the associated nearby ear, "For Christsakes get on with it buster or I'll kick your head in." Admittedly it's an oblique approach to the question but it does help to concentrate the man's mind and restore undivided attention, visibility and audibility to the waiter. So be careful, pin-head! It may be your nostril next.

******

PART TWO
A born leader

I have dealt broadly with the individual job skills that make possible the running of a hotel and a restaurant. Very little has been said about management. That is probably because management is more directly responsible to the public and the public and its godawful ways has yet to be discussed in Part 2.

However, before we leave the behind the scenes scene, I would like to deal with two events, the descriptions of which should prove to the discerning reader that in myself, we have a restaurateur who is not afraid to go in there and do whatever his staff have to do. "I never ask you to do what I can't or won't do" I proudly tell the lads and lasses as I take up a carrot and a peeler or go out into the car park to sweep it or roll my right shirt sleeve up before I unblock an 'en-suite' lavatory.

I firmly believe it is the duty of management to lead, not from the panelled boardroom, but from down in the front line.

Let me give you an example.

I had two young trainee chefs at the time. At about 9.0am, I came back from the Manchester fish market with two stones of fresh herrings and one stone of fresh mackerel. I'd watched these two trainee lads faffing about with a boning knife before, filleting their fingers mostly. I decided to show them how an old pro sets about it.

Surreptitiously, I saved a minute or two by sharpening my knives, by preparing a sink and a cutting board and the waste bin, and I got kitchen cloths to hand before making my shock announcement.

"I have here," I said, "before your very eyes, two stone of herrings and one stone of mackerel. The way you have been shaping up, it would take the pair of you, working together, two hours to get this lot ready. I want you to make a careful note of the time. It is just 9.15am. Now watch. Watch closely, because the like of this you will never have seen before."

Swiftly I scaled the herring, then I took the heads and the tails off — my staff were dazzled, hypnotised by the flashing knife blade. Again the knife was twisting in my lithe, lean, brown hand. Knife tip into the vent, slit the length of the fish, out with the guts, and wipe the cavities clean with the cloth. Two stones of herrings were gutted and cleaned in thirty minutes. Then I started on the mackerel, silver and blue striped, my knife twisting and turning, too fast for the eye to follow. One stone of mackerel ready for the grill in sixteen minutes. The whole lot of fish done in a shade over three quarters of an hour.

I expected applause as I exultantly cried, *"Voila, c'est tout fait"* and threw down the last fish and the knife, but I don't think they understood my French. One lad had drifted into a light doze while the other was sizing up page three of the 'Sun'. The two kitchen women had sat down to their tea, butter and toast.

"Just over three quarters of an hour the lot," I reminded them again. "So that's your time in future, not the couple of hours you take but my time plus a quarter of an hour allowance for your lack of experience, say one hour, no, I'll be generous, say seventy minutes maximum." I *was* being generous. No slave driver, me. I'm the first to recognise that all men are *not* equal.

Conscious of having set a good example, of having established a precedent, I stumbled from the kitchen, nearly missing the doorway.

I stumbled through the bar lounge and despite the spots dancing before my eyes, I found the stairs up to my flat and pulled myself up them with the bannister.

Flo was shocked.

"What on earth has happened to you?" she said. "You look terrible. You're wet with sweat. It must be Asian flu. You had better get to bed and I'll call the doctor."

"No need," I said, "it's not the flu. I've got palpitations again, that's all."

"You're doing too much," Flo said.

"I know," I replied. "Don't I know."

******

I'm all for saving the company money, and in any event, I always say, "anything that they can do, I can do better." I believe that's why I'm the boss, intelligence, drive and not a little brilliance.

Late on Saturday night, I looked at the hotel bedroom chart and saw that we had only two residents.

"Phone the breakfast cook and the breakfast waitress and tell them not to come in on Sunday morning," I told the receptionist. "There's one couple in the hotel. They've already indicated that they want breakfast at 9.30. I'll do their breakfasts myself."

I set my illuminated, two-tone digital alarm clock for 8.15am Sunday and I went to bed. At 20 minute intervals throughout the night, I woke up to check that there hadn't been a power cut and that I had pressed in, or alternatively, pulled out, all the right knobs and levers. Whether or not I'd got it right and the alarm went off, I'll never know.

I awoke in a panic at ten to nine.

I rushed through my shower, scrambled into my clothes and went down to the kitchen. I had forgotten the keys to the stores and refrigerators. I rushed back upstairs for the keys, grabbed them off my tallboy and then fell back down the stairs and into the kitchen. I couldn't open the store room or the refrigerators with my car keys so I rushed upstairs for the proper bunch.

By the time I had found the right keys and opened up the stores,

I had my palpitations again and it was now ten past nine.

I got out the Alpen, the fruit juices, the sausages, the bacon and the tomatoes. As I carried out a tray of eggs, the tray buckled in the middle and three eggs dropped on the floor. They must have had very thin shells because every one of them broke wide open. All three of them.

I filled the staff kettle in case my guests wanted tea and got out a packet of ground coffee. I lit an oven and put some plates in. Then I went into the restaurant and switched on the coffee machine, waited until the light went out and poured a flask full of water in through the hole in the top. When all the water had run through, I had to do the whole thing again, because the first time I'd forgotten to put the coffee into the filter paper.

Back in the kitchen, I switched on the big electric grill, put six slices of bread into the toaster ready to switch on and I got frying pans ready for fried or poached eggs, lard in one and water in the other.

******

Bang on 9.30, the couple sat down in the restaurant. But I was ready for them, nay, even eager to show my paces.

The man studied the breakfast menu which I had failed to notice was on his table.

"Two fresh grapefruit please," said the man. "Then I'd like a kipper and my wife would like porridge, followed by a scrambled egg and sausages for me and poached egg, bacon and tomato for my wife."

Grapefruit? Kippers? Porridge?

"I've got some lovely fruit juices," I said hopefully, "and some really great Alpen. Smashing Alpen. The grapefruit aren't much cop, not this week they're not." He couldn't have heard me.

"As I said, we'd like fresh grapefruit," he replied, "then porrridge for the wife and a kipper for me — the rest to follow.

106

Would you like to write it down?"

"The Alpen is very fresh," I said, "The Alpen is a lot fresher than the kipper."

"Just what we've ordered, please," he said. "Nothing else."

I'm always telling my waitresses to get something on the table — quickly — when people are waiting for their breakfast order. Toast and butter, the tea or coffee, a fruit juice. Get something on the table.

The nearest things were a bowl of flowers, a candleholder and a glass with toothpicks in it, so I gave them those. Better than nothing at all.

Back in the kitchen, I switched on the toaster.

While I was cutting up the first grapefruit, I cut my finger and some of the blood got on to a grapefruit segment. It was very red blood, quite scarlet in fact. I couldn't find any cherries — 'cerises' as we call them in the trade — and rejecting the idea of a beetroot garnish as being altogether too bizarre, I threw the scarlet spotted segment away. In spreading out the remaining pieces of grapefruit to fill the gap, I spotted them too so I threw the whole bloody grapefruit away, put on a Band Aid and started again.

The toaster was making that fizzy noise it makes when it can't pop-up so I switched it off, picked the toast out, put the toast out and scraped the cindery bits off. I put the pieces that I hadn't cracked into the toast rack.

I poured water from the kettle into the teapot into which I had remembered to put the tea bags. Unfortunately, I had not remembered to light the gas under the kettle and the water was cold. I threw the waterlogged tea bags away, refilled the kettle and started again, with fresh tea bags and the kettle on a lighted gas ring.

I put some sausages and tomatoes under the hot grill and I ran out to the breakfast table with pristine grapefruit, the crackly toast and the coffee. I had over-filled the coffee pot and, on the way to the table, some of the coffee ran out of the coffee pot spout on to some of the toast, but I didn't worry too much about that, as I think it improved it, texturewise. Softened it up a bit.

"Could we have some milk," the lady asked, "**and** some butter? If you don't mind," she said, very toffee-nosed she was.

"Milk? I said — not too tersely, I hope. "Butter? I was just getting them, Madam. Only one pair of hands," I joked. "Can only be in one place at a time," I quipped.

"And the tea, please," she said.

"All in good time," I called back to the table, "Got to brew, through all those little perforations. Not made in a minute, you know, good tea. Nothing instant served here, none of your fast food at the Old Rectory."

I got some milk and butter from the refrigerator but, half way back to the table, I decided not to serve the milk from the bottle and I went back for the milk jug.

As I found a jug for the milk, I noticed that the tomatoes were welded to the grill pan and the sausages were on fire.

I opened the window to let out the smoke and to throw out the blazing sausages. In throwing out the sausages, I inadvertently let go of the hot grill pan and the sausages and grill pan disappeared into the car park.

I took the milk and butter back to the table and then I went out to the car park to look for the grill pan, intending to re-use it to complete the couple's cooked breakfast. A neighbour, digging his garden, said over the fence: "Some bloody fool just threw a burning pan at me out of your kitchen window."

I had no time for Sunday morning pleasantries. "Oh get stuffed," I shouted, perhaps somewhat rudely.

I found the grill pan in the bed of nasturtiums and back in the kitchen, I cleaned and reloaded it with sausage and tomatoes. I then made the tea and took it to the table.

"Kipper and porridge coming up," I assured them, but churlishly they made no reply.

I put porridge oats into a pan and a kipper into a jug and poured boiling hot water on to both. The jug cracked, so I picked the kipper up out of the pool of hot water on the floor, washed it well under the hot tap and put it on a plate in the oven to dry out a bit.

I scraped the annealed lumps of porridge into the liquidiser and I switched it on. Unfortunately, I had forgotten the liquidiser lid. I added more boiling water to such of the porridge that wasn't hanging from the ceiling and when it was of the right consistency, I poured it into a soup bowl. The bowl was cold but I figured that the hot porridge mixture would soon warm it up. Anyway, you can't win them all.

I took the kipper and the porridge out to the table. My guests were sitting there with their elbows deep in snapped off bits of charred toast, just staring moodily out of the window. I think they may have had a quarrel. They certainly weren't very chatty, not with each other, nor with me.

"The garden's nice at this time of the year," I ventured, just for something to say, to break the ice as it were. Again they made no response.

Back in the kitchen, the tomatoes and sausages didn't look at all bad so I transferred them to the oven and I replaced them under the grill with the bacon rashers.

I took five eggs off the tray — three to scramble and two to poach — and, knowing what eggs are like and how they can wobble about, I wedged them on the table with a circle of those nasty, little wrapped portions of butter.

I added vinegar to the poaching pan water and I put butter into the bottom of a small pan for the three eggs I had beaten up. Unfortunately, the butter I put into the pan was the nasty little wrapped portions of butter I had wedged the eggs with. I wasn't just thinking you see.

I had to replace the eggs for poaching as, in falling to the floor, their thin shells had broken right through. I don't think that these days the hens get enough grit in their mash, the egg shells are certainly very fragile.

The yolk of one of the replacement eggs also broke as I cracked it into the poaching water so I fished it out with a perforated draining spoon, through which I was surprised to find it ran quite freely, all over my suede shoes.

I put another egg into the pan and I had a quick look at the bacon which by now had shrivelled up a bit and was beginning to flambé around the edges. I turned the grill down, turned the bacon over and then wiped the resultant hot bacon-fat splashes off my silk tie.

The vinegar in the egg poaching pan must have been double strength because, although the eggs poached very firmly, especially the yolks, they definitely came out of the pan 'vinaigrette'. In tilting the plate to drain excess vinaigrette water off the eggs, one of them slipped off the plate on to the stove, but, fortunately, instead of breaking, it bounced.

The heat under the scrambled eggs was perhaps a little too high because whilst I had been busy elsewhere, they had gone quite solid. Undeterred, I stirred them up vigorously with a fork and as they began to break up and the dark brown bits came up from the bottom, they took on a most pleasing two-toned marbled and mottled effect.

You never know how people like their bacon, so to be safe, I cooked the bacon rashers well-done on one side and rare on the other.

When I took the plates out to my guests it was still only twenty past ten.

The chap had dozed off so I woke him up. "There you are," I said cheerily. "All good things are worth waiting for. Better late than never."

"I'm not too sure about that," he said, in a most unpleasant tone.

"What can you expect?" I asked my wife later. They were

the sort of people who order far too much and then have to leave half of it. It was all on their plates, it was. Eyes bigger than their bellies."

My wife and I finished cleaning up the kitchen just before lunchtime.

"A job well done," I said "and my word, I've certainly saved us some money."

"You really are a remarkable man," she said. "Quite remarkable."

Modest to a fault as I am, I must confess I had to agree with her.

******

Wedding Bells

It was a Saturday morning and we had a big wedding reception booked for eighty guests to sit down at 2.0pm to three courses and coffee. The day started quite normally. There were eleven wrong entries in the bedroom reservation chart and five in the restaurant book. I detected errors in cash-totalling, showing an irretrievable loss to the company of sixty-two pounds. The shaving light in room 24 was kaput as were the electric alarm and teasmaid in room 16. The lavatory seat in room 3 had come adrift and the lavatory in room 8 was blocked. The post included a cheque for £97.00 returned 'Refer to Drawer.'

The few guests in the hotel had breakfasted and either gone back to their rooms with the papers or gone out for the day. The breakfast staff had gone home to their godforbids and their godforbids Dad, still bleary-eyed and furry-tongued from Friday night with the lads. The restaurant extractor fans were busy taking the mixed smells of coffee and burnt toast, kippers and finnan haddock and passing them to the gentle breezes that blow around the tower blocks of Haughton Green.

There was a message that the cleaner was ill and wouldn't be coming in.

The only chambermaid working that morning complained that with seven bedrooms to do, she wouldn't have time to vacuum the restaurant, not even a lick and spit job. It wasn't her job anyway, it was the cleaner's job and she'd like to point out that this was the second time in a month that she's been in on a Saturday; mark you, it's not that she minded for herself, not likely, no she wasn't one to complain, not never, everybody knew that, she'd always do whatever needed to be done even when she was being used and put upon; no, it wasn't her. It was him.

"Just ask anyone what he's like, Mr Chadwick, you have no

idea, you've got to live with someone before you get to know them and if I'm not back by twelve to take the kids off his hands so he can get back to the Old Dog with his mates, well he's like a bear with a sore head, not that he's ever violent, not even when he's had a skinful, never laid a finger on me in twenty years, he hasn't, still, as I said, it's not me, it's him, if it was left to me, I'd be working here all the hours that God sends, not just for the money neither, I've always been a grafter, born to it I was, well you mustn't keep me here talking, Mr Chadwick, I've got too much on my plate."

I took her point and went back to the kitchen where I found that a supplier had delivered a box of aubergines and Betty had accepted it. She had no way of knowing it should have been a box of capsicum.

The microwave oven was blowing fuses.

In mid-morning the receptionist also fell ill and had to go off.

The two barmaids both turned up on time but one had to go back home almost immediately when a neighbour phoned to say that her son had fallen and cut his knee badly.

As I say, it was a normal start to just another Saturday.

The menu for the wedding was pheasant consommé, boeuf bourguignonne, fruit salad and coffee. Not exactly 'haute cuisine' but 'haute' enough.

After my chat with Mavis, I rushed into the kitchen, a bit behind schedule, and my apron caught on the edge of the bain-marie and tore across the corner.

I was jerked suddenly to a halt and my snap-on braces unsnapped and shot up my back. Bending forwards, one hand groping for them up my back under my chef's jacket, my glasses fell off my nose into the boeuf bourguignonne.

Fishing them out, I noticed that the boeuf bourguignonne had an unusual, but vaguely familiar bouquet. I looked around and I found a pan containing red wine, tomato puree, and *beef* stock. It should not have been there, not without the beef, onions and

"My glasses fell off my nose into the boeuf bourguignonne."

mushrooms. It was the bourguignonne part of the beoeuf bourguignonne. What *was* in the boeuf bourguignonne was tomato puree and the *fish* stock that I had prepared to make fish soup. Desperate as I was, I knew that red wine, tomato puree and beef stock make a very poor fish soup so I forgot about fish soup and added the bourguignonne to the fish-flavoured, boeuf bourguignonne, hoping that some of the beef stock flavour would come through. This made the boeuf bourguignonne very wettish. I ladled some of the surplus wet into the liquidiser and added some flour and switched on and because the wet was hot, the liquidiser lid blew off. Multi-flavoured, wet flour dripped from the ceiling.

I was moving a flask of black coffee out of the way of the drips when I slipped on the wet and floury floor. In trying to recover my balance, I inadvertently tipped the flask of coffee into the pan of pheasant consomme. Fortunately the coffee and the consomme were about the same colour so I gave them a good stir and nothing showed. Just for once, no harm done, I hoped.

I was in time to make some more consomme but I was short on coffee, so I kept the mixture back for the finish.

Even so, I suddenly felt despondent, suffering a malaise of my normally exuberant spirit. I needed to take some of my pills, the blue ones, and lie down for a while. As I left the kitchen, the sharp corner on the bain marie snagged me again and tore the back pocket off my chef's trousers. Once more my braces unclipped and shot up my back, the metal bits hitting me a sharp blow between the shoulder blades. "They can bloody well stay there," I decided. Anyway, because I'm a pessimist, I always wear a belt as well as braces.

"Think that's funny, do you?" I snarled, shaking my fist at the kitchen ceiling, somewhere high up on the far side of which I imagined God to be. I've been a life long atheist but that's not to say I don't know who to blame when it's one of those days.

******

The guests arrived half an hour early, as always.

Passing through the crowded restaurant, I came across this woman in her late twenties got up in the flowing, flouncy dress and flowery little hat you associate with these sad occasions.

She was in the final days of her pregnancy.

"Congratulations," I said, "I wish you both a long and happy future."

"What are you talking about?" she asked, quite sharp she was too. I thought that perhaps, what with one thing and another, even in these permissive days, the strain was getting too much for her.

"Congratulations," I said again, giving her one of my warmest smiles. "You are the bride, aren't you?"

"Indeed I'm not," she snapped. "I'm the bride's sister. I'm one of the bridesmaids."

"Oh," I said, momentarily put out. "Oh dear. Well in that case, if you like what we do today for your sister, perhaps when *you* get married you'll let us handle *your* wedding reception."

I don't like touting for business but you must strike while the iron is hot.

******

In the event, it all went very well. The father of the bride was very pleased and settled up in full. "How was your meal?" I asked him.

"Great," he said, "that soup was very tasty and so was that stewed beef. We all said we'd never had anything like it before."

I believed him.

******

Weddings! On another occasion I answered the 'phone to a young girl who asked "Is that the manager?"

There was no point in telling her that we couldn't afford a manager so she had to make do with the chairman.

"Yes madam," I said. "Speaking."

"It's just an enquiry. Do you do weddings?"

"Weddings?" I said. "Do we do weddings?! Madam we do the best weddings in the United Kingdom."

"Weddings? Weddings?" I murmured throatily, with just the merest touch of Charles Boyer. "To have and to hold from this day forward, for better, for worse, for richer for poorer, in sickness and in health, to love and to cherish, till death do us part."

"Excuse me," she butted in. "If you don't mind ......" but I hadn't finished yet. "With this ring, I thee wed," and my voice dropped to a spine tingling, passionate whisper, "with my body, I thee worship." That's enough of the eroticism, I thought, after all, this is an innocent young virgin maid. "If that's the sort of thing you mean," I said, "Yes, we do weddings."

"Sod off, you creepy old fruit," she rasped and hung up.

******

Still, one or two brides-to-be persevere and having fixed the wedding date by telephone and tentatively reserved the restaurant, turn up by appointment with a committee to fix the grisly details.

For example:

The *dramatis personae,* shortly to act out this time-honoured tragedy, arrives as a cast of six. First, the principal, the father of the bride-to-be, glazed of eye, disconsolate, downcast, his face a sickly hue and twitching like a poleaxed steer as he hears the costs mount steadily; his wife, flushed and gushing as she plans the poshest possible send-off for her daughter. Proving to the groom's parents on the other side of the table that cost is no object, she tosses Dad's paper blood about as if it were the first of the confetti to come.

The groom's father, blessing the luck that gave him a son and nowt much to pay for on this occasion, except for the flowers or the taxis or something, he's got it all written down somewhere. He hopes they can get things settled quickly then he can have a pint. He smiles and nods at every suggestion; with nowt much for *him* to pay for, he can agree to everything. The groom's mother, conveying by an attitude of calm regality, her royal acceptance of whatever the other side is prepared to offer as down payment for ridding themselves of the encumbrance of a daughter. Even so, despite her superior manner, she is beginning to wonder whether she should have invited Uncle George and Auntie Edith, he with his yellow celluloid-type false teeth that click when he talks and splatter wet food about when he eats with his lips apart, and her with her dropped aitches.

The prospective bridegroom, trapped, stares sullenly and silently out of the bars of the cage he finds closing in on him, day by day. The bride-to-be, bold in the security of the pill — a marriage of choice this is, not of necessity, love, true love, that's what it is, but still no reason, now that it's got to this stage not to let him see the other side of the coin, the nitty-gritty. 'Start as you mean to go on' her mother said and that's just what she's doing now, after all, it's all about her, isn't it, it's her day! The play was written with her in mind and already she dominates the stage, rehearsing the part of the wife she intends to be, tough, argumentative, positive, knowing and getting what she wants, the all-time, all-purpose boss 'woman.

The embattled would-be director of this comedy of errors, the restaurateur, tries patiently to get it all together sensibly whilst pleasing everyone or, at least, pleasing those who pick up the bill.

Initially they want a late church service. I convince them that, as many of their guests will be travelling some distance, a late church service will be inaudible behind a barrage of belly rumbles, hungry belches and feverish farting. I roundly declare that guests need to eat no later than 2.0pm, or must be allowed a meals-on-wheels tray service, in the church itself.

They want to start the meal with melon but I say no to that because I cannot guarantee a supply of sweet, ripe melons on a day several months ahead. How about a prawn cocktail then? Yes, I *can* give them a prawn cocktail but it puts the cost up considerably and not everyone likes prawns or, shall we say, some people like shellfish but shellfish doesn't like them. "Puts the costs up considerably?" Dad puts in his piece. "Nobody," he says, "eats prawns these days. Far too dicey. Fish poisoning. No. Prawns are out. Mr Chadwick knows best. Prawns are definitely out."

We only cook fresh vegetables and inevitably we have some left each day. Homemade vegetable soup with us is not just the soup of the day but the soup of yesterday, of all last week, and daily for the past decade or two. We tend to become inundated with it. It must be regularly syphoned off or given to Oxfam. "Everybody," I say with absolute confidence and a certain degree of truth, "likes our homemade vegetable soup." I appeal to Dad. "I can do it at one third of the price of a prawn cocktail, a tenth of the price of half a lobster." This is the first mention of lobster but at a saving of ninety per cent, it convinces Dad. "Mr Chadwick's the expert," he says. "We must be guided by the chap who's doing it all the time. Vegetable soup it is then, what? Everybody likes home-made vegetable soup."

The bride-to-be wants *gazpacho*. The bitch, with all that vegetable soup just waiting to be eaten.

The bride-to-be knows about *gazpacho,* she had it on a Thompson's package holiday in Benidorm. "Garlic," I say to Dad, "Stiff with garlic and costs half as much again as the veggie soup." "Vegetable soup, it is. No more argument," Dad says. "Can't stand garlic. Stinks. Not surprised it keeps vampires away."

One of the bride's friends has suggested *osso buco* but I convince her it would hardly be proper to slaughter twenty calves to give us enough shin through the bone for one hundred people. Nor, as she now suggests, can I successfully grill one hundred steaks, some peppered, some plain, some rare, some medium, some well-done and have them all hot and ready to serve at the same moment.

The groom's father suggests a free bar before the meal. He would like that, the groom's father.

No, I say, it's a nice idea to have a free bar before you all sit down, nice that is if you are Tiny Rowlands or even a medium-sized Arab oil sheikh. It will cost an arm and a leg. "It's my daughter's wedding day," Dad says. "We don't want a booze up." Right then, a welcoming drink, hot punch or cold cup according to season or the customary sherry — a most liverish drink in its dry form — all the year round. Neither will we open the bar, before the meal, even to people buying their own drinks, or some people will fall down instead of sitting down or sit down shouting across the tables, "It's alright Fred, I've got 'em in," before falling forward and rendering themselves unconscious on top of six, full pint pots. Not the sort of thing we want on somebody's wedding day.

Then there's the discussion of the toast wine. Champagne is out of the question, especially as half of the guests would be hard put to it to distinguish between a Tesco Reisling and Strongbow Cider if it wasn't for the fizz in one if not the other. That's where those other labels come in handy, Asti Spumante or Moussec for the toast wine at a reasonable price. I talk them out of a cheese course — after all, I just want to make a decent living decently without financially raping a captive client. "It's a waste of money and even worse," I say, "it's a waste of cheese." "Get your priorities right," says Dad, "I'm not bothered about the waste of cheese. It's the waste of money that knocks me sick."

I didn't go to a grammar school for nothing. At this stage, I try to introduce a note of culture with an appropriate French proverb: "*Le marriage est comme une fortresse assiegeé; ceux qui sont dehors veulent y entrer et ceux qui sont dedans en sortir.*" "Eh," they say together. "What are you on about? Did you say something?"

"Marriage," I translate, "is like a besieged fortress, those who are outside (it) want to get in and those inside (it) want to get out."

"Gerraway.," Dad says, his eyes no longer glazed but now misting over. "That's lovely that is and so bloody true."

They said they wanted us to supply the flowers for the tables.

I am in like a flash with yet another touch of scholarship and erudition.

"I have loved flowers that fade,"I breathe.

"Within those magic tents
Rich hues have marriage made
With sweet unmemoried scents," I quote, rather smugly, I must confess.

"Rich Jews?" Dad says. "I wish we were! We're Christians we are, and skint. Left Footers both sides." We left it at that.

******

At least we'd fixed our menu. The vegetable soup, roast turkey and apple pie with cream.

On the day itself it all seemed to be coming together perfectly until I tasted that vegetable soup.

We've all read about the man who checked the football coupon and found he had the only eight draws in a £5 eight out of ten permutation and also found that in a coat pocket, he had that week's only unposted winning coupon. Well he couldn't have felt any worse that I did when I tasted the soup.

It was a big wedding for us, one hundred guests for a three course meal. The guests were to arrive at one, having a cold claret cup whilst the photographs were being taken and to sit down to eat at about one-thirty.

We had roasted two forty-pound turkeys that morning, jointing them before cooking, breaking the back of the birds, dividing the legs with a cleaver and cooking them, with the wings, in roasting dishes at the bottom of the oven, the heavier double-breasted halves being cooked at the top. This way we had perfect control over the cooking with perfectly finished meat, juicy and succulent.

Both families were Catholic and, if you are going to be religious on your wedding day, it certainly pays to be a Catholic because the weather turned suddenly warm and sunny, almost close, which was much better than Protestants would have been entitled to expect at that time of the year, let alone chapel-goers, agnostics or atheists.

Let it be said that to restaurateurs, with the food ordered and prepared to a strict time schedule, wedding photographers are a nightmare. "The same again, but this time without first or second cousins or relatives by previous marriage. What I want now are the mother and father of the confectioner who made the cake, hurry please whilst the light is just right."

As usual, the photographer went berserk, prancing around the gardens, framing the fountain with his hands, rabbiting on about the contrasting dark green verdure of the conifers and yews with the *contre dur* effect of the sunlight. He moved everything he could, his camera and tripod, the bride's headdress and veil and her bouquet. He even made the bridegroom move his smile to the far side of his face where it was less in his viewfinder.

God save us from these Cecil Beaton clones, prancing about with the agonised concentration of male ballet dancers in tights two sizes too small. The bored-rigid guests stood about with their cold cup chambreéing whilst the seeing eye had the girl hold out her dress, first against the fountain and then the ancient elm tree, now brown, not with autumn tints but with the ravages of the Dutch death beetle.

"Just once more," the maniac cried. "If I could have the whole family again in front of the compost heap but this time without the children, especially the teenager with acne and bad breath. That's lovely, that's really lovely. If someone out there on the right could pick Grandad up and hold him up somewhere near the centre? No, darling, it doesn't matter that he's just had a fatal coronary, so long as you hold him up in a lifelike position and put his teeth back in, in case his face comes out clearly. That's

122

"No darling it doesn't matter that he's just had a fatal coronary so long as you hold him up and put his teeth back in."

lovely. He really looks as if he's enjoying himself. Now, would the relatives from Ireland please come forward and form a group in front of this oil tank."

The rest of the guests milled about, stared at the pictures on the restaurant walls, yawned, finger de-waxed their ears, scratched themselves here and there. It was turning out even worse than they thought it would be.

******

After a good hour or so of this, my son, Lee, came into the kitchen.

"That maniac's almost finished and they're starting to come in. Are we all ready?" he asked.

It was then that I tasted the soup, which had been heating up steadily on the stove.

Gallons of it, perfect the day before! Now? All gone sour!

My assistant chef tasted it.

Lee tasted it.

"Well?" I asked, as if I didn't know.

"Sour!!" they both said.

"The Chinese do a very nice *hot* and sour soup," I gabbled, panic-stricken. "Peking style, *hot and* sour soup. Pass me the cayenne pepper."

"Not that damned sour," Lee said morosely.

"Right then, be bloody minded. Chinese *sweet* and sour soup, Cantonese style. Give me that bag of demerara sugar."

"It's supposed to be vegetable soup," the chef reminded me.

"For God's sake stop nit-picking. What we've got is the best of both worlds; Chinese style, hot, sweet and sour vegetable soup. With curry." I cried, chucking in a handful of Hot Madras and stirring vigorously, "hot sweet and sour mulligatawny vegetable soup." Happily the photographer was still into his David Bailey bit.

We liquidised celery and added it to the soup, we liquidised watercress, carrots, and even liquidised some unidentified liquid. They all went in. Ten pints of milk, some instant potato powder, all went in to this bubbling, boiling mixture. The guests came in just as I was about to add rough-cut Oxford marmalade, dessicated coconut and lime jelly. We skimmed off all the crud and waited until it had stopped frothing and fizzing before slipping out of our wetsuits.

Flo came in. "They're sitting down," she said.

"Taste the soup," I said. Flo, Lee, the chef tasted it. I tasted it. It was superb, soup such as there had never been, soup par excellence, with a strangely seductive smatch to it that was absolutely riveting.

Nobody left a spoonful. Some asked if they could have seconds. For an hour after they had had their coffee, we sat with pen and paper remembering and writing down what we had done. One day, not too soon perhaps, but one day, I'll create once again that most noble soup which is to the world of *potages* what Beethoven is to the world of music.

"Emperor Soup," that's what I'll call it.

******

One Saturday and for a most welcome change, the photographer at a wedding party was an attractive young woman, very well spoken and holding a Hasselbad. Better than that, cameras do not come.

"A Hasselbad," I said. "That's a great camera. A professional camera."

"I'm not really a professional," she told me. "During the week, I'm a barrister's clerk in a law firm. This is my paying hobby."

"Well, well," I prattled, "how very interesting, I must say. I'm not sure but I seem to remember that the young Cecil Beaton had something to do with wedding pictures."

"Cecil who?" she asked.

Sic transit gloria Beaton!

******

It has always seemed to me to be quite ludicrous that because a young couple fall prey to that temporary, mental sickness we call love and decide to get married, two entirely unrelated and often ill-matched families are arbitrarily brought together on the wedding day and, at an horrendous cost to the bride's father, are given a couple of drinks and some food and then expected to get along as if they had known each other all their lives.

If the bride and groom share a similar social background and up-bringing, then there is a reasonable chance that their respective families, even if they do not become bosom friends for the day, will manage to get through a few tedious hours together without being too much ill-at-ease and wary of each other.

On the other hand, anyone who has ever been at a wedding where love has managed to breach the class barrier will know what a traumatic experience it can be. In these egalitarian days, it is quite usual for both sides to produce one or two of those who have made it or had it made for them, the odd total failures, and certainly a drunk or even an alcoholic or two. The age spectrum will range from incontinent and unintelligible infants to incontinent and near incoherent geriatrics.

However, there is no disguising the class difference. Here, on the one side, we have my class, the one that used to be referred to as the working class, mostly ill-at-ease in the up-market setting. Surrounded by people talking la-di-da, they either keep nervously quiet or are just as nervously loud and hearty with their own clan.

The women will have painfully poshed up for the day, their blouse sleeves down and buttoned, hiding the blue tattooes, 'I love Fred' and 'Guinness is Good for You', on their forearms. Their freshly permed hair is stiff with sneeze-inducing lacquer under repellant, fluffy pink hats. Their fur capes smell of mothballs and at certain times of the year, are in moult.

Their men, uncomfortable in a suit just back from the cleaners, sport a carnation with cooking-foil wrapped around its stem and shoved through their buttonhole or fastened to their lapel with a safety pin, sellotape or bluetack. As soon as they can, they dump their sherry or glass of claret cup behind a bowl of flowers and go back to the bar for a sensible pint of beer. They hope that whatever they are going to be given to eat will also be sensible, something they can get down without too much messing about with their knife and fork. Most of them will hold their knife, and sometimes their fork, like a pen or, in extreme cases, like a dagger because somehow they have been convinced that's the smart thing to do. Sensibly, they don't put either knife or fork down from starting to finishing the plate, in case an over zealous waiter thinks they have eaten enough and removes their plate.

The other side is horsey and tweedy and far back. Their women don't smell of hair lacquer or mothballs but of special soaps and subtle perfumes. They don't wear once in a while, special-occasion furs but all-the-time mink and their fellahs are relaxed and confident, whether they be in well-cut formal suits or tweed and cavalry twill. They don't worry too much about what the food is going to be, they are equally at ease with whatever comes, artichoke or asparagus, lamb or lobster, prunes or peaches. Above all, they know that it's socially acceptable to use your fingers when eating certain dishes provided you don't wipe them on the tablecloth or the person next to you.

The congratulatory telegrams and the speeches also bear witness to which side they came from. The working class Dads and lads have laboured long with books of quotations and after dinner jokes and cobbled together a speech that sounds like a club-comic's cast-offs.

The other lot launch, without hesitation, into threadbare but well-worded chat, larded with chamber pot references, Rugby club smut and nudge-nudge inferences that tonight's marital bed will be more of a trampoline than a place of repose. That is, if the young couple can wait until tonight and do not rush off soon to their honeymoon suite, to do roodies and umpy tumpy away like goats. As if they hadn't been hard at it for a couple of years, exhausting all possible permutations, just to make sure that they both liked it and everything was in good working order.

In the meantime, the Rugby types will have sent out their scouts to embellish the groom's car with inflated condoms and strings of beer cans, and festoon it with rolls of toilet paper. There is nothing more comical to the British than blown-up baby stoppers and yards of bum paper.

At last the atavistic orgy is over and the bride and groom leave.

Sweating and red faced with laughter, their guests fall about as the car clatters away down the drive, all its available surfaces daubed with mild obscenities.

Inside the restaurant, the bride's father has been given the bill and if he is from the working class side, is in a state of shock.

If from the other, he takes the bill calmly, because he's going to pay by cheque and that not for a long time.

The staff set about searching for glasses, sweeping up the confetti and replacing the toilet rolls.

There'll be another wedding next Saturday. If it is true that a second marriage is the triumph of hope over experience, then it must be true that a first marriage is the triumph of hope over your parent's experience. But then, Sophocles said, speaking in Greek, of course, "It is hope which maintains most of mankind."

******

Finally, a recent survey has shown that two wedding reception jokes have, over many years, proved more durable and popular than all the others. **Joke One:** (rather old-fashioned and in these permissive days, factually unconvincing). It was a wild and bitterly cold morning when the hotelier met the bridal couple emerging from the bridal suite on their way to a late breakfast. "Good morning. A bit raw this morning," he called cheerily. "Mind your own business," the bride snapped.

Well, at least it's short. That can be quite important if the speaker who tells it has a bad stammer or a weak bladder. **Joke Two:** The day before his wedding, the prospective bridegroom gave the best man a shopping list of honeymoon requirements on which were a pot of green paint and a mallet.

"What on earth do you want with a pot of green paint and a mallet? On your honeymoon?"

"Joan swears she's a virgin," the groom said. "Innocent of all physical experience other than a kiss, she claims. I'm going to paint my wedding tackle green and if she say's she's never seen a green one before, I'm going to hit her on the head with the mallet."

Enough!

******

It tolls for thee

Wedding parties and funeral parties have a lot in common when you think about it.

It was my day off, a cold but sunny day in February and I had gone to Blackpool, truly the Nice of the North.

I had my usual long walk along the nearly deserted promenade, of necessity swivelling my lambent gaze from the winter sparkle of the sea to the pavement at my feet as I slalomed between and around the mounds of dog turds, all apparently deposited by massive mastiffs.

I dropped in at the odd bar for a morning bracer then made my way down to the Clifton Hotel for lunch.

It has given way now to the ultra-modern Ramsbottom's Restaurant but then, the Clifton Hotel still boasted one of the most elegant, Edwardian style, high-ceilinged restaurants in the North and it was there that I went for a bottle of wine to accompany my three course lunch at an incredible price of £3.95. Would it were still so.

Seven people sat at a nearby table, all dressed in black. With only one exception, they were all elderly, grey or white-haired and some of them showing a strong family likeness. The one exception was a fair-haired young man in his late forties in the uniform of a Merchant Navy Officer. They were obviously a funeral party but of the seven, it was only the younger man whose face was shadowed by sorrow.

The luncheon party started quietly enough but for some reason — perhaps since disposing of their dead, they had had a quick reading of the will and found it good, I don't know how these matters are managed, but for whatever reason and after a brief conferring, they ordered a bottle of champagne. "Better make it two" the most senior man called after the wine waiter. A man of sound judgement, obviously.

The corks were popped with a merry sound and soon their faces eased into gentle smiles. Only the younger man remained quiet and unsmiling, presumably lost in his sad thoughts. Had he lost a loved grandparent, I wondered? Or was he sad because he was reminded, even in his youth, that sooner or later, he too would come to the grave? The older ones, wallowing verbally in a sea of nostalgia, were now calling for a third bottle and now turning one to another with animated gaze and happy smiles, as they mentally queued to deliver their own anecdote of times gone by. Were they even now laughing aloud, not just because of the champagne but with relief and gratitude because they had heard the hiss of Death's scythe and on this occasion, had been passed over?

The party ordered brandies with their coffee and one lady ordered a large gin and tonic. The chatter flowed on when the champagne was gone. Romeo said: "All these woes shall serve For sweet discourses in our time to come."

The most senior man there was less poetic, more direct. "You know," he said, happily, letting his veined, liver-spotted hand fall over that of the old woman next to him, "we really should do this more often."

"Never fear," I thought. "You will. Oh, you will."

******

131

Oh Christ, it's Christmas again

To a child, the time between Boxing Day one year and Christmas Eve the next seems at least a century. To the child's grandparents, it is hardly worth while taking down the decorations and throwing out the tree. Next Christmas will be around so fast they'll still be making sandwiches from the old turkey when they're putting the fresh one in the oven. Better to throw a dust sheet over the tree, sit down with a cup of tea and wait.

My wife Flo, my son Lee and his wife Margaret, grandson Neil and the triplet granddaughters Clair, Britt and Ann, all insisted on being present to help me to put up and decorate the Christmas tree.

From the outset, I took a firm hold of the situation. I didn't need their services but, if they insisted on being there, they might as well do something useful.

I started to delegate.

"Margaret and the girls can fetch the boxes of decorations from the store-room. Flo, you find a large plastic bucket, there's one in the preparation room, I think, near the sink. Lee and Neil can bring the tree in from the car park, it's pretty heavy so it will need the pair of you. I'll stay here and work out just where I'm going to put it." I have always been a first class organiser, delegation and command come very easily to me.

When they had reassembled, I put down my coffee cup and continued to mastermind the situation.

"Just lean the tree up in the corner, Lee, while you and Neil bring a couple of those full sandbags from behind the toolshed."

"You'll need a bigger bucket than that," Lee said, "I'll go and look for one. Neil can bring the sandbags in. One at a time." Bit of a dodger, Lee is, when it comes to the heavy going.

"Anyone can see that tree is too tall," Flo said. "It'll never fit in. That tree is two feet too tall. Aren't you going to shorten it?"

"Anyone can see that tree is too tall ..."

"No I'm not going to shorten it. I'm going to take up a floor board or two to let the bucket down lower, then, if necessary, I'll cut a hole in the ceiling to accommodate the fairy on the top," I said with heavy but wasted sarcasm. It's not that Flo doesn't recognise sarcasm, it's just that over the years she's got into the habit of listening to me without hearing what I say, if you know what I mean.

"I think you're making a lot of work for yourself for nothing. It would be a lot easier to shorten it. With a saw," she explained. "Take it off the bottom. Saw a couple of feet of the bottom. It'll fit then."

Lee came back. "I couldn't find a bigger bucket but I've brought the saw. You're going to have to shorten it. That tree's too long."

"I'm glad you've told him," Flo said. "He was going to cut holes in the floor and ceiling."

Neil had come back with the sandbags so I shortened the tree by letting him saw two feet off the bottom. I carefully placed the bucket where I wanted it then I stood the tree up in the bucket and got it vertical, well, at least as vertical as you can ever get a Christmas tree in a bucket, even when you're as good at it as I am. I was getting rather tired with all this physical exertion whilst everyone just stood about watching. I decided to delegate again. "While I hold the tree vertical or as vertical as you can ever get a Christmas tree, Lee and Neil drape those sandbags around the trunk inside the bucket. That's right. Now drobble them firm with your heel."

"Drobble? Drobble? What's drobble?" Neil asked.

"He's made it up," Flo said. "I've been married to him for forty three years and I've never heard him say 'drobble' before. He's just made it up."

I began to lose my temper. "If any of you ever took time off from staring at the goggle box to play a mind-improving game of Scrabble you would know that 'drobble' is what people do with their heels to sandbags when they want to firm the sandbags up around the trunk of a Christmas tree, inside a bucket, in order to keep the tree vertical, or as vertical as you can ever get a Christmas tree. That's what 'drobble' means."

"I challenge that word," Clair said. A bit bolshie is Clair.

"Now just you shut up, Clair. Children should be seen and not heard." It sounded just as daft then as when my mother used to say it to me. Or 'Little pitchers have big handles' which was another of her pretty fatuous clichés. But neither, it must be admitted, quite as fatuous as the time when my father got confused and said to my mother "And another thing. Do not refer to me as a shit in front of the k-i-d-s."

I climbed the steps. They were placed quite close to the bottom of the tree but because of the conical nature of Christmas trees, I was too far from the top. I came down, moved them in even more and climbed up again. I really was a bit fed up with the whole thing, especially as we seemed to have gone through all this only two or three weeks before.

I looked down from the top of the steps.

"Would you *please* stop those girls from putting those glass balls on the tree?" I begged Margaret. "They're all in the wrong places and anyway it's the tinsel that goes on first. It's always the tinsel first. You should know that, at your age. There may be some excuse for the children but ......"

"It's the lights first," Flo interrupted. "You *always* do the lights first. Then it's the tinsel *after* the lights and *then* the glass balls. You remember, one year you did the glass balls *before* the lights and it wasn't at all satisfactory. They were all in the wrong place."

Ann started to cry.

"Grandad won't let us put the balls on the tree," she snivelled.

Now Margaret got shirty. "Really, I do think you're a bit mean," she said. "After all, Christmas *is* for the children, you know. You could have let them put the balls on the tree. They're only trying to help. After all it's a family tree, not your personal

135

property."

"I know Christmas is for the bloody children," I ground out. "You don't think I'm frigging about up this ladder at my age and in my state of health to please Flo — or you and Lee. It's the brats I'm knocking myself out for. Trying to please the brats."

Now Britt started to cry.

I tried to cool it.

"Look," I said soothingly, "let's not get quarrelsome. If you'll all stop arguing and being so dreadfully unpleasant and just pass me that blasted tinsel, I'll be able to get the job finished and come down off here before I *fall* down off here." They passed me the tinsel and I got on with the job. I've always been pretty good at draping the tinsel, it's a sort of knack, comes from forty years of tinsel-draping experience.

"Round the back," Neil said.

"What?"

"It needs some round the back. There's not enough round the back. You've got it all at the front."

"Shut up Neil," I said.

"It's very bare at the back."

"I said shut up Neil!"

"Grandad's spoiling it," Clair said. "He's not put any tinsel round the back. It's all at the front." '

"And you shut up Clair."

"He won't be told," Flo said. "If he'd done the lights first, he'd have been able to see round the back and see that there's not enough tinsel. Not round the back, there isn't."

"He's always the same when he's trying to lose weight and not drinking," Margaret said. "Grandad was a lot nicer when he drank his whisky, wasn't he children?"

"Only imperceptibly," Lee muttered.

"No, he wasn't nicer," Britt said. "He was just the same."

"His eyes were always red and watery," Ann said.

"So, what's different?" Neil asked.

"They're still a *bit* red," Britt added.

"That's quite enough," I shouted. "In fact, more than enough. Just be quiet all of you and someone pass me those lights, pass the end without the plug. Now behave yourselves. Less of your impudence."

"You should plug them in first, *then* drape them around the tree," Flo said. "That's what you usually do. Plug them in first. They light up and you can see whether they work or not."

"Oh God," I snarled. "Now your Grandma's a lighting technician. She couldn't light a bloody cigarette, she couldn't, but she knows how to light a Christmas tree. Oh yes."

"Grandma doesn't smoke," Ann said, "so she doesn't need to light a cigarette, does she? You're just being silly."

"Shut up Ann! Now be quiet."

I started at the top of the tree and draped the lights down in a regularly descending spiral but either someone had shortened the flex since last year without telling me or some fool had put the bucket with the tree in it too far from the skirting board. At full stretch, the plug was two feet short of the electric socket.

"Now see that you've made me do," I cried. "I'm fed up with this. You're all so smart, you do the blasted tree. I'm going out for a walk." And without a shred of sympathy for them, I left them to their own devices. I jacked it in and went out.

What a mess they made of it! It was pathetic. That night, when they'd all gone to bed, I spent over an hour getting it right, including the drobbling.

Not that I ever get any thanks for it. Not likely, not from my lot!

******

There is nothing that the restaurateur dreads and fears more than the advent of the office Christmas party season.

You would think that it is in the best interests of all concerned to agree on a fixed menu before the event. A fixed menu obviates the need for taking orders on the day, greatly assists kitchen planning and vastly speeds up the service. The majority of organisers recognise this and sensibly make all arrangements well in advance of the event.

Not so, however, with the rebels. The rebel organiser insists that his, or more likely if a rebel, *her* party, anything from a dozen to twenty-five strong, should be allowed to eat a la carte. Thus each person present will need to have sight of the menu and ten minutes to decide what they want.

It's a restaurateur's nightmare.

They tumble through the door, giggling with the effects of the aperitifs they have already had at the office, gin and orange, Babycham and Cherry B's drunk from thick glasses or, in extremity, from chipped teacups in the general office. They start again, asking for all the drinks we haven't got, Green Goddesses, Parfait d'Amour or whichever way-out concoction is currently receiving saturation Christmas advertising on television.

As the drinks go down, the level of aggro goes up. The badinage becomes increasingly banal, the shrieks of laughter become more ear-splitting. Taking the orders is sheer hell.

"What's Onions Monegasque?" one asks.

"Ooh, you're not eating onions, are you Mary? Don't forget we're going back to the office party. I wouldn't eat onions if I were you."

"Don't be daft. Of course I'm not eating onions. I just wanted to know what they were."

They never order for themselves until they've checked what the others are having.

"What are you having, Joan?"

"I don't know yet. What are you having, Elsa?"

"I don't know. What's Mary having?"

"What are you having Mary?"

"I don't know what I'm having. What are you having? I don't fancy any of this."

"Me neither. We should have gone to the Carillon."

"It's no good crying over spilt milk. I'm going to try this one," and Joan points to something on the menu.

I'm trying to take the order.

"Which is this one?" I ask.

"The beef thing," she says. There are three beef dishes on the menu. I try again.

"I haven't got a menu," I say. "They are all out with your party. Which particular beef thing do you mean?"

"This one," she says pointing again. "This one here."

Mary helps me out.

"She means the fourth one down after the fish. And I'll have the same."

"Me too," says Mabel. "I'll have the same."

As I said, I haven't got a menu, so I write on my order pad, "Three of the beef thing, the fourth one down after the fish" and move along a bit.

"Has John ordered yet?", I am asked. "I always have what John has."

"Who's John?"

"He's sitting next to Peter over there."

"Which one is Peter?" I asked patiently. Surprisingly she doesn't say, "He's the one sitting next to John," She says "Peter's our Yorkshire rep."

"Oh yes," I say, "*that* Peter."

"Well ask John what he's having then I'll have whatever he has."

"What's Mushrooms a la Greque?" Betty asks. She's sitting next to Henry who's in the drawing office. Or is it Peter who's in the drawing office? No, of course not. Peter is the Yorkshire rep. Peter is sitting next to John. I tell Betty "Mushrooms a la Greque? Mushrooms cooked with finely chopped onion and carrot with tomato purée, spices, white wine, lemon juice and a touch of garlic."

"I don't like mushrooms," she says. "I can't stand the texture. Don't you have a prawn cocktail?"

"I'm afraid not."

"They do a prawn cocktail at the Carillon," Henry says. "*And* they do melon balls."

"All the melons in the market were female melons," I quip.

"Very droll," says Henry.

"But we're not at the Carillon," Betty says. "More's the pity."

"Perhaps it's not too late," I say. "I could ring them for you." She takes me seriously.

"No chance. They've been fully booked since July. We left it too late. That's why we're here. We couldn't get into the Carillon."

"This is the only place we could get in," says Henry. "We left the rest too late."

"Very droll," I reply.

******

When the orders finally come from the kitchen, the waitresses mill about hawking the plates around the tables, crying their wares whilst the revellers try to remember what they ordered or claim the first dish they fancy as they see it going past.

Someone who ordered the carbonnade refuses to accept it.

"It said on the menu it's made with a Cuban steak cooked in beer. That's not a steak."

"This *is* steak," Maureen tells her, "cubed steak cooked with onions in beer."

"That's not a steak. That's meat. It said a steak on the menu. That's bits of meat."

By the end of the meal, the girls start to quarrel and bitch among themselves. The chaps sit there taking alternate sips from their coffee and a flat pint of beer and trying to remember from last year whether Yvonne's bristols are for real or just push-ups. The boss has had enough and wisely decides it's time for him to scarper. "Sorry I have to dash, Chad," he says. "look after them for me, will you?"

It's about now that a girl, make-up smeared and crying hysterically, is led out by her friends to be sick on the carpet in the ladies room. Someone has already chucked up in the washbasin.

At last it's all over. On their way out they steal anything which isn't screwed down and finish with a brief punch-up in the car park.

When the heat's off, I phone John at the Carillon. "I know it's a bit early John but I'd like to book Weston's office party in for lunch next December," I say. "No way," he says. "They tried that on this year. I told them I'd been fully booked since July."

"And had you?"

"You must be joking. Anyway I'm glad you phoned. I was going to ring you. I want to book Blenkinsop's in with you, twenty-three of them. The Thursday before next Christmas Day."

"Get stuffed," I say. And hang up.

******

Christmas Eve and New Year's Eve are our big party nights. Admission is by ticket only and we go berserk with a disco, crackers, paper hats, and false noses that are only marginally less absurd or repellent than those the clients grow for themselves.

Instead of the white tie and tails of Klemperer, Karajan or Bruno Walter, the conductor wears the checked trousers, white jacket and hat of the chef. Tonight is the once only performance of the 'Concerto for New Year's Eve', completely sold out at the box office.

The first ticket holders have arrived and have found the cloakroom, rapidly filling with near virgin, unstained Gannex and sheepskin coats, Christmas presents from loving partners.

141

Here and there, the stench of mothball marks out the ladies who got their sheepskin last year and this year, a new cooker or a set of gardening tools. The air is scented with the clean smell of aftershave and the men are not left out of it either, with their hair lacquer. There is a lively buzz of conversation.

"For Christ's sake, where's the Gents? I'm bursting for a pee."

"It's bloody cold in here. I hope the clown's remembered to turn the heat up."

"Whatever you do, don't have the pork. He always overcooks it. Remember it last year? I had the pork last year. Dry as a witch's tit."

The barmaids start in on their stately ballet, pirouetting from customer to glass, from glass to ice, from ice to lemon, from lemon to the optic measure.

The massed orchestra waits expectantly, tensely in the kitchen. The waitresses are in there already, preparing their cheese boards and the gateaux that they will introduce, *molto doce,* as the concerto nears its end.

The kitchen staff bend over their instruments tuning them; the grills, the ovens, the dishwasher, clashing the pan-lid cymbals. There are the usual pre-performance nerves and minor acts of professional jealousy.

Beryl drops the freezer lid on Jean's fingers; Betty lets the kitchen door swing back on Maureen who is carrying a tray of glasses, but out in the restaurant auditorium the patrons are now taking their seats, and at last, the moment comes when the conductor takes up his wooden spoon baton and raps sharply on the *plongeur's* head, calling the orchestra to order. Then, as they quieten into silence, he raises his stirring-spoon and leads them into the opening of the first, slow movement.

Johanna moves plaintively in with a little turkey broth, *allegro misterioso* and Andrew picks up the theme with chicken liver paté, *Con brio.* "Table 17 are sitting down. Four broth please. Fish course for the eight on six. Four main courses for three."

The waitresses move in and out of the harmony as the conductor beats a livelier tempo with his spoon and introduces the majestic, and all but overpowering, 'game-pie *furioso*.' Oven doors open and close, glasses and faces steam up, cheeks and eyes redden and all the time, the pace quickens.

The game-pie is soon supported by the 'chicken a la king', making octave leaps, climbing, then descending again in thirds and fifths to a bridge passage, where the 'pork bonne femme' takes increasing steps into a mood of violent conflict, terminating in a dominant statement of triumph and despair, which the conductor cleverly sustains by a lavish and barely controlled use of the double bass and the double whisky.

The final *adagio,* in which the mood becomes more tranquil, is led by the mince pies and Christmas pudding before surrendering to the *largo* and the sweeter notes of the sherry trifle and fresh cream gateaux.

The Concerto is finally brought to its triumphant conclusion by a brief *pizzicato* on the petits fours leading into the last solemn chords of coffee and cream.

The Concerto is over.

The orchestra stands still over its instruments. They have given of their best, now they are drained, exhausted, scarcely believing that, once again, they have achieved what should have been impossible. For a moment, there is silence. Then from the restaurant auditorium, the kitchen players hear what is their reward, the gales of laughter, the waves of noisy chatter, the pulling of crackers, the blowings on hooters, the bursting of balloons. This is their applause.

The conductor leans against the bain-marie, totally overcome by emotion and alcohol. Once again he raps on the *plongeur's* head and the orchestra waits for his words. They do not wait for long.

"Tonight," he says, "and, once again, together, we have been privileged to look up on the face of the eternal. Together we have created a night of such power and glory that in all the days to come, wherever and whenever men and women gather together with tales of noble deeds, then shall our names be spoken and, so too ......" He stops. The old fellow closes his eyes and, for a moment or two, has a good look at the back of his eyelids. Then, apparently satisfied with what he sees, he opens them again.

"Come on," he cries persuasively, "let's all get proper pissed."

******

Well, that was New Year's Eve. Now it's New Year's Day. The restaurant is closed and I stand down there, ankle deep in paper streamers, torn, cracked crackers, bursted balloons and discarded paper hats.

Here on a table, a creme de menthe, once *frappé*, now *chambré*, a full wine glass, a half-smoked cigar extinguished in a brandy and soda, speak out against our suicidally profligate, consumer society. But who is to change it?

This was the stage on which, only a few hours ago, a motley crew of Lancelots and Guineveres in silver cardboard crowns, bright feathered Hiawathas in lounge suits and Pocahontases in long dresses, skull and cross-boned pirates from the Spanish Main and second hand car dealers from Oldham, sharp-eyed in golden masks, poured one drink after another through the same orifices that had already taken in sherry, pints of beer, gee and tees, cream of carrot soup, salmon mayonnaise, lemon sorbet, beef or pork or coq au vin or game pie, blue Stilton, sherry trifle, coffee, petit fours, mints, brandies, liqueurs and God knows what all else, because that's what having a rare good old time is. If you don't live in Africa. Or India.

They pulled their crackers and then, once things started to warm up, once the chill of British reserve was washed away, they put on their paper hats and blew on their blowers and dipped their cotton wool throw-balls in wine to give them a bit more

"Once the chill of British reserve was washed away ..."

weight and striking force. Then, a drink or two later, they stood on their chairs and threw the throw-balls at each other, with increasing violence, hoping perhaps to put out an eye or, at the least, a front tooth or two, wishing they had some steel ball-bearings or cricket balls or hand grenades.

The alcoholic excitement became euphoria verging on anaesthesia. They looked at each other and sat smiling at nothing.

Strangers spoke to each other as if they were friends. Husbands and wives almost, but not quite, loved each other again, just for a while, for a golden moment or two before the anaesthetic turned to a slow poison, before voices were raised, before faces that had shone with pleasure now became flushed with the anger of old resentments and eyes that had shone with love froze into the old indifference.

It was all over. The Old Year had died, the New Year had been born.

Now there was only the way home, heavy with the silence of unspoken recrimination, heads aching and a police car waiting round every bend. A day or two off to recover and to count the cost and then back to the old two and nine, back to the what's-happened-to-it-all, what's it all about? Where are we going, where are we at?

That was yesterday. The Old Rectory is closed and Flo has gone down the lane to the river, not to chuck herself in but for a breath of air and to see what colour it is now that the dye works are closed for the holidays.

It's four in the afternoon, New Year's Day, another year starting. There can't be a lot more of them to come, not for me. I sit in my armchair, the daylight is fading but the last of the sunset silhouettes the winter branches. I put on a record and Barenboim is having a go at Mozart's 21st Piano Concerto. There is good coffee in the pot and I have just poured a measure of Mentzendorff's Kummel onto the ice cubes in my glass. If I'm really careful and don't think too much about things, perhaps this time, perhaps just this once, I'll be able to listen to the andante second movement without feeling Mozart's hand squeezing at my heart.

******

As I've said, there are not many restaurateurs who enjoy the Christmas season. We are all more than a little relieved when

146

we find that once again we have come through it still with our sanity and are into the first week of January, forty odd weeks to go before it all starts up again.

And yet, at the peak of a murderously heavy night when the restaurateur has had enough and is about to take a cleaver from the kitchen and rage round his restaurant crying "Have at ye, take that — and this — and this —" always when he's just about at breaking point, ready to abandon himself to total manic misanthropy, some sweating, red-faced chap will throw an arm around his shoulder, pump his hand up and down and, with eyes wet with emotion or leaked whisky and water, will say "I just want to tell you on behalf of my wife and myself, and all that lot at our table over there, that we've had a really smashing night, thanks to you and your lot. It's been bloody marvellous. Happy bloody Christmas. Now sit down and have a bloody good drink with me."

Then, hands still clasped, the restaurateur and the customer look mistily at each other and suddenly it's all there again, the kindness, the appreciation, the fellowship from the customer and the deep satisfaction of having done a good job well.

The stupid, the arrogant, the ill-mannered, the greedy, the phoney, the imposters, the bully boys, are all forgotten. The back-breaking ninety hour week, the heat in the kitchen, the clanging headache, the hot and aching feet are all forgotten.

The restaurateur and his team have made this man, his family and his friends, happy. They have made at least one night of their lives memorable, even if it's only memorable for a month or two. They have done a good job, as well as they know how, and they can respect themselves for it.

"We'll have that drink," the restaurateur says to the man, "but we'll have it on me. I can get it wholesale and it comes off the top for tax."

******

Just two more tales, before we finish with Christmas.

It was a year when Rowntrees in York had suffered some sort of labour dispute and during the Christmas season, there was an acute shortage of After Eight Mints. Our printed matter detailed our fixed-price, ticket-only, six-course meal and concluded 'Coffee and After Eight Mints'.

Throughout December, I had scoured the area, calling even on side-street, corner toffee shops gathering in mints daily but even so, on Christmas Eve with just one hundred diners, I was eleven mints short.

Ten people either didn't notice or didn't care much. Not so the eleventh.

The meal was all but over, even at the tables last to be occupied. The hullaballoo with whistles and hooters and God knows what else was indescribable.

I was wandering about between the tables half-stoned and totally knackered. A thin, earnest, bespectacled chap in his late fifties, ludicrous with a small paper maché policeman's helmet stuck on his balding head, stopped me. "Excuse me, are you the manager?" he asked.

"Yes," I said, "after a fashion. You could put it that way."

"I'm awfully sorry to bother you, but I've got a complaint."

"Bad luck," I said. "You ought to see your doctor. It might be catching."

"No, no," he said, "You don't understand," — yes, he did really. "I mean, we're one After Eight mint short on our table. There's six of us you see, and there's only five mints. It said on your prospectus 'Coffee with Mints.' We're one mint short."

I just couldn't believe it. Neither could I be bothered to explain why he was a mint short.

"I'm awfully sorry," I said. "Would it help at all if I gave you a small discount in cash?" and I gave him a five-penny piece.

"Thank's awfully," he said, pocketing it. "I knew you wouldn't let me down. We're regulars, you know. We came here last

Christmas Eve." True! Every single word.

The other tale concerns a packed lunchtime session a day or two before Christmas Day. At the end of our restaurant we have three, large, ceiling to floor plate-glass windows which, in the summer, we slide out of the way, opening the restaurant up to the terrace and the gardens. Naturally enough, the windows were tight closed in December but it was a bright and sunny day.

A senior executive, a regular customer, called me to his table by the window. "Can you do anything about this sun, Chad?" he asked. "It's shining in my eyes!"

"I can lend you some sunglasses," I said.

"Oh come on," he insisted, a shade petulantly. "You must be able to do something."

I folded my hands in prayer, bowed my head and closed my eyes.

"Excuse me God for bothering You at what must be, like ours, one of Your busiest times, what with your Son's birthday in the offing and all the hairs on the heads to be counted together with those falling sparrows. Unfortunately, someone has just complained about Your sun. No sir, not Your Son, but Your sun, that glowing orb which by some miracle, You hold permanently suspended in the exact geometric centre of our solar system and from which, from the kindness of Your heart even if perhaps not often enough, You occasionally allow we poor Brits the odd warm and golden beam or two, one of which is now striking through my windows on what would otherwise have been a bleak day in December.

Unhappily, Sire, it is striking one of my most valued customers straight in his mince pies so, on his behalf, I respectfully ask You to consider dimming it down a bit. Don't put it out, whatever You do, nothing serious, perhaps a partial eclipse or, if that fouls up the celestial calendar, perhaps an itsy-bitsy cloud no bigger than a man's hand. I'll be eternally grateful if You can do something to oblige this chap because otherwise he'll go on nitching right through lunch, and frankly Sire, I don't think I can put up with any more of it, not the way I am feeling at the moment. Thanking you in anticipation, I remain Sire, Your obedient servant. For ever and ever, Amen."

"That's blasphemous," the chap said. His colleagues laughed. "No, I don't like that sort of humour," he said, dead sniffy. "That's not at all funny."

Just then, a cloud came over the sun. It was a big cloud. After all it was December.

"I'm sorry you were offended," I said, "but you've got to admit it proves one thing. If you want something doing, get straight through to the Boss!"

******

A Glarse of Whane

"As much as Wine has played the infidel And robbed me of my Robe of Honour — Well, I wonder often what the Vintners buy, One half so precious as the stuff they sell." A good question from Omar Khayyam.

Wine is certainly a good thing to have around and you could fill a book with quotations from the wise and mighty down the ages to that effect. There are those who consider the drinking of wine to be some sacred rite and the wine itself to be some holy elixir to be reverenced and humbly worshipped. I am not one of those. To me wine is a welcome accompaniment to food and no more than that and I feel that those who can pay a couple of hundred pounds for a bottle of wine must be off their trolley, have probably stolen the money even if in a legalised way and should more properly be behind bars.

In my own restaurant, I am constantly amused, despite the sense of *deja vu,* by the antics of the top flight executives when it comes to ordering the wine.

They have at last made their agonised choice from the menu. "I'm *torn* between the chef's bear's foot paté or the dandelion and burdock broth. Then this shark's fin stuffed with red cabbage sounds rather exciting. What are you having, Henry?"

"I'll *try* the melon and the roast beef," says Henry.

"Jolly good idea," says George. "I'll *take* the same."

Now comes the ritual wine dance.

The host engagingly crinkles up his face until the eye bags look like prunes. He purses his lips and says, coyly, to the other. "Shall we have a glarse of whane?" Both of them have every intention of getting as pissed as newts as long as the firm is paying but the guest pretends to consider the question for a moment or so. Cogitation corrugates his brow. Then quickly, in case the offer is withdrawn, a happy smile replaces the look of thoughtful concern. "Way not, indeed!" he gurgles. The ceremonial rites having been observed, they now get into the after-you-Cecil, after-you-Claude liturgy.

"Come along," says the host winningly. "You're the wine expert. You choose."

"Oh no, no, no," splutters the other, "please, you choose. I'm no expert. I like just anything."

"You're just being modest," the host says. "You choose the wine old boy."

The fact is that neither of them knows the first thing about wine except that it's red, white or half-way between and if it's a sparkling wine or a very old one, you shouldn't shake the bottle.

They take the easy way out. "Let's see what this chappie thinks."

"What do you suggest?" they say to the wine waiter. The wine waiter is getting his back pains again and his feet are hurting. He wouldn't care if they ordered a bottle of the '85 Sanatogen.

"Bull's Blood, Sir," he says, he hopes with some conviction. "Bull's Blood, eminently drinkable." He always recommends Bull's Blood because he finds it a lot easier to say Bull's Blood than 'Cru Larrivet-Haut-Brion' or 'Chateaux Larose-Trintauden', never mind the German stuff.

"Capital idea. Bull's Blood it is then."

******

Many years ago, I went with a friend to the Blue Angel in Berkeley Street, London. We wanted a bite to eat and a glass or two.

We had already had a convivial time and, as sometimes happens to even the best of us, I was on the turn. The Blue Angel management in those days, kept the club in near darkness. The waiter handed out the menus and a small torch. "That side's the food," he said helpfully, "and that side's the wine." I ground my teeth with irritation.

"I'm so glad you told me," I said, childishly. "I was just about to order a Hock, done rare and with french beans."

"There you are then sir," he said. "You see. It's as well I said."

We ordered the cheapest bottle on the list, a red Vin du Table.

He brought our bottle of fearsome plonk with the cork already drawn. I was still bitchy and he got a bollocking and was made to bring the cork to the table. I sniffed at it, delicately flaring my nostrils. I'd just read Postgate on Wine and I knew exactly what to do, even if I didn't know why I was doing it.

I went through the whole routine, the glass held lightly by its base between my thumb and index finger, swirling the wine around.

Then the bread and salt drill, the over and under the tongue bit, the sniffing the snorting, the gurgling. The waiter thought that, at last, he had met Derek Cooper. My friend thought that I was having a stroke. Eventually, I signalled to the waiter with a languid wave of the hand that, whilst the wine was pretty grotty and they certainly didn't fool a wine buff like me by claiming it was an appellation controlled, Vin du Table, Tres Ordinaire, he could slop out a couple of glasses of the stuff.

Later we ordered another bottle. The wine waiter was a quick learner. This time, the bottle was still corked when he brought it to the table. Instead of hitting me over the head with it, as he was entitled to, he thrust the bottle excitedly between his knees, drew the cork with a theatrical flourish, wound it rapidly off the corkscrew, jammed it half-way up one of his nasty, hairy nostrils, sniffed at it noisily, then, after a bit of a struggle, got it back down his nose and pushed it into my face saying, "Have a smell at that, sir. It's lovely."

******

I watched on television, the annual Hospice de Beaune wine auction. The wine buffs there were also doing the whole thing. Screwing up their faces, snorting air fiercely up and over the palate before spitting the wine out into the tubs of sawdust; what a waste I thought, these people don't appreciate a glass of wine. I mean, it couldn't have been all that bad, could it, not in Beaune? Not so bad you had to spit it out, surely.

It was the comments 'crisp, dry, a little full, lacks balance, a nice finish' that reminded me of an occasion in Bulgaria, also a little full, lacking balance but with a nice finish, when Flo and I went to a vineyard, wine tasting.

Our party of twenty or so, of mixed nationalities, were shown over and around the vineyard and then shepherded down into the village, and taken into a large village hall, divided down its length by a ceiling to floor curtain. On our side of the curtain, long tables were laid with a large slivovic and a bottle of the local red wine at each place setting and down the centre of the table, plates of smoked meats and sausage, especially a superb smoked ham, cheeses, olives and pickled cucumbers. And of course, the thing we have all but forgotten about in Britain, proper bread. On the other side of the curtain were the locals, the liberated peasantry. It was obvious that for the purpose of raising hard currency, the locals had been pushed into half of their watering hole and were not expected to meet or get in the way of the tourists.

We sat down at the table. On our left were a civilised Belgian couple who spoke excellent English. Opposite us were a party of cynically unappreciative French, and on our right, an earnest, bespectacled English couple with that showered, scrubbed, pink-faced, clear-eyed, direct gaze that could only come from an intimate acquaintance with the Marxist Leninist Library and a fully stamped up, British Communist Party card.

We, or those of us who could stomach it, drank our slivovic, then got started on the food and the red wine. It was then that the waitresses — naturally in national costume — went crazy. They opened bottles of a different red wine and two or three white wines and they bestowed the bottles most liberally down the table despite the fact that there was already a bottle of red at each plate.

It was obvious that my English party-member neighbour was taking the wine tasting very seriously. After all, the tour had been advertised in the hotels as 'A visit to a typical Bulgarian vineyard to be followed by a wine-tasting in the village', and not as a monumental piss-up although it would have seemed that the Finns present had got the intention right.

My English friend had carefully written the numbers one to twelve on a pad and as each bottle was opened and sampled, he copied the name of the wine against the number of its appearance and then described it. 'Sistowa. Red. Very dry. Plenty of grape' and so on.

Unfortunately, neither he nor anyone else in the room was a fully qualified wine taster. We didn't spit it into the sawdust. There wasn't any sawdust. So we actually swallowed the stuff.

The Belgian couple hadn't drunk a lot and about the time they had gone out onto the hard clay street for a 'bit of air', the Germans, remembering their Hun ancestry, had locked their arms and had started to shout their boot-stamping, table-thumping songs, including the Horst Wessel.

The Finns, between noisy and perceptibly wet belches, were drinking straight from the bottle and the French were taking the mickey out of both the food and the wine, and everyone else.

My friend's writing, like his lyrical judgements of the wine, had become less than precise.

Wine No. 6 was described as 'Great man! Sweet. White. Sticky'. By now he had abandoned dialectic objectivity and described No. 7 in revisionist terms as 'Bloody smashing. Real gutsy'.

I couldn't read his valuation of No. 8 because his writing had become spidery and, as a spider would, had wandered off the page and out across the tablecloth. His wife had laid her forehead to rest on a dish of fat, black olives and gone to sleep.

For some reason, our Bulgarian courier didn't like it when Flo and I picked up a couple of bottles apiece and went around the curtain to have a drink with the locals.

There's no doubt about it, Communism keeps the workers ignorant. Would you believe it, not one of those vineyard workers spoke English. They laughed a lot, they seemed happy to see us, they threw their arms around our shoulders, they offered us drinks but it was obvious that when it came to English, they were illiterate. Undoubtedly kept so by their Marxist masters.

Happily we found a French speaking priest to act as a linguistic bridge between us. He was an old, handsome, grey-haired Hemingway look-alike, snuff and snot down his filthy habit. He was our interpreter.

We continued with the wine tasting, occasionally cleaning our palate with a shot of slivovic.

Arms around shoulders and locked together in a spirit of good will, we tried, desperately, the pair of us, to remember the words in French of the Internationale. Even sober and with a dictionary, it's not easy to translate 'Arise ye starvelings from your slumbers, awake ye criminals of want, for Reason in revolt now thunders and at last ends the age of cant'.

(A friend of mine was once put off joining the Communist Party because he'd misheard the last word of that verse and thought they were trying to do away with sex.)

The Bulgarian priest and I were suddenly joined by the English wine tasting comrade. He didn't make much of a contribution to our evening. His unconscious body crashed through the curtain to fall recumbent, but still breathing stertorously, at our feet. He had apparently, incautiously and, no doubt driven on by No. 11, referred audibly to the German platoon as 'Fascist Krauts', and had been summarily expelled from their 'lebensraum'.

156

"... and for some time, the comrade, the priest and I were recumbent together."

I immmediately fell over him and the priest fell over me and for some time, the comrade, the priest and I were recumbent together, the Englishman snoring, the priest and I now attempting the Marseillaise but not with remarkable success. Suffice it to say that I have heard it sung in France to better effect.

It was a superb and a life-long memorable night. All in all we seemed to have much more fun than those people in Beaune spitting it all out. I think they would have done a whole lot better to have swallowed the stuff.

After all, once you've acquired a taste for it, it's not at all bad and swallowing it is certainly a lot more fun.

******

It's a year or two now since the Observer published a letter from a Mr Albion F. Watkinson of Lydd. Mr Watkinson had an astonishing tale to tell. Under the heading *'Chateau Plonk'* he wrote: *'The widely observed convention that restaurateurs offer the sealed bottle of wine for inspection and open it at the table is a necessary protection for the consumer, who is paying quite a high price for a dinner wine, and does not expect to be served cheap and indigestable 'plonk' disguised as the wine of his choice by having been poured into an empty bottle of that vintage. The reluctance of 'diners out' to risk a scene by making any sort of complaint in public and doubt of their own judgement of the wine must surely explain why in three different restaurants recently, in Oxfordshire, Northamptonshire and Kent, I have observed the waiter/proprietor continue bringing bottles ready opened from the kitchen to other tables even after my insisting on the proper procedure with my own order. I wonder whether some energetic salesman of cheap bulk wine has been increasing his commission by reminding less scrupulous clients of this ancient trick?'* You can imagine the consternation that this acutely perceptive letter caused to the serried ranks of the hotel and catering workers. Hitherto strong men, now rumbled by Albion and exposed to the readers of the Observer as coldy calculating crooks, broke down and wept bitterly before fleeing the country.

In my own case it was not a wine salesman who put me onto this 'ancient trick' but my ancient grandfather.

"Do ee cum 'ere," he wheezed, pulling me by the arm. "I be going to show ee an ancient trick that were shown me by *my* ancient grandfather, that's how ancient this trick be!"

158

We slipped and clambered over a pile of empty wine bottles covering the kitchen floor — like the restaurants in Oxfordshire. Northamptonshire and Kent. we serve all our wine from the kitchen and our soups from the bar.

I saw with amazement that all the bottles bore the great names of the vintner's craft. Romanee Conti '34. Mouton-Rothschild '29. Tesco Ruby Red '98 (98 pence per bottle. that is.) Just then our sommelier fell into the kitchen. He has this 'taste-vin' thing hanging around his neck. you see. and he will keep using it to taste the wine. He's a swallower too. not a spitter outer.

"A bottle of Schmok's Hock '43 and a '38 Magnum Special." he hiccupped.

It took us only twenty minutes or so. rooting and rattling through the bottles. to find the right labels. A jugful from the white wine tank poured through a funnel and we were in business. ready to pull the ancient trick once again.

Of course that was in the old days. before we introduced mechanisation and the micro-chip. Nowadays our kitchen computer. programmed with our current wine list. is fed by a junior with the customer's choice of label. A correctly-shaped bottle ready filled with 'cheap and indigestible plonk' is automatically presented to the photo-printing labeller and the chosen name and year are printed and fixed to the bottle.

Whites are chilled by the blast freezer and reds chambréed in the microwave and it all works very well.

Mark you. it doesn't stop there! We employ an ex-TV producer. wise in the way of it. to produce whisky look-alikes from cold tea and bacardi. gin and vodka types from tap water synthetically flavoured and spiked with industrial alcohol.

A well-wrapped retired stonemason sits in our cold room chiselling simulated trout from blocks of frozen dog fish. From a Japanese export firm. we get rolls of plastic trout skin and stick on trout eyes. with that opaque white. freshly-grilled look. They also supply us with replica rabbit skeletons in edible plastic.

With their non-toxic glue, we glue blocks of chicken meat at 56 pence a pound onto the frames to produce phoney rabbits at 69 pence a pound, which we can then chop up to make our Lapin au Deux Moutardes.

We make up packets of Polycell using half the stated amount of water and that gives us our sago pudding. Kipper fillets sliced with a surgeon's scalpel become smoked salmon, fat starlings go into the pigeon pie and chunks of zoo-surplus camel in the jugged hare, there's no end to our cunning. Grandad would be proud, he would.

Even so, whatever racket we machiavellian crooks of the restaurant trade are into, we must always keep a sharp lookout for Albion F. Watkinson. There's no fooling perfidious Albion.

******

More about wine

We have a simple wine list at the Old Rectory. Even so, there's always the fellow who wants to make Grand Opera out of it. For five or six pounds a bottle, he wants to go through the absurd tasting routine then have each glass poured for him, it being terribly demeaning to pick up the bottle and pour your own. This odd attitude is encouraged by wine and food writers, one of whom complained in her column that correct service at the table is not the same thing as looking after people. *"So many times it seems,"* she wrote plaintively of eating out, *"my table setting has been re-arranged so that cutlery is straight; care is taken to see that wine is poured into the right glass, that food is served and plates removed from the right side"* (she meant the correct side.) Well, so far so good.

It's certainly better that wine should be poured into the right glass. Poured into the wrong glass, especially that nasty little smeary one that they keep the toothpicks in, and it's not the same thing at all. Just as true with the service of food. I have seen more than one previously voluble and happy dinner party shocked into sudden, unbelieving silence when food has been served from the wrong side, the right side.

"How much happier one would be," the expert went on, *"if staff were geared to keep an eye on what the customer might really want. To refill a wine glass, for example ...."* That's it, no messing about. Straight to the heart of the matter. *"To refill a wine glass for example."* That's what the customer wants above all else, someone to refill the wine glass.

Picture the scene, going well so far, table settings re-arranged so that the cutlery is straight, the wine poured into the right glasses, the food served and the plates removed from the correct side. Then, oh my God, the wine glasses need refilling and the servitors have not been geared to do it.

Knives and forks are laid down beside plates of cooling food, the erstwhile jolly conversation dies away. There is a brooding silence whilst Pater, slowly empurpling, stares stonily at his empty glass whilst Mater, terrified of Pater's rages, seeks desperately to catch the eye of the sommelier or at least that nice, fat old waitress, Edith.

Their son, Tony, is the first to crack. "Oh, for heaven's sake," he says, reaching out for the bottle of Golden Guinea. In a second he finds his wrist pinioned in Pater's iron grip. "What in God's name do you think you are doing?" his father snarls. "I've had men drummed out of the mess for less than that. Touch that bottle, sir, and you're disowned. No son of mine is going to act in public like a bloody wine waiter."

I'm sorry, but just picturing that scene has got me so upset that I'm going to have a sip of water and lie down for a minute. Do excuse me.

*****

There. That's better.

I must quarrel, however, with the lady food writer's final statement in her article. *"Most guests will forgive the occasional badged plate facing the wrong way or a vegetable served from the wrong side, in exchange for a little caring attention to their needs."* Not here they don't. Ours are an unforgiving lot, so just to be on the safe side we serve our vegetables right over the tops of their heads with little warning cries like "Oops, watch your nut" or "Duck or grouse" — very witty that last one.

Our plates are chipped not badged. When a chap complains about his chipped plate being arsy-wersy, I take the writer's advice and offer *'a little caring attention to his needs.'* "Can we sponge and press the old whistle and flute, sir? Clean and polish your daisy roots? Trim those nasty little hairs sticking out of your hooter? How about a massage. With special services?" I leer. Caring attention is our speciality.

I don't always know what my customers need but I certainly know what they deserve.

I do hope they get it.

*****

In an attempt to get some sense into it, our wine list bears the following homely message:-'*No need for a sommelier to handle our wine, it's just good plonk! So don't mess about, pour your own, get it supped and order another one. Why not, indeed!*" Despite this warm and friendly advice, we still get the occasional Charlie fishing out his little vintage card.

Wearing my waiter's white jacket, I said to one such, a complete stranger, "No need to bother with that sir, all the wines here are fresh." He looked at me as if I'd taken leave of my senses.

"Me and my wife went out for a bit of dinner the other night," I went on, now that I had his attention, "and it's not that we get out very often, the wages here being what they are and us having to rely on our tips, if you take my meaning. Anyway the food was fine but the wine list was terrible, it was all old stock going right back to '43 some of them. '52, '55 clarets and burgundies. '53, '59 and '62 hocks and not even marked down or on special offer. He must have been dead green when he first started buying wines because the oldest were the dearest, they really did rip him off way back and it was thirty years before he started buying and selling at the right price. No wonder he'd been left with the stuff at what he was asking for bottles long past their shelf life."

The customer was fascinated. "I'll tell you this," I said, warming to my theme. "The boss here is a realist. He would have got rid of all that sour old crap on the cooking and got fresh stuff in to drink. Not that he needs to dump stuff, the boss. He went to France one year and saw how they shifted their white wine by putting cassis in it, you know, their Ribena. Straight away, back home, he started some innovations of his own, to keep the stock turning over. Blue Nun with Soya sauce, Montrachet with Lee and Perrins, Riesling and Ginger wine, Barsac and Peppermint, you name it. Still, mustn't keep you from your dinner, sir. Now, what would you like? We have red and white and, if you like rosé, we can blend you a bottle. If you like it fizzy, just put your thumb on it and give it a shake. It's all fresh and it'll fizz like crazy."

"Do you have draught Guinness?" he asked.

"Yes, sir," I said. "Have you ever tried it with a splash of Mouton Cadet?"

******

Because I am very modest I haven't, so far, disclosed to you that I am something of an expert if not on wines then certainly on spirits. I've never heard from John Arlott or Derek Cooper but I do have a treasured couple of postcards from Pamela Van Dyke Price — one of them written in red ink — and she doesn't write to just anybody, not even in blue or black ink.

I've just finished my Sunday lunch. Before I sat down I had one or two gins and tonic and we've had a bottle of Beaune with the beef. I don't know why I opened Beaune because Flo's not very fond of Beaune and whenever we have it, I have to drink most of it myself. The Stilton was just a shade on the ripe side but my 1966 port helped it along considerably.

Now, as the expert, this is my considered opinion; vintage Port is alright. Beaune, being a Burgundy, is also alright, as is a gin and tonic, or a Gee and Tee as the *congnoscenti* like Pamela and I say. Gee and Tee is not quite as alright as a dry sherry or even as a dry vermouth, both of which are very alright, but a Gee and Tee is alright just the same, and two or three Gee and Tees is absolutely alright.

Now vintage Port doesn't go a long way as it's very moreish and I seem to have come to an end of that bottle. I forgot to decant it — well no, not really, let's be honest, I only have one decanter and it's half empty or half full, according to whether you're a pessimist or an optimist, with a very unusual wine called Windok. Windok is produced and bottled by the Yates' Wine Lodge people and the label says it's *'meat and malt extract blended with specially selected, vintage Australian wine.'* That's what the label says so I put it in the decanter. The man who sold it to me says that doctors are very partial to it and use it a lot but he didn't say what they used it for. When the sun shines through the decanter, it makes all those cut-glass nobbly bits look like staring, bloodshot eyes. It's a sort of warning.

Where was I? Oh yes, the vintage Port.

I didn't decant it but if you're careful you can sort of suck most of the last muddy glass of it through your teeth and trap all the crap and then get it out from between your lips and your choppers using your finger or a bit of bread crust. Well, the port's gone now and I don't want to waste this big pot of coffee so I'd better have a brandy with it.

I've just tried the Armagnac, Courvoisier Three Star and the Hine V.S.O.P. and as an expert on spirits I can give it as my considered opinion that these brandies are alright. The coffee is good but the brandies are really alright, even more alright than the coffee which is quite alright as coffee goes. Rum is alright too. I haven't drunk any rum today except only a little to use up that old bottle of Coke that could have been going off, but I can't write a definitive article on spirits without explaining rum. Rum is light or is dark, the light doesn't smell but the dark smells rum. Rum comes in bottles of different shapes and sizes. That's enough about rum.

Clarets — the red wines from Bordeaux are always referred to by experts like myself and Pamela as Clarets — Clarets are alright, especially as a change from Burgundies, not that Burgundies are not alright because they are. German whines, hocks and that are pretty all write sometimes excapt the hecks are all wite and don't ever come in rod. Where was I? Where am I?!

There's vodka, the most alright comes from Polelant or Roosia although there's no bad vodka, it's just that the best vodka is

"The most alright vodka comes from Polelant or Roosia ..."

166

better. Then there's anus and pasties and ouzwho and arrack and slipovich which are all okay except that slippyvich which is only okay for Yugoslavs and other nut cases and then only if they like it.

Now what else is protty tip hole is that Yates Windok which I am now finishing off as I nead the decantor for another gottle of port once I have scoured it. Windowk throws a crost like what port does and some of it is stucking to my teef and stucking my teef to my laps and now my teef are itchink.

I can taste the molt and I think the meet is bits of wallabies wangers they have dissolved in it, like it has just dissolved some of my teef and a bit of my tong and now I have tort you all I no about whine and spits, I thing I am goink to have a lye down.

Oh dere, I've just bumpt my hed on the skirtink bored.

******

I was in a small restaurant in Burnley and was being served by a charming, grey-haired and plump old lady anxious to please.

I ordered a bottle of Chambertin. "It won't take a moment, sir. I'll have to go down to the cellar for it," she said. I rapidly changed my mind. "Don't bother love," I said. "I'll have something else, it'll be too cold down there."

"That doesn't matter," she said. "I'll put my cardy on."

******

The definitive last words on wine must have been written by Jancis Robinson in the Sunday Times.

Let me explain.

One of the first things that Flo and I did when we started our long and painful climb from the ranks of the lower working class to the ranks of the middle working class was to change our Sunday papers.

By then, we had acquired one of those genuine reproduction,

teak-type blockboard, home-assembly coffee tables and I must say that, lightly displayed there, the News of the World, Sunday People and Sunday Express seemed rather squalid and down-market. We replaced them with the Sunday Telegraph, the Sunday Times and the Observer.

Our life instantly took a turn for the better. Especially on Sunday. The papers were a little difficult to get used to, no tarty tits, no poking perverts, no Nigel Dempster or John Junor. Lots of specialist good advice though, in fact they were more like training manuals on how to climb the social ladder without falling off and how to behave once you had made it to a social class you hadn't been born into.

We got cookery courses with photographs of the Roux brothers, both of them, not just Albert. We got details on how to set a table for a seven course dinner for twenty guests, three of whom are titled or are pals of Princess Margaret. We had special offers from Fortnum and Mason, Harrods, Heals and even Habitat. Laura Ashley, Yves St. Laurent, Terry Wogan, the names of the world's leaders of fashion and foolishness dripped from the columnists' pens. We learned to refer to the sitting room instead of the lounge, the loo instead of the lav. Flo stopped appearing publicly with rollers in her hair and I bought an anti-dandruff preparation and a male deodorant, not the roll-on-ball type, it was for under my arms. (Sorry. Same old joke).

Now that we 'entertained guests' instead of 'having company', we were soon into things like Quiches, percolated fresh coffee instead of Nescafe and strangulated vowels and bowels, both induced by socially nervous tension.

Well, now back to Jancis Robinson.

It was God, of course, who first thought of laying down the guide-lines for best behaviour, the Ten Commandments. There were originally more but He offered them around and no one wanted them, the Syrians, the Greeks, the Romans. Until He offered them to the Jews. "I've got some nice Commandments

I think you could use," God told Moses.

"Commandments? How much are they then, these nice Commandments?"

"Nothing," said God, "each one is free. No charge."

"In that case," said Moses, "we'll take ten."

In the Sunday Times, Jancis Robinson had her ten Commandments telling *'the thirsty diner-out how to order wine.'* I would have thought that a thirsty diner-out would do better to order a pint of lager or even a pot of tea, especially as ordering a bottle of wine appears to be a 'a ritual', but never mind. *"Few social rituals,"* Jancis goes on, *"offer more scope for embarrassment and humiliation than choosing wine in a restaurant."* That's very true. Pamela Vandyke Price and John Arlott have been known to colour up and falter when trying to decide whether to have Flora Blanche or Sainsbury's Super Red with their pheasant. Even Derek Cooper, afraid of being 'embarrassed and humiliated' when handed the wine list, has said "Please take that away and bring me a pint of best mild."

But Jancis wasn't all discouragement. *"Assume the wine waiter knows less about wine than you do,"* she wrote, *"the snootier he looks, the more desperately he's trying to cover up his ignorance."* So if the chap looks very snooty, I mean, really the pits at snootiness, don't waste your time asking him for a dry white wine or a full-bodied red, he'll only look at you in abject misery at being publicly exposed as a fraud who doesn't know what you're wittering on about.

On the other side of the coin, Jancis tells us in an illuminating aside that *"Master Sommelier Kevin Crooks, of Maxim's, is a fund of good advice but looks and sounds reassuringly like Eric Morecambe."* I have thought long and hard about what Jancis wishes to convey by this fascinating revelation.

Does she mean that (1) a fund of good advice can be daunting unless it emanates from someone who *'looks and sounds reassuringly like Eric Morecambe?'* (2) That although Kevin

Crooks may know 'less about wine than you do', and may even be 'desperately trying to cover up his ignorance', he is not doing it by looking snooty. Eric Morecambe didn't look snooty and Kevin Crooks looks reassuringly like him. (3) If Kevin Crooks looks reassuringly like Eric Morecambe, then the vice versa must be true. (4) Those close acquaintances of Eric Morecambe who dined at Maxim's used to think that although Eric looked and sounded reassuringly like Kevin Crooks, he didn't really know much about wine and should have looked much snootier than he did. He would have made a lousy wine waiter and was wise to stick to Wise, tap dancing and telling jokes.

Jancis makes her seventh Commandment, watch out for sweetness in some white wines and ask the wine waiter for guidance. Which in view of the fact that she has already warned us that *"the wine waiter knows less about wine than you do,"* seems a bit daft. Unless the wine waiter looks like Eric Morecambe. Or even Patrick Moore. But not Lord Longford. And certainly not Auberon Waugh, Lord Hailsham or President Reagan. In fact, I'd be so far from being reassured if my wine waiter looked anything like that lot and another hundred I could name — I'd leave the restaurant instantly, never to return.

Her tenth Commandment adjures you to *"make sure your wine is not corked."* She must mean not corked when you or the wine waiter are trying to pour it from the bottle into the glass. If it is still corked, it won't come out will it? On the other hand, it has to be corked when the bottle is lying on its side in the cellar or wine rack. It would pour out all over the place, otherwise. It stands to reason. I really think she should have been clearer on that point.

One thing she doesn't tell us, however, is how we will ever learn enough about wine not to need advice like ...... *"Refuse to be rushed into choosing a more expensive bottle than you can afford."*

"Don't ignore the house wine, especially if it's quite

expensive."

"*Wines at the top of the list are usually poor value.*" Well, all that may be confusing, but at least it's expert advice. They only have experts in the Sunday Telegraph, the Sunday Times and the Observer.

******

Keep it clean

We've always been very keen on kitchen hygiene ever since we sat in on a lecture being given to his staff by the well-known hotelier and restaurateur, Mr Sam O. Kneller.

He knew his stuff backwards and he laid it all on the line.

"One of the most important bits of this here hygiene caper is what you do when you go to the lav and that. That's where most of your troubles start, infestations, infections and that, all in that old smallest room. Nobody in their right mind wants to get all them dangerous food germs onto their private parts and that's just what you're going to get, a bad case of silverfish in the water-works or steam flies on your down-unders if, after handling all that food without gloves on, you don't wash your hands before going to the toilet.

It has been reported to me that certain members of the staff are in the habit of cleaning out pans by spitting on the crusty bits and rubbing at them with the floor cloth. Now let me make it clear. Floor cloths are not never to be used on the pans and dishes. We've got floor cloths and we've got dish-rags and as the names imply, floor cloths is for doing floors and dish-rags is for doing dishes. If you want to know which is which, the floor cloths often have a trod-on cockroach sticking to them, while the dish-rags feel dead greasy and pong a bit.

And talking about grease, you've got to get some of this grease and that off the kitchen floor. If the chef drops a steak or a chop or a rasher of bacon on that floor, the way it is, it's going to come up pretty tacky. He can't put it on the customer's plate covered in fag ash and fluff and mouse dirt and that and he can't keep wiping it clean on his trousers. Them trousers he has put on Monday have got to last him out the week and he can't go getting 'em greasy and stuck all over with fluff and mouse dirt, at least not before Thursday at the earliest.

Now, about your hygiene hats. Some of you ain't wearing 'em. I want you all wearing your hygiene hats because, let's face it and no offence, most of you lot are getting on a bit and you suffer from falling hair and dandruff and without your hat on, you only have to cough hard or sneeze and all that debris starts falling off your scalp and getting about all over the place and there's nothing worse to a high class caterer like me than having to watch my punters skimming floating flakes of dandruff off their soup before it sinks in or pulling greasy, grey hairs out of their grub before they can get stuck into it.

Don't never clip your nails where they can flirt about and get in the mash and if you've got a sore finger and the bandage slips off into the grub, don't you dare give up rooting about until you've found it and stuck it back on again. I can tell you, there's nothing like a grotty finger bandage turning up in their din-dins to put some of them la-di-da squeamish types off eating up. And it's most likely that if it gets them feeling honky, they're going to have no pudding and that's another two quid light on the bill what with VAT and service.

It also appears that we have a joker amongst us. Oh yes, a real card, a dab hand at the comic stuff, emptying the dead flies from the Insectocutor tray into the currants, shoving frog spawn into the sago pudding and dead maggots into the patna rice. Fortunately, the customers haven't yet noticed anything wrong but I'm telling this joker that if I find out who ......" We never heard what he was telling the joker. We had finished our own lunch there with a piece of their currant sponge and we said how nice and full and moist the currants were.

We had to leave rather suddenly.

******

Hydrolised and Stabilised Haute Cuisine

Restaurateurs are far too modest by nature and are generally loath to let the public know just how hard they slave away over their hot stoves.

Take, for instance, the following menu. The fact that you are offered five dishes, not the customary starter, main course and pud, and the carefully balanced choice of dishes instantly tells you that you are in a superior, 'haute cuisine' restaurant at least the equal of Le Gavroche or the Connaught.

Thick Vegetable Soup
Duck Paté
Cod in Butter Sauce
Beef Pie with Gravy
Lemon Mousse

What else do you learn from this menu? Absolutely nothing. There is no hint there of the dedication to modern culinary technology that has gone into the creation of these dishes. Indeed stated so baldly Thick Vegetable Soup ...... Duck Paté ...... one might even question whether it was worth eating.

How much more exciting, how much more tempting to the jaded palate if the dishes were accredited and described in full as they should be, like so ......

Knorr Thick Vegetable Soup (Wheat flour, noodles, dehydrated vegetables — potato, carrot, leek — with preservative, salt, edible fat with anti-oxidant, cornflour, hydrolised vegetable protein, onion powder, monosodium glutamate, ascorbic acid, sodium nitrite).

Ross Cod in Butter Sauce (Cod, butter, starch, dried skimmed milk, vegetable fat, salt, monosodium glutamate, emulsifying salts, onion powder, sugar, spices, emulsifier, herbs, citric acid, colour, cheese flavour).

Birds Eye Beef Pie (Flour, edible fat, beef salt, hydrolised vegetable protein, starch, powdered dextrose, stabiliser, colour, monosodium glutamate, onion, spice, emulsifying salts, sodium alginate, emulsifier).

Maggi's Gravy (Potato starch, wheat flour, hydrolised vegetable protein, vegetable oil, monosodium glutamate, whey powder, caramel, onion powder, sugar, yeast extract, beef extract, herbs, spices, onion extract).

Bird's Lemon Flavour Mousse (Sugar, hydrogenated vegetable oil, gelling agents (E331, E410, E341) emulsifiers (E477, E322) adipic acid, lactose, caseinate, whey powder, flavourings, artificial sweetener (sodium saccharin), colors (E102, E160a) antioxidant (E320).

******

By heaven, that's a bit more like it, isn't it? No one can argue that that little lot isn't well worth whatever you are asked to pay for it, all that hydrolising, emulsifying, stabilising, to say nothing of the sodium nitrite and both the ascorbic *and* the citric acids. That sodium alginate doesn't come cheap neither, not the refined, pale blue one doesn't. It has to be imported, you know.

******

At the Old Rectory, we've stopped messing about in the kitchen cooking food and we've gone along with the technical revolution. We don't have a chef any more. His place has been filled by an industrial chemist called Harry. Neither do we use recipes any more, only formulae now. On Harry's day off, we write the formulae out as a prescription and we take it down to our local branch of Boots, where we get it made up. It's been a bit of a blow, the Government putting up the prescription charges, but for the time being we are stabilising our own charges and absorbing the extra costs ourselves.

******

Well that's one sort of technology, as applied to food. There are, of course, many more aspects to the march of progress in the hotel and restaurant business.

The bain-marie is the thing that Carveries keep roasts drying out on and the vegetables hot in. I read somewhere that the latest bain-marie service units have sneeze-guards as well as four heating lamps. Sneeze-guard? That's nothing. Our bain-marie is an even later model. It has a sneeze-guard *and* a falling hair and floating dandruff deflector plate, bleary-eye polishing pads, a nose-drippings containment trough, a micro-mesh entrapment for nail-clippings and a de-stencher for noisome and noxious odours with vents for suck-pump extractors at garlic-breath, foetid-farts and gamey-foot levels. Cap that!

******

We've also long been into freezing techniques as used in our trade. One of the processes we use here extensively is the freezing into one-inch, solid cubes of water, drawn from the cold tap. I'm happy to pass on the tip that these cubes, which we call 'ice-cubes', are extremely useful for cooling down warm gin and tonic and other drinks. Should the local authority have reason to turn off the water supply in order to make repairs or should there be a summer drought, large quantities of these 'ice-cubes' can be taken from store and left for some time in an ambient temperature above 0 Centigrade or 32 Fahrenheit, when they will 'thaw out' and provide almost the same quantity of water for any kitchen use. If later you find out that you have 'thawed' too many cubes and you now have an excess of water, the water can readily be re-converted to 'ice-cubes' by the application of the freezing process.

These fascinating revelations have been prompted by an almost equally illuminative article in our trade press about a new, fast-food product, frozen scrambled eggs. Not as you might think, part of an Eskimo's breakfast, but a major breakthrough of inestimable value to the busy hotelier as the writer of the article explains. *"The idea of frozen scrambled eggs is likely to be greeted with a degree of scepticism by many chefs. Yet, as with so many simple dishes, a lot can go wrong with scrambled eggs. The fact that they need careful heat control and virtually continuous stirring adds up to the recipe for a potentially nasty result. Take into consideration, too, the fact that scrambled eggs are most popular at breakfast — a time when kitchen staff may not be truly awake or alert — and the preparation of a simple dish begins to look more complex."* There can be nothing more compelling than an authoritative, well researched article such as this one.

No one with the least practical experience would deny that *'scrambled eggs are most popular at breakfast'*. As are fried eggs and sausages, bacon and tomatoes, grilled kippers, porridge, Weetabix, Sugar Pops, and even foreign Johnny-come-lately's like Alpen, all chewy bits and sticky pieces when you have only just cleaned your choppers. These persistent and fairly rigid breakfast preferences have never yet been satisfactorily explained. Just as no researcher has ever been able to give a definitive reason why few Brits, if any, ever breakfast off brown Windsor soup, roast beef and Yorkshire pudding and jam roly-poly, even although some, even at breakfast, may have spotted dick.

It is certainly true that kitchen staff are not yet fully aware or alert at breakfast time and that they will go on yawning, stretching, scratching themselves and bumping into each other until it's time for their elevenses.

Happily the bits and pieces such as brown gravy, custard, mayonnaise, vinaigrette dressing, rice pudding and chocolate mousse are more popular for lunch or dinner and can be made when the staff are wide awake and as alert as their lobotomy will permit and capable of 'careful heat control and virtually continuous stirring' without falling over.

We used to freeze not just scrambled eggs, but all breakfast items and serve them as breakfast lollies but this wasn't as popular a move as we had hoped. We then hit upon the idea of freezing some of our kitchen staff when they were fully awake and alert, that is about seven-thirty in the evening, and thawing them out, wide awake and full of beans, at seven am the next day. It worked well with the 'simple but complex' dish of scrambled eggs but it took half the staff out of circulation for too much of each working day. Admittedly, it cut down on the consumption in the kitchen of tea and butter with toast, but stored overnight, the staff took up too much room in the walk-in freezer.

Then we had a brainwave. Each bedroom was skilfully and unobtrusively converted into a blast-freezer unit. Two minutes after the resident had used his key to get into his room a timing device switched the system on and he was blast-frozen solid in eighty six seconds. Careful monitoring from reception ensured that he was thawed out in good time to vacate his room before eleven am on the day of his departure. The cost of installing the freezer units was enormous but the benefits were immediate. No need to cook and serve breakfast or, indeed, any other meal. No need for waiting staff whether truly awake and alert or not. No need for lighting, laundry, chambermaids. No mess made, so no need for cleaners. No need for heating; an eighty per cent saving all round.

I think that frozen scrambled eggs have had their day. Frozen residents or diners are much more cost effective. Even with the *'need for careful heat control and continuous storing'.*

******

Restaurateurs eventually come to realise that for years they've been like King Canute, trying to hold back the tide of progress. Going down to the market several times a week, testing by hand, by eye, by smell, trying to form accurate judgement, here hares or pheasants or mallard ducks, there boxes of real finnan haddock, Loch Fyne kippers and smoked cod's roe. Somewhere else it's sprouts and celeriac, chicory and cabbage. For why? For what? For whom? For customers whose proudest statement is "I don't like my food messed about" and who will eat anything out of a packet or a tin as long as it is hot, cheap and doesn't irritate their piles or give them diarrhoea.

Reading their trade papers, restaurateurs see where they have been wrong, missing out on what surely must be the very zenith of comfort and ease of achievement for the caterer.

Disposable cups and saucers, disposable cutlery, napkins and tablecloths, all of them such close simulations of the real thing as to deceive the senses. Ready prepared and dead weight, portion controlled, individually vacuum-wrapped steaks and fish, pies and pizzas and quiches, vegetables and miracle-whip top desserts. Stuff to boil-in-the-bag, or blast from frozen to burn-the-mouth in the microwave. Poly this and that, saturated or non-saturated, vitamin enriched and protein extended ...... now there's something, soya bean flour as a protein and bulk extender of fish, beef, pork, lamb. Wonderful! You can even get an extender for your soya bean extender, fine ground sawdust or soluble cellulose or something and all guaranteed free of wireworm, beetles and thrip, to be practically non-toxic and certainly devoid of calorie bearing food value.

We contacted these various companies and moved into the twentieth century. No more early morning trips to the market.

No more preparing of fresh vegetables, cleaning fish or boning and cubing meat. Just add half a litre of boiling water, stir, bring back to the boil and simmer for twenty minutes before folding in the contents of the enclosed packet of genuine, synthesised, country-cooking type, flavourising, stabilising compound.

Our clients loved it. Business executives to a man, they continued to arrive smoking their stinking, palate polluting pipes, sharpening their appetites with an aperitif of three or more large gee and tees or a couple of pints of bitter. The roast baron of beef, hydrolised like crazy, micro-shredded, mixed with bislocated oxiovic dimethaline before being pressure moulded in easy-to-slice, bone and fat free, baron of beef type shape, 'best before' tomorrow afternoon, was a knockout. No one seemed to care that they could have got more sustenance and better flavour out of sucking on a bad tooth.

******

A nicer class of person

We had frequently been embarrassed by the number of empty seats in our restaurant. "You're quiet tonight. What have you done to them?" and "If we'd known it was going to be as dead as this we would have come on another night," had more than once proved hurtful to us.

Well, now we were into plastic food, why not some plastic people to pack those otherwise empty tables? Keep the lights down low and they would pass for real. A local sex-aid shop was advertising life-sized, male and female plug-in, undulating and vibrating, silently complaisant and compliant bed-partners. In warm and smooth to the touch, flesh-textured plastic, guaranteed washable, no less.

We had to have them slightly re-designed because even in Denton, women diners do not sit at the table in suspender belts and peep hole brassieres and drawers. Nor does even our pig's head brawn have such a visible effect on the mens' potency, even when they are wearing only a black-lace suspensory bandage. Re-designed and wearing their new plastic clothes and with the chaps now discreetly detumescent, we were able to use them to fill the tables in the shadier parts of the restaurant.

In no time at all, we realised that the blown-up, plastic people were one hell of a sight more pleasant to have around than the blown-up real people.

We had long and in-depth discussions with our Japanese clients, one of the biggest in micro-chip electronics. Their ingenuity has now given us our plastic customer Mark 2. Not the original, silent static one but an all-singing, all-dancing, micro-chip activated plastic customer who now wields a plastic knife and fork to eat plastic food off his plastic plate. The food

"Our inflatables are exact copies of our previous clients."

passes through a totally aseptic plastic gullet into a container lined with a sterile bag, from which, through a spring loaded, hinged, abdominal flap it is regularly removed for recycling and re-use by our fully automated android plastic waiters and waitresses.

We have now entirely filled the restaurant with our inflatables and, as it has always been our policy that your table is yours for the night and we don't have second sittings, I refuse all outside bookings. "Terribly sorry, sir, but I'm afraid every table has gone."

Our inflatables are exact copies of our previous clients, with the same sagging cheeks, the petulant mouths and double chins, the purple faces and dull eyes, the same corpulent and flatulant bodies. But unlike the old whingeing live lot, these are programmed to say nothing but nice things. "Absolutely superb. How kind of you to have us here. Excellent food. We're really not worthy. So grateful. Out of this world. You really must let me pay you twice what you ask." In fact all the phrases those other bastards should have used but in their time, never did.

Since we got rid of the live lot, we've also been able to get rid of the entire staff, the lot, and we have enough plastic food and enough spare plastic people in the stores to keep us going for years.

We've switched off the coolers and the freezers and fridges and the ice-maker, the plate warmer and the bain-marie, the slicers and fryers, the mixers, the mincers and the ovens. We need neither the cloakroom nor the toilets; no need for toilet rolls or soap or towels. No need to unlock the restaurant door when we open or to lock it when we close, they're all in there already and they are going nowhere when we finish. We can get up when we like and go to bed when we like, it's only a matter of switching on or off.

I say *we* but I suppose that's a royal 'we'. Flo's gone off to see her sister in Australia and says she might not be coming back and Lee's resigned from the company and gone with his wife and family to run some pub somewhere. He phones occasionally to see how I am. He says he's not really into plastic people. For better or for worse he preferred the old-fashioned live type. He says no matter how clever the technology, plastic is never as warm as flesh and blood and they never get the look in their eyes that real people have.

183

It's a bit quieter here than it used to be, with just me and the inflatables. There are starlings in the eaves and they make a lot of noise and just now and then, the phone rings but I never answer it.

It's bound to be one of those other people, the arguing, demanding ones trying to get back in by booking a room or a table.

I sit in my flat a lot, listening to Mahler or very loud Beethoven and when I get fed up, I go down to the restaurant for a bit of company. The curtains are closed but whether it's lunch or dinner, I leave them that way. I used to switch all the lights on before I started *them* up, the chandeliers, the picture-lights, the wall-lights. I don't anymore, there's no point in it. I know what they look like and just who is sitting with whom, they never change tables nor even places.

In the dark, I sit at the remote control console and I press the start button. They all sit up straight and the tape comes on. The waiters move past me from the plastic food hoppers in the old kitchen to the restaurant tables. The knives and forks don't make the same clatter on the pates as the old silver on Royal Doulton used to do but you can hear them and "Truly remarkable. Delicious" over the muted background of Chopin's Nocturnes. When I think they've eaten enough and enjoyed themselves and had a good night out, I switch them off.

I may not open up again for a day or two but, when I do, the androids will bring the plastic food back to the hoppers and I'll be ready to start all over again.

It *is* a bit lonely with Flo gone and Lee and Margaret and the kids gone, just me pressing the buttons and talking to the plastic people. "I hope everything has been satisfactory, sir?" I say or sometimes, if I am feeling more confident, "May I say, madame, how very beautiful you are." Some of them look as if they are smiling but they never answer me. Until last Wednesday, that is. One of them spoke to me last Wednesday, not a lot, but he spoke to me. "How are you these days Chad?" he said. At least I think he did. And I think that since the ice was broken, one or two more have had a quiet word. They're inclined to whisper but I'm sure they are beginning to talk to me.

Tonight, when I switch them on, I'm hoping that at last one of them will stand up. If it's a woman-type inflatable, I'll ask her for a dance. If she says no, it won't really matter. After all, they're not really human, are they! They're plastic people.

******

Money matters

Do you remember the old days when, with the exception of the Royal Family, people had money in their pockets or handbags. I mean real money, coins of the realm and banknotes upon which the Chief Cashier of the Bank of England roundly declared his promise to pay the bearer on demand the sum of five, ten or whatever pounds.

Then there was the cheque book. There are still a few cheque books about but now the new and undisputable master of the cash till is no longer cash but the credit card. Top people no longer carry money and their cheque books are left to gather dust at home. Business executives now leave their bases for tours at home or abroad armed only with a concertina of stitched, transparent envelopes each guarding its own plastic card designed to command an unquestioned and immediate supply of anything that used to be bought for money; petrol, travel, accommodation, food, drink, clothing, just anything at all, including services and the humble obeisance that goes with them, without the need to produce a single coin of the realm.

"Which one do you want?" asks the jet-setter, unfolding his concertina and dangling it before our dazzled eyes, and there the magic Abracadabra is displayed, American Express, Diner's Club, Barclays, Access, Meals-on-Wheels, Giro Scope ...... dozens of them.

"None of them," we used to say, and that's when the fertiliser hit the fan.

*****

We spent a lot of time quite precious to us explaining to those for whom we had supplied goods and services, that the cost of

186

those goods and services was owed directly to us. By the consumer. We saw no reason why moneylenders should interpose themselves between him and us, simply for his convenience and for their own profit, moneylenders who would have us clutter up our already beleaguered lives with their sliding print-out machines and piles of blanks, involve us in a lot of clerical work, posting entries in cash books and claim forms in post boxes and then have us sit back patiently waiting for our cheque, less their levied commission. Commission? For what? Any service they had rendered was to their client, not to us, but they dare not charge their client a commission because he would cease to be their client. He wouldn't pay it. Nor would we. A reward for having put us to a great deal of trouble by shoving their sticky fingers into our pie? I should think not.

We will take that old-fashioned thing called money, there is still some of it about and it is still legal tender. We will take a cheque with or without a banker's card. We have often said "Take the bill with you and post us your cheque when you get back." We have not yet said "Have that on us." But I think that 'in extremis' we might have done rather than give in.

Like the man at the petrol station.

I pulled up at these self-service, petrol pumps that I had never used before and filled my car's tank with four-star. "Twenty-three pounds eighteen pee," the man in the office said. I brought out my Access card.

"Sorry, sir," he said, "We don't accept credit cards." I was dumbfounded. In this day and age! Don't accept credit cards! Incredible, and I told him so.

"I'm sorry you don't like it but let me put it in this way. I've just supplied you with petrol for which you owe me money. That's a direct transaction between us. Now why on earth should some money lenders interpose themselves between you and me simply for your convenience and their profit?"

"Utter rubbish!" I said, but he went on regardless. "Money

lenders who would expect me to clutter up my already beleaguered life with a sliding print out machine and piles of blanks, involve myself in a lot of clerical work, posting entries in cash books and claim forms in post boxes."

"Have you finished?" I asked. "Have you finished, for God's sake?" "And then sit back," he wittered on, "awaiting their cheque less commission. Commission? For what? Any service rendered has been to you, not to me. They want rewarding by me for shoving their sticky fingers into my pie. No way," he concluded on a dramatic rising note. I'd never heard such claptrap.

I've never been afraid to tell people what I think. Especially when they are five foot two, weigh nine stone and have one arm in plaster.

"No offence meant," I told him, "but you're a boring old fart. You certainly won't see me again." "No offence taken," he said, "provided that's a promise and you keep your word."

What a way to run a business. I ask you! Unbelievable, wasn't it?

All in the past. Perhaps the petrol station man is still bravely holding out but not the Old Rectory. I've capitulated. We take credit cards.

Yes, sir, that will do nicely, sir.

******

Even so, the arrival on my desk of a parcel of bumph from American Express gave me an idea for a rear-guard advertising campaign in our local paper.

THE OLD RECTORY HOTEL

...... a peaceful haven in a

troubled world, a gentle reminder of a bygone age.

Money, known in paper form as 'currency' and in metal as 'coins of the realm', the two combined as 'cash', can still be obtained from your friendly, listening bank manager. Surprise him and ask for some. Then, armed with these time-honoured, ancient tokens, come to the Old Rectory for an olde worlde nyte to remember.

See the joy in the eyes of the barmaid as you hand her some of those differently shaped and coloured pieces of metal, those 'coins' just as they were used in the days of Rome, Greece and Old Manchester. Listen to the merry music they make as they cascade into the 'cash' register, renovated for just this and similar occasions.

Marvel at the ancient, handed-down skills of the craftsman who engraved the pictures, the intricate whirly patterns and the quaintly archaic oath 'I promise to pay the bearer on demand' on those coloured slips of paper you now know as 'banknotes'.

Learn also that each variation in size and colour marks a difference in purchasing power. Enjoy a feeling of having done a good, a noble deed as you observe the pleasure, nay, the gratitude of your host as you help him to fill another biscuit tin with these antique artifacts!

Enjoy the feeling of 'change' being put into your hand. Change, a careful selection of those metal pieces, that you can take home to examine at your leisure or better still, distribute to the staff as a souvenir of your visit.

Most of all, luxuriate in the feeling of having 'paid your way', 'paid on the nail', 'settled for cash', all those laudatory archaic phrases from the days of yesteryear which eulogise you as a worthy and honourable guest, the sort we want at ....

THE OLD RECTORY
Open to receive 'money', six days a week.
Write, phone or call for a reservation.

*****

189

Elsewhere I read about a Cornish hotelier who made an extra charge, plus VAT for *warm* toast at breakfast time. *"I have to keep overheads down and I can't afford to have someone making hot toast for each customer when they come down to breakfast,"* the hotelier stated. *"Breakfast is served between 8.0am and 9.0am, so we have to make our toast at 7.0am."* (Sic). Well that makes sense, making your toast at least an hour before you need it. It gives the stuff time to cool down. We have all heard of the third degree burns that hot toast can inflict on sensitive finger tips or the roofs of mouths. Very nasty they can be!

Hoteliers and restaurateurs will be forever grateful to that pioneering Cornish hotelier. In making his major breakthough into a more rational and equitable system of charges, he has opened all our eyes to the numerous possibilities upon which we have hitherto failed to capitalise.

We had always insisted upon telephone restaurant reservations. We now impose a booking fee to cover the cost of having telephones the customer can telephone, having staff available to answer their calls and the cost of entering these reservations in the restaurant diary, itself quite an expensive thing to supply.

We have installed parking meters on the car park and poking meters on the bedroom doors, both of which the client can feed if he needs to, without penalty.

The cloakroom is doing very well at 20 pence per individual article deposited plus a further 20 pence search fee when the articles are reclaimed, plus a final 20 pence should the customer go away with something better than whatever it was he came with.

The coin slots on the toilet doors are more than paying for themselves — our chef's concoctions are a great help in this connection — and it was a shrewd commerical stroke to remove the old toilet rolls from the twenty-six bathrooms and adopt, instead, the Eastern European system of installing at a table on each corridor, a fat old lady with a begging bowl and a pile of assorted lavatory paper.

In order to leave the customer with some element of choice, we have installed a three-tier rating system in other areas; Tier A, no surcharge at all; Tier B, Fifty pence surcharge; and Tier C, One pound surcharge. For instance, a resident can now choose between: Tier A) fairly clean bedsheets used previously that week only by people known to come from a good background. Tier B) the same used sheets but freshened up, stains removed and lightly ironed and Tier C) sheets out from the laundry for the first time that week.

There is a choice between: (A) indescribable towels, (B) towels described as 'cleanish' and (C), towels that are 'cleanish' and fairly dry. The resident can have (A) two ex-Army blankets, (B) two ex-RAF blankets or (C) one ex-RAF blanket and Maud.

In the restaurant the diner can choose between (A) utter rubbish, lukewarm and badly cooked, (B) average rubbish, badly cooked but really warm and (C) above average rubbish, badly cooked but very, very hot.

It is also possible to discount or increase the extra charges by cross matching them to a choice of (A) arrogant and indifferent service, (B) arrogant service but different and (C) warm and friendly indifferent service, but the permutations become too complicated to go into here. Write, enclosing a S.A.E. for our pamphlet 'What you're being done for and why'. It doesn't make much sense but it's beautifully printed.

******

"That was an excellent dinner, Chad."

"I'm glad you enjoyed it, sir."

"This is only our second meal here but my guests and myself have found the food and service excellent. I hope you don't mind me calling you Chad."

"Not at all, sir. Feel free, as they say."

"Only as it looks as though we are going to do a lot of business with you, we may as well be on friendly terms."

"I quite agree."

"You may have noticed that we have taken five rooms for next Tuesday night and booked a table for eight for dinner."

"Yes I have seen the booking, sir, for which I thank you."

"Well, whilst we are talking business in such a friendly and agreeable fashion, what discount do you give for quantity?"

"One third. Thirty three and one third per cent discount."

"Good Lord, that's very generous, I must say."

"No less than our clients deserve, sir and, in these hard times, no less than they need. To avoid any accusation of favouritism, we give one third discount to everyone."

"One third discount to everyone? Then how can it be a Quantity discount?"

"Not everyone qualifies for a Quantity discount, sir. What we give is a General Purpose discount which the client can use in any fashion. In your case it is a Quantity discount because you've booked five rooms and eight for dinner. Each case is classed individually. For someone else it could be a *'Welcome On Your First Visit'* discount or a *'How Nice To See You Again'* discount. Some people claim it for *'Not Wetting The Bed'* or for *'Wearing A Jacket And Tie In The Restaurant'*. It has been awarded for *'Flattering The Proprietor'*. We have one client who has an astonishingly ugly wife. He gets a *'Thanks For Leaving Your Wife At Home'* discount."

"Well, I can't say I've ever heard of that before. Still, it's not for me to argue. Room, bath, full English breakfast is reasonable enough at £30 including VAT and service. At £20 it's a steal."

"I'm afraid it doesn't quite work like that, sir. You see the room rate is really £50 a night but we first of all deduct 10% bringing it down to £45 and then we deduct your Quantity discount of one third and arrive at £30 which is the rate printed in the tariff. The discounts are built into the asking price."

"Ten per cent? You've not said anything about ten per cent."

"Haven't I? I thought I had. The ten per cent is an overall discount for Dissatisfaction. You see, we only have two chambermaids, one permanently on Valium, the other a seventy-two year old alcoholic with a bad leg, neither of them up to much but the best we could get. They tend to be forgetful. They forget toilet rolls and clean towels. They forget to change the sheets. That 10% discount is a sweetener because it's ten to one there'll be a cock-up. It's just the same in the bar. Lipstick on your gin and tonic glass, barmaid's cigarette ash in your whisky and ginger, alright, not £1.50 but £1.35 is what you pay. Ten per cent Dissatisfaction Discount comes off the top before any other discounts are calculated."

"Very reasonable."

"It even applies to your restaurant bill, sir, you cop the same ten per cent Dissatisfaction discount. You'll probably get lukewarm soup in a chipped bowl, with the waitress's thumb or even a dead fly in it. You could find fag ash in the mash or a fag-end in the fegato. Ten per cent off straight away to stop you snivelling and then the All Purpose discount of one third. That's how we can let you have the main course including vegetables for a modest £9 instead of the proper rate of £15."

"I'll just check that with my pocket calculator. Fifteen pounds less one pound fifty equals thirteen pounds fifty. Thirteen pounds fifty less one third, that is less four pounds fifty, equals nine pounds. Remarkable. You're exactly right."

"Well, like yourself, sir, I've got a good head for figures. I just wish you hadn't mentioned how much you enjoyed the food, sir."

"Oh? Why is that?"

"Excellent dinner, I think you said. Well, under the circumstances, you can hardly expect to benefit from the ten per cent Dissatisfaction discount, now can you sir, which amounts to four pounds in your case. Be fair. You are just about to pay

193

me twenty-four pounds which is thirty-six pounds less one third 'All Purpose' discount. Thirty-six pounds is forty pounds less 10% Dissatisfaction discount. We have agreed that the 'Dissatisfaction' discount is not applicable. Ergo you owe me a further four pounds."

"In that case, the All Purpose discount one third of £40 would be £13.33 and not £12.00."

"I stand corrected sir. My apologies. The correct balance owing to me is not £4 but £2.67."

"That's better. Now what discount do you give if I pay you in cash and not with a credit card?"

"I'm sure we can come to some arrangement, sir. Whilst you still have your calculator to hand, shall we sit down ......"

******

Rules
of the House

All the best hotels have a set of rules that they would like the residents to observe. Rules make for good living and an ordered existence, rules does. Take for instance the rules of the Hotel Keban in Istanbul, displayed in each bedroom in English, French and Turkish. The English version reads as follows:-*1. It is kindly required from our guests, on the arrival in our hotel, to present at the desk, their passport, I.D. card and son on, signing in the same time the usual form required by the Police.*

2. Important ammounts of money or any valuable object are to be deposited in our Reception's Office in order to be kept in the safe. Management do not assume any responsibility in case non-observance of the present article.

3. The travellers who have to leave the hotel are bagged to advise the Reception's Office till 13h at latest.

4. It is strictly forbidden to cook in the room till 13h at latest.

5. It is forbidden to use in the rooms, electric irons, friers and other similar apparates in order to avoid fires.

6. It is kindly requested from our guests to avoid dirting and doing rumours in the rooms.

7. It is kindly requested to shut slowly the door of the elevator.

8. It is kindly requested from our customers to check their bill, in case of necessity, require the tarriff.

9. Tariff below indicated has been approver by the Ministry of Tourism.

Please write your complains in our reclamation book.

Nomber of the Room 504

Price 2 per 245   3 per 295

I suppose that it's when there are three in the room, 'menage a trois' as we savants say, that the management is most likely to have to invoke Article 6.

******

I stood outside a Spanish restaurant in Majorca and read the rules of the menu as posted up in a display case. *'Menu del Dia (Menu of the day) inclusing bread, desserts and 1/2 litre of commun wein the wein can be substitute if the client wish to for a bottle of water without charging anything over the price.*
Notes: On these prices is inclusing the tax, services, porcentages and all taxis, excise taxis that are legally authoritive. In case of runing of some plates that form the Menu of the day, this enterprize is obligatedt to sustitud by anotherone which is characterist are similars without emplagip any variation on the price of it.' Well I was glad they made that clear.

No emplagip any variation on the price of it seem pretty reasonable to me.

******

Mark you the Spanish have always excelled at making everything clear. Take this extract from the booklet published for tourists by the Compania Telefonica Nacional de Espana. I have never come across a more explicit explanation of the charging system for international calls which, for the edification of all, I now quote from page 16 of that booklet.

'Great Britain. Connection charges (No. of pulses) 25 Interval between pulses 0.92 sec. Initial perceptions are expressed as authomatic counter pulses and the number of seconds an authomatic conter pulse takes is shown.

NOTE A metering pulse = 1.45 pts.
Example: for a two minute call to Germany:
$25 + \dfrac{120''}{0.92} = 155$ *pulses.*

$155 \times 1.45 = 225$ *pts.*

When I first read that explanation of the charging systems, it all seemed so clear that I felt really put out that I didn't know anyone in Germany that I could have telephoned and talked to for two minutes. If I had, I would certainly have taken up the option of $25 + \dfrac{120''}{0.92} = 155$ pulses.

The very idea fairly makes the pulses race.

Whether the errors are in translation or typesetting, the result can be very much the same thing. Over the years, our menus typed daily have listed such arcane culinary achievements as Vegetable Soap, Fresh Prunes in the Shell, Pork and Beef Brown, Roast Leg of Lamp, Roast Dick and Hungarian Pork Goolies. The girl who typed the last two had to go, her hang-ups were showing.

I thought we had a particularly jolly crowd in one night. In fact, I said so to Lee. "We have a particularly jolly crowd in tonight," I remember telling him. I went to take their order. "I would have had the fillets of sole poached with tarragon in shite wine but I'm not very fond of tarragon," one of the chaps told me "so I'll have the blanket of lamb instead."

******

We don't have a lot of rules of the house at the Old Rectory and those that we do have are mostly ignored or defied by the iconoclasts, sometimes quite pathetically.

Our bar has a very narrow frontage. If people treat it as a pub bar and stand around it facing Mecca they make it impossible for people either to move freely into the bar lounge — the doorway is opposite the bar — or, once in, to get to the bar to be served. Neither the volume nor the economics of our trade have ever allowed us to employ a bar waiter, only a barmaid. This alone is a serious culture shock to residents or first time diners who can't believe that they are expected to manage the short walk from their bar lounge seat to the bar, and back again, this time carrying a drink.

Because congestion around the bar fouls up the whole situation, a sign hangs above the bar, gold letters on a mahogany panel.

'Gentlemen are requested not to stand at the bar'.

Oh dear, Oh, my goodness! Good heavens!

Portly, purple-faced captains of industry read the simple request then kneel or sit on the floor whilst their acolytes fall about neighing with sycophantic laughter. Oh, what a prankster the chairman is, to be sure. Or they call up their women-folk and, looking archly around for appreciation, say "I'm afraid I'm not allowed to stand here darling, so you take my place whilst I go and sit down." Ha-bloody-ha. Or most stupidly of all, some rat-trap mouthed, Yankee overlord, over here to oversee his company's British serfs, will say, "Sure I've read your notice but I'm no gentleman," inviting and getting the obvious reply, "That is quite evident. Gentlemen are *requested* not to stand at the bar. Others are *told* not to."

******

We also have a small notice in each bedroom and on the reception desk asking male residents using the dining room to wear a jacket and tie, or at the least, one or the other.

Oh dear, Oh, my goodness. Good heavens!

Ninety five per cent of our residents are business executives. I have yet to see one of them leave our hotel, after breakfasting, without a jacket or tie, their shirt sleeves rolled up and their shirts open to the waist. Not bloody likely. There they go, sober business suit, crisp shirt, clean, well tied tie, socks worn and pulled up, shoes polished. Why? Why don't they treat their business environment with the same bold, individualistic sod-you approach that they use against restaurateurs.

A couple come out for dinner. For them, it is something of an occasion, certainly it costs a lot of money. They will polish and preen themselves, look forward to being 'out', to be looked after, nurtured, cossetted. Sitting next to and surrounded by a bunch of thugs dressed as if they've come to clean out the drains!

"Don't complain if the barmaid is in jeans and a dirty anorak ..."

It's not on, matey. You fellows who want to relax into informal scruff should save it until the next time your wife has one of her elegant dinner parties for your more important business and social friends. Let that lot see what a screw-the-rules macho male you are.

Alternatively, don't complain if, the next time you go out to dinner, the barmaid is in jeans and a dirty anorak and your waiter is wearing yeti boots, bahama shorts, a prominent cricketer's-box, a see-through nightie and a fireman's helmet.

But you would complain, wouldn't you? You would be the first to complain, you horrible little man.

******

An eminent member of our trade once wrote — and I like to think that upon reflection, he wished he hadn't — of the days *when hotel tables were laid with military precision, napkins were linen, silver was heavy, everything was polished until it shone. There were serried ranks of waiters in their immaculate black dinner jackets marching through the room, reflections in the mirrors of the chandeliers, the ladies in their evening dresses, the toastmaster majestic in his decorum.'* A truly evocative word picture of what were, to some of us, the past days of better style and better manners. But now?

Well now, the man wrote, people eating out are *'Yearning for informality, light-weight, light-coloured suits or open-necked shirts and jeans, disposable shoes they can throw away when the soles wear through. They don't care if their food is served from left or right or from a great height and they get steamed up if some toffee-nosed twit asks them if they have booked.'* That last bit really got through to me. I only cooked from fresh ingredients and even the simplest things, roast potatoes, roast meats, anything but grills, take time to prepare. As I've never had a glass ball — no, not that, I mean the type you read fortunes in — I needed to have a good idea of numbers so that I could balance things out without too much waste. I was one of those toffee-nosed twits who asked them if they had booked and whatever the question did to *them*, *I* certainly got 'steamed up' if they just walked in and expected everything to be available and first class. "There are six of us. We haven't booked," they would say breezily. "That's alright, I haven't cooked for you so push off." "Try it on your wife when you get home tonight," I would say. "Walk in on her six handed, and see if, at the drop of a hat and within twenty minutes of your arrival, she'll be able to offer you a choice of fourteen starters and eight main courses with five fresh vegetables." Christ, the average housewife would need a fortnight's notice to serve you and your guests with tinned soup and beefburgers and chips.

Well, that was me, one of the toffee-nosed twits. But not any more, not since I read that article and saw the light. Now, with the back up of the freezer, the microwave oven, the tin, the packet, the boil-in-the-bag, the only-add-water-heat-and-stir compounds, you can drop in any time. Nobody gets steamed up anymore by being asked if they've booked because nobody asks the question any more. It's irrelevant. Unfortunately, they do get 'steamed up' when they taste the 'fast' food and instant mush they now get on their plates.

We are also into the informality that people are *'yearning for'*. Lee and I shave only once a week and have given up bathing altogether. Flo can't leave her teeth out because they are her own and she's very attached to them so she blacks one or two out with shoe polish just for the informal effect.

Our waitresses barge their way through to the tables. They are barefooted because they have worn out the soles on their disposable shoes and disposed of them and new supplies are late in arriving from Taiwan. *'From left or right or from a great height'*, they slurp our instant gunge out onto the plates from plastic buckets.

Staff and customers belch and break wind and when I want the punters to sod off, that is, when I've got their money safely in the till, I walk about shouting "Come on you mothers, time to haul ass," and kicking the open-neck, shirted little weak ones, right in the tight seat of their jeans.

Formality was real heavy, all those troops of waiters in their *'immaculate black dinner jackets'*, all those *'reflections in the mirrors of the chandeliers'*, all those *'ladies in evening dress'*. Formality was heavy, man. Informality is cool, informality is way out, informality is right in there.

******

John Mortimer, playwright, Q.C., and bon vivant is all for informality. In restaurants, that is. Writing in the Oberserver supplement some years ago he exhorted all diners out to *'avoid all restaurants which attempt to dictate the way you dress'*, and said that *'if the other diners only feel socially secure eating in a room full of ties and blazers, then it is a good place to avoid'*. One might have thought he would have felt the same about the Old Bailey and all the other seats of justice or otherwise at which he earns his living. Blazers and ties seem far less oppressive or absurd to me than all the archaic flummery of wig and gown but we have yet to see Mortimer pleading his client's case, dressed as he was photographed on this occasion in the restaurant of his choice, jacket-less, shirt sleeves flapping, shirt unbuttoned to the waist, let alone in a blazer and tie.

But Mr Mortimer hadn't finished yet. *'The happiest thing about the best French restaurants is that they are entirely classless. In the old 'Chien qui Fume' in Les Halles, meat porters in blood-stained overalls used to get their choucroute beside after-theatre eaters in diamonds and Dior.'* Well, I know that to be true. Flo and I were never out of the place after L'Opera or La Comedie Francaise, she in her diamonds, me in my Dior. It really made our night, sitting next to those classless meat porters in their blood-stained overalls. It was just as *haut monde* at *Le Baquet du Merde* down the road. You could tell it was one of the best French restaurants because it was full of workers from the vast Parisian sewer system, squelching in in their wellies, sitting at up-wind tables in sewage-stained overalls. And what a giggle it was when their symbiotic bluebottles came across to our table to puke on our *pain* and piss in our *vin.* There was one difference. Unlike diners at *Le Chien qui Fume,* very few at *Le Baquet du Merde* chose the choucroute. They seemed to be put off by the frankfurters.

******

We once stayed at a particular seaside hotel in Britain where the proprietor believed strongly in Rules of the House. For instance, amongst the many notices and admonitions in our bedroom was one that read: GRATUITIES *No percentage is charged unless requested — when you settle your account we will ask whether this should be added or not — this is left to guests' discretion but guests wishing to show their appreciation are reminded that there are three separate departments in the hotel: DINING ROOM, KITCHEN AND BEDROOM STAFF.*

It is requested that unless guests wish to show their appreciation to a particular member of staff, gratuities should be left at reception when you settle your account as this will be shared fairly between all the staff.

THE RATE ACCEPTED GENERALLY IS 10 PER CENT. Now I reckon that was most helpful and clarified the tipping situation enormously. No service charge would be added to your bill but when you came to pay it you would be asked publicly and in the hearing of other guests whether or not you agree to parting with another 10 per cent, this, of course, being left entirely at your discretion.

Their printed breakfast menu was even more illuminating, concise and precise.

BREAKFAST MENU

A. FULL HOUSE. Fried Egg, Sausage, Bacon and Tomato or any combination of these.

B. Boiled Egg, Scrambled Egg or Poached Egg.

N.B. We regret that experience has taught us that a combination of Part A and Part B confuses and impedes service of breakfast so we are regrettably not able to offer this. I couldn't believe it!

"Could I have a Scrambled Egg, Sausage and Tomato please?" I asked the waitress. "I'm afraid not, sir," she replied. "Quite out of the question."

"Well, how about a couple of Poached Eggs, with Sausages and Bacon?"

"Definitely not permitted. That's a combination of Part A and Part B and is confusing. It is not only confusing but will seriously impede service."

The proprietor came to the table, urbane, unruffled, the perfect host.

"I'll attend to this Mabel," he said. "Now then, sir, what appears to be the trouble?"

"Well, actually I'd rather like to have Scrambled Egg, Sausage and Tomato." He gravely shook his shead. "Terribly sorry, sir."

"Well, Poached Egg, Sausage and Bacon? How about that then?"

"Come, come, sir, you're getting worse. I do recommend our Full House. Fried Egg, Sausage, Bacon and Tomato or any combination of these."

"Right," I said. "I don't like Fried Egg, Sausage, Bacon and Tomato. I'll have Bacon and Tomato with Sausage and Fried Egg. Or an even better combination, Sausage, Egg and Tomato with Bacon."

"That will be quite in order, sir, as long as the Egg is Fried

Egg and not Boiled, Scrambled or Poached." I didn't want to impede the service any more than I had, so I gave in. Even so, I'd only just reached the toast, marmalade and coffee, *or* the toast, honey and tea, *or* the brown bap, blackberry jam and hot milk alternatives as the first soups were being served for lunch.

******

I've had to change our own Rules of the House more than once.

Business gets worse year by year. Last year we put up a big sign at the end of our drive. *'This way to the world famous Butterfly Valley picnic area! Tea, Coffee, Ice-Creams, Snacks! Trading stamps with all purchases! Twenty per cent off list prices. Free car parking and use of Toilets. Your laundry done while-U-wait. Shoes soled and heeled at competitive prices. Suits pressed, hair washed and cut, fortunes told'.* It didn't work. Business got worse.

We tried 'feature' nights in our restaurant, first Ye Olde English Mediaeval Night. To set the scene and recapture the atmosphere of the Middle Ages, we tipped untreated sewage over the drive. Members of the staff with dentures, or the odd glass eye, left them out and rubbed any remaining teeth with green shoe polish. Our receptionist, who was active in the local amateur dramatic society, made us up for scrofula, scabies, scurvy, smallpox, the King's Evil and the Black Death. The good old days.

Then we had a 'French Night'. We put Edith Piaf on the tapes and 'Pissoire' on the toilet doors. We had Gauloises and Garlic coffee. We hired a Jamaican girl to impersonate Josephine Baker but when she turned up, she had only one leg so we changed the bill and put her on as Sarah Bernhardt with a sun tan.

'Novelty Surprise night' was good. We cleaned and polished the cutlery, taking particular care to get crut out from between the tines of the forks and off the necks of the HP sauce bottles. We gave them proper soup made on purpose and home made paté instead of that imported rubbish we'd got away with for years. Unfortunately they'd acquired a taste for the imported rubbish and left most of mine. In the course of the evening, I smiled quite a few times, that was a novelty, and not once did I refer to any customer as 'that purple-faced prick on table six'. I even gave people the correct change when they paid their bill, instead of keeping a bit back to make up for possible shortages. What with my amiability and one thing and another, it really was quite a novelty night.

Even so, nothing worked. I still can't understand why. After all, something rather similar in 'themes' seems to work for pubs, otherwise the breweries wouldn't keep on doing it, would they? I mean, making what they call 'theme' pubs.

You know what they do. They convert their old Victorian pubs, ripping out the polished mahogany, the Minton and the Doulton wall tiles, the stained or etched glass and the bevelled plate-glass mirrors, replacing them with polystyrene ships spars, nylon ropes and nets hung with coloured glass floats and a plastic crab or two. What was the 'Rose and Crown' becomes 'The Frigate' or the 'Man O'War' and, as you enter, someone pipes you aboard, fits you with a papier maché lifebelt and, using a compass, guides you to a seat. The landlord becomes the 'Cap'n' and addresses everyone as 'shipmate'.

He wears a black eye-patch and he lurches about drinking Lamb's Navy Rum from the bottle, with a parrot on his shoulder, intermittently sicking down his front and squitting down his back. You sit at your place in the galley with a pint of grog bitter, eating deep fried scampi off a wooden-leg platter.

A great idea, 'theme' pubs. There's one near us that used to be called 'The OK Corral'. It didn't really take off so the brewery has torn out the plaster-of-paris bunkhouse walls, swept up the plastic horse shit, returned the landlord's Wagon Master's Stetson to brewery stores with the mothball cocooned Indian braves and changed the name back to the 'Rose and Crown'. God knows where they got them from but they've fitted it out with mahogany, Minton wall tiles, stained and etched glass and bevelled plate glass mirrors.

The landlord wears a tie, a clean shirt and a gold watch chain across his waistcoat. When you go in, he smiles and says 'Good Evening, Sir. What can I get you?" instead of "Howdy cowpoke. Name your pizen." The place is packed out.

******

"I am holding a pistol to my head, an empty one as I can't afford any cartridges ..."

Well, we don't have to convert the Old Rectory into a 'theme' restaurant and hotel, the recession has done it for us. The tired business executive can now relax in the ambience to which he has become increasingly accustomed, one of quiet despair at the slow erosion and dissolution of all that it has taken him a lifetime to build up.

A visitor to the Old Rectory now approaches up a weed-grown drive, noticing the broken roof tiles and the peeling paintwork. Through the grimy and cracked kitchen windows, he sees a dim chiaroscuro of cobwebbed casseroles and rusting cooking pots.

Once into the building, he avoids the mould patches on the grease-trap gunge and slutch-toned carpet and finds his way to the all but empty bar, where a rat peers at him hoping he's brought something to eat. The bar is empty but for my presence.

I am sitting there before a very large Scotch and a pile of final demands. I am holding a pistol to my head, an empty one as I can't afford any cartridges. At my feet is the skeletal, emaciated body of a bailiff. No need to bury him and cover his grave with rocks, as the only jackals and birds of prey in Haughton Green have been killed for food and eaten by my starving staff.

I'm still not beaten. As I lay down the pistol and straighten myself up, you can almost hear the faint bugle notes and see the old flag flying behind me, fluttering in the English breeze. "Stands the church clock at ten to three, and is there honey still for tea?" I murmur.

"No," the customer says. "It's not ten to three. It's much later than that, it's half past seven. It's not tea with or without honey that I'm after but a spot of dinner. If I may be so bold."

The first customer I've had in for weeks but no sign of weakness on my part. I compose my features in my well known scowl of welcome and go straight into the *'Rules of the House'.* "I hope you've booked a table," I snarl. "It's not a café, you know, or a fast food outlet. No instant potato nor boil-in-the-bag here. If I'm going to cook for you, I need to know you're coming. *And* you need a jacket and tie in the restaurant."

I'm a little bit rusty but I soon warm to my theme. "No cigars or pipes in the restaurant. No credit given or credit cards accepted. No discounts or refunds. I can only accept your cheque if presented five clear days before you owe me anything. No responsibility accepted for cars or their contents left on, or even near, the car park, or coats, hats, sticks, umbrellas, cameras and their cases, cigarette cases, brief cases or briefs, deposited in the cloakroom. Or for any of your property, or parts of such property, left anywhere, in or on these premises or part of these premises, now, then or at any time in the future, weekdays, Sundays or Bank Holidays, notwithstanding the provisions and exclusion clauses under the laws of Scotland.

No cats, dogs, budgerigars, tapeworms, goldfish, mynah birds, pythons or killer bees. No children under the age of eighteen. No circulars, no hawkers, no hawking and spitting. Reps seen only by appointment and only if wearing a hat. Hats off in the mess. No singing in the restaurant nor cycling in the corridors. No ball games except in the bedrooms. No more than two or three in a bed. No loosing of noxious vapours. No dirty feet or smelly socks ......"

"That's alright," the man butts in. "I understand all that. You've got to have *'Rules of the House'.* We could do with a lot more discipline these days. Talk about the permissive society! Some people think that just because they're customers, they can have whatever they want, when they want it. I'm a firm believer in *Caveat emptor,* I am. I've had my let-the-buyer-beware-warning and I accept your terms and conditions as stated or understood by written or verbal ......"

"Cut the bullshit," I say. "You really mean that you agree to the *'Rules of the House'?*"

"Absolutely, old chap. Totally and absolutely."

"You mean you're not going to break the rules?" I am quite put out. Quite off balance. Out of kilter, one might say.

"Not the teeniest, itsy bitsy one. Now could I please have a drink and order my dinner?"

"Ah," I say, happily, back in charge again, back in the saddle. "Dinner! I'm afraid you're too late for dinner. We've stopped serving dinner. Awfully sorry and all that!"

"But it's not eight o'clock yet and in your brochure, you say that you take orders for dinner until nine pm."

"So it does, sir," I agree, "but if you'll look at the small print — here — just under where it says, *'This brochure is now obsolete and should be replaced by the one which will follow it'* there's a clear statement that *'The management reserves the right to alter, delete or deny anything at all, at any time, without prior or subsequent notice'.* "Good lord," the chap cries, "I'm most frightfully sorry. I'm afraid I'd missed that bit."

He's so decent about it that I unbend a little.

"Well, I must admit that the print *is* rather fine. You really *are* frightfully sorry? I mean, you're just not saying it? You're not putting me on?"

"Shattered! It's all my fault and I apologise for wasting your valuable time."

"In that case," I say generously, "I just might be able to let you have a sandwich. I just might."

"If it's not too much trouble."

"Well, it is trouble, but not too much. Just don't make a habit of it, that's all. Now what's it to be, cheese and onion, cheese and tomato or cheese without onion or tomato?"

"You're very kind," he says.

"I know," I reply, modestly.

******

210

Brief Encounters of the Nice Kind

Flo and I were on a touring holiday in the Irish Republic based on three days stay in each of four hotels belonging to the same well-known group.

One night in one of these hotels, I was about to start my dinner with a plate of smoked Irish salmon. I asked the waitress if I could have a little brown bread to go along with it.

"It's sorry that I am, sir, not being able to oblige you." she said, "but it's melba toast and rolls at dinner, so it is, and there's brown bread tomorrow with your breakfast. If you're still wanting it."

"Tell me that again," I asked. She did. "There's no brown bread at all at night but we do have very thin white bread toasted, Melba toast we call it, or a white dinner cob. In the morning for breakfast we have wholemeal crusty rolls and sliced Hovis."

"Well, I'd like to change my order then. If you'll put this smoked salmon on one side for me I'll have it for breakfast after some soup or an hors d'oeuvre and now, if I may, I'd like a little porridge, followed by grilled bacon and tomato, please, with a white dinner cob and some Melba toast."

She laughed. "Sure, sir, you must be having a joke with me. You know full well that we don't serve soup and smoked salmon at breakfast time. Neither do we serve porridge or bacon and tomato at night. You've been listening to too many of those Irish jokes, so you have."

******

By the end of the holiday, I was a nervous wreck and suffering from an attack of shingles on the sciatic nerve. We were in Dublin.

As a youngster, I had soaked up the works of the Irish writers. O'Casey, O'Faolain, O'Flaherty, Yeats and Joyce. Now, limping down or up O'Connell Street, around the Abbey and the Gate and then across to Phoenix Park, sweating with pain, I had found one famous pub after another to have been gutted by brewers as vandalistic as any in Britain. Gone were the smoky pews, the etched plate-glass, the mahogany and the marble-topped bars. When you ordered a pint of the draught Guinness, the bartender still said to you "Sure, sir, and what will you have while you're waiting?" But now it was in a setting of juke-box, strip-lighting, black glass and formica.

On our very last day, I was desperate for us to have dinner in a famous Dublin fish restaurant which friendly Dubliners told me was extant and untouched by the Gaelic Goths.

With difficulty, I parked my car in what I thought was the the vicinity of the restaurant, and, leaning heavily on my stick, made further enquiries of a passing citizen.

"Do you have a car wit' you?" he asked.

"Parked just round that corner," I said.

"Well, you don't need a car," he said, "you can walk it easily enough, so you can." And he gave me explicit directions. It was a very long walk. It nearly killed me! After almost an hour, with Flo pulling on my arm begging me to give it up and get a taxi back to the car, I saw the famed, named restaurant on a corner a hundred yards ahead.

The actual restaurant was above the ground-floor bar. Flo and I went into the bar and ordered the Guinness, having a drop of the Irish while the bartender struggled to get the Guinness to stay in the glasses. I told him we had come halfway across Dublin because of their international reputation for fish.

"And don't we serve the finest cooked fish in all of Ireland,"

Jean & Roger 01-907-9465

he declaimed rhetorically.

"That's what I've heard. Do you think we could have a look at your menu?"

"That you can, sir."

"Obviously, we have to eat upstairs," I said. "In the restaurant up there."

"You do, sir, and like a king at that."

I was struck with a sudden fear. "Do we have to book a table?"

"Only on Saturday night, sir."

"Thank heaven for that. And is all this on?" I asked, salivating.

"Every night, sir," he said, "every single night." Our drinks finished, we slipped off the bar stools and moved towards the stairs leading up to the restaurant. "Every single night, that is except tonight, sir," he went on, "tonight being Monday, and the restaurant being closed on a Monday."

******

So after that harrowing two weeks, I wasn't really put out by a later encounter in my restaurant wit chust anutter Oirishman.

The Irish resident asked me if the beef was rare and it was so. Pink and juicy it was, and just for once, as near as dammit, perfect. I half expected him to say "In that case I'll have something else" but he didn't, he ordered the rare roast beef.

When his plate came back into the kitchen, all the vegetables had been eaten but the beef was scarcely touched. I must have got it wrong and he wanted his beef well done. I rushed out in a panic to his table.

"Sure," he said, "and the beef was great, just the way it should be." "But you left it." "Well, to tell you the truth, it's only two days since I had all my teeth out. They've fitted me with this temporary set so I could go about my business and they're hurting me terrible I can't chew a thing at all.

"Why didn't you have one of those stews then?" I asked. "The blanquette of lamb is easy eating. Soft. Mushy. Sludgy."

213

"I never eat stews," he said. "It's only rare roast beef that I enjoy and that's the way of it."

******

A waitress told me that the man at table six would like a word. He drew me down and whispered conspiratorially "I don't want to make a fuss. I don't believe in drawing attention," he said, "but something's got on to those sprouts." "Got onto the sprouts?" I was puzzled. I studied them closely and then I said, "Oh, that's chopped walnuts." "There," he said, "I knew something had got on to them. I thought it was mouse droppings. If you wouldn't mind just changing them."

******

Another old toff said he'd had a really nice dinner. If I didn't mind him saying so, it was a bit spoiled because the vegetables weren't cooked properly. "We try to cook all our vegetables 'al dente'," I told him, in my most dignified manner. "That may be so," he replied, "but you slipped up tonight. They weren't cooked properly, they were chewy."

******

A woman said of her braised fennel that she didn't often get cooked celery heart and she'd never before had it the way we had cooked it, 'in Pernod'. She was going to recommend us to the Good Food Guide.

******

This other woman said she'd have the 'Coq au Vin, *a quarter of a chicken cooked with diced bacon, button onions and mushrooms, tomato, garlic and herbs in a red wine sauce.*' As she only ever drank white wine, 'the reds being too sour', could she have her chicken 'quite plain with no dressing.'

Smoking

Some years ago I thought it would be amusing to print at the bottom of our menu the message:

Smoking in the Restaurant

Much as you may enjoy your after dinner smoke, it can interfere with other diner's enjoyment of their food. You are respectfully asked not to smoke cigars or pipes in the restaurant. Cigarette smokers should inhale only. There you are, an obvious joke! The Today presenters thought so. Brian Redhead and John Timpson had me down to Manchester's BBC studio to talk about it. Other restaurateurs asked for and were given permission to use it. It was quoted here and there. The Daily Mirror got on to it and Cyril Fletcher on Rantzen's programme, quoted it to prove what an idiot I must be, an opinion shared by a purple-faced, white-haired and military-moustached Colonel type reading the menu in my bar lounge. I was wearing my white cotton jacket and taking the orders. He snapped his fingers at me. "You there!"

I doubled forward and waited, half way between standing easy and standing to attention. He was spluttering with rage.

"What the devil's all this drivel about smoking? How the devil am I supposed to inhale only?" he jibbered, stabbing at the offending line with his finger. "Absolute bloody nonsense."

I put on my Lancashire accent. "Eeh, ah don't rightly know, sir, it's boss who's said that. It gets folk proper aggravated that does and it's all his fault."

"The boss, the boss? Is he about, this boss? I'd like a word with him," he fizzed.

"I should think, sir, that he's probably up in his flat pleasuring one of the more pliant female staff. I'll fetch him down." I shot up the stairs and put on the jacket approximately matching my trousers — I get my suits from M & S and the light's not always good down on their lower sales floor — I swear to you that it wasn't four or five minutes before I was back, with my face brushed and my hair combed.

Now, using a far-back, upper-bracket tone, I said, "Excuse me, sir, but I understand you wish to have a word." He was still on full fizz.

"You the boss?" he snapped.

"When my wife is absent," I said. "Can I be of any help?"

"So this is your bloody silly idea," he started, accusingly, then he slowed down to do the proverbial double-take. "You look remarkably like that waiter-johnny I was just speaking to," he said, peering up at me. "Almost identical."

"Oh dear," I sighed. "I was hoping you wouldn't notice. That chap is, in fact, my elder brother, the black sheep of the family. Out of love and respect for our dear mother, I employ him but, unfortunately, he's an alcoholic. I do hope he hasn't been rude to you." The Colonel was softening, visibly.

"Not at all," he said. "He was quite civil, in fact. I must say, I admire your family spirit. Not a lot of it about these days. Jolly decent of you to care for a member of the family on hard times." Then he came back to the boil. "The point is, this bloody footling nonsense here. How in the blazes am I supposed to inhale only?"

"I'm a non-smoker myself so I'm afraid I can't help you." I told him, airily. "I'm sure it could well be rather difficult for smokers, especially those on more than forty a day, but I'm also sure, that as a gentleman of the old school, you'll have a damn good shot at it."

******

216

Professionalism

Over the years, I have repeatedly had occasion to ask myself what is the definitive difference between the amateur and the professional. Allowing reasonably equal efficiency and profitability, I think that the difference lies in the urbanity of the professional, the ability to keep cool when the going gets rough and, like the old nursery toy, to rock smoothly back upright whenever put down. The professional, like the amateur, enjoys his moments of deep, personal satisfaction but it's not he but the amateur who feels anger and anguish, hurt pride, a sense of frustration or personal failure when something goes radically wrong.

The professional totally ignores those boorish customers who, in his hearing, talk disparagingly about the paintings on the walls, as if he were deaf or merely part of the furnishings. "Call that a painting. Our three year old Damian could paint better than that." It is the amateur who icily asks for which publication they are the art critics. Or if they represent Sotheby's or Christies.

"Is this all you've got on tonight? Not much choice," someone else says of the menu, "nothing there that I fancy." The professional smiles charmingly, bows his head sadly and spreads his hands in a gesture which is, at the same time, apologetic and appealing. The amateur raps back "In that case, sir, may I recommend the Chinese chippy at the top of the lane. A wooden fork and curry sauce on the chips. More your scene, I should think."

When a beautiful young woman arrives in a low-cut evening dress, it is the amateur who says "Cor, what knockers!" It is the professional who tells his waiter, "Leave this to me. I will serve the soup to the lady." Later, when the nervous waiter drops

"When the nervous waiter drops the Poire Belle Helene down between Helen's belle pair."

the Poire Belle Helene down between Helen's Belle Paire, it is the amateur who tries to slide it back up with a cold hand or a serving spoon. The professional takes a large gin and tonic out onto the car park and stares up at the stars, sipping his drink until the hullaballoo is over.

I wish *I* were a professional. I particularly wished that on one memorable Sunday morning.

On Saturday, the previous day, the receptionist was going off at lunchtime for the weekend. She was putting me in the picture. "The couple in Room 25 paid their bill in advance as they are leaving first thing in the morning. They're not having breakfast.

They'll be gone before eight o'clock."

Sunday morning, I went down to the restaurant at ten-fifteen. Mrs Pegg, who had come in to cook and serve three breakfasts, was sitting at the restaurant desk, reading a paper.

"What are you still doing here at this time?" I asked.

I'm waiting for the couple in Room 25," she said. That's the trouble with the Old Rectory, not enough inter-communication. I tut-tutted impatiently. "I'm sorry you weren't told. They left early this morning. I should think they left before you got here."

"I don't think they have, Mr Chadwick."

"I know they have," I told her firmly. "So just turn everything off and clean up the kitchen. Thank you Mrs Pegg." And I went across to the office. "Blast it," I thought, searching the key board. "That's just what happens when there's no one in reception. They've taken the key with them. Or left it in the room." I got the master key and went down the corridor. Taught by previous experience, I knocked several times and waited a moment before opening the door.

I had a quick flash of a woman's naked back as she nipped into the bathroom and her equally stark husband leapt behind the door calling out in a high-pitched panic "In a minute. What is it? What do you want?"

Jesus!

"Breakfast," I bawled, equally panic stricken, through the narrowing opening. "Breakfast. If you're having breakfast, you've got just five minutes to get in. We stopped serving half an hour ago." I whipped off, sweating copiously and found something to do in the office. When, minutes later, I went back into the restaurant, the couple were sitting at a table, giving their order to a red-faced Mrs Pegg. It was obvious there had been words said.

"I'd like to know," the man asked, "are you the lunatic who just came bursting into our bedroom?"

"It was I," I said, "who after knocking and receiving no

answer, started to enter your bedroom. In a proper manner."

"With what object, may I ask?"

"I was looking for your room key. I wanted to know whether you wanted breakfast. I can't keep my staff hanging about indefinitely."

"You could have used the 'phone."

"I thought you had left. Left early this morning. Taking the key with you." I didn't seem to be making much sense.

"Well, we haven't left. With or without the key," the woman said, unnecessarily I thought, under the circumstances.

"In any event," the fellow said, "your brochure says you serve breakfast until 10.0am so I don't see how we can be keeping your staff hanging about."

"So we do serve breakfast until ten but," I said sternly, tapping my Omega, "you will observe that it is now twenty-five to eleven."

"Yesterday it would have been twenty-five to eleven. All last week it would have been twenty-five to eleven. This morning it is twenty-five to ten. Summer time ended last night and the clocks went back one hour." he said.

"Summer time ...... clocks going back ...... what on earth has that got to do with it? I've never heard such nonsense." And then, as always, the better side of my nature came to the fore. I had made my point, I was the master of what could have been a tricky situation. I could afford to be generous. "Well, no point in nit picking. I'll overlook it this time. Now that you *have* got up at last, you may as well have your brekky. Have a nice day." I said and not waiting for them to express their gratitude, I strode quickly out to the garden where I took up a contemplative stance behind the tool shed and stayed there, just looking at the trees and things, until I heard them drive off in their car.

Nowadays people are so difficult, so bloody minded, so abrasive, that it's nice now and then to have a quiet moment to yourself.

Plenty of choice

Although we regularly go through the farce of handing out menus and pretending that the customer has a free choice, it is of paramount importance that the customer chooses only that dish which we wish him to have. In order to achieve a high score in this game, the restaurateur needs a pretty sound knowledge of human psychology.

Customer A is a pushover. He is so used to being bullied, as a youth at public school, and later by his wife, his boss and now, by his growing children, that he is prepared to order anything you wish provided you speak kindly to him. Often he will just say "Bring me something nice," but abject, total surrender is no contest and a very unsatisfactory victory.

"The beef is good today."

"Fine," he acquiesces. This won't do at all.

"On the other hand, so is the lamb. The lamb is exceptionally good."

"Righto then, the lamb it is." What is the matter with this man?

"On second thoughts, I recollect you had our lamb on Tuesday. How about the salmon?"

"Lovely. Salmon," he breathes nodding vigorous agreement.

It's like dynamiting a trout stream and you move on, frustrated at the lack of battle to Customer B, who is an entirely different kettle of fish.

Customer B is a captain of industry, not one of its other ranks and he prides himself on his perspicacity and his ability to see through your crafty tricks. You need the 'Double Sell' technique for Customer B.

"What do you recommend?" he asks, fixing you with a keen and penetrating stare and clenching his strong yellow teeth about the stem of his pipe. You must recommend anything at all that you don't want him to have.

"The lamb is superb," you say.

"I'm sure it is," says your pigeon in a let's-have-no-nonsense tone "but I'm having lamb when I get home tonight. I'll have the beef." Your pigeon is in the net. You have plenty of beef and would be quite pleased to move a slice or two. But all is not well. If he has the beef, he's still having what *he* wants and that's no way to play this game. Time for your master move in beef.

"I'm awfully sorry. I have such a poor memory. You like your beef rare I think." Now you have him. If he says "Yes," you tell him that your chef has cocked it up and the beef has come from the oven black and crisp. If he says no, he likes his beef well done, you tell him that each slice is so bloody it comes with a tourniquet and a Band-Aid.

Reluctantly, you let him order the pork chop. Reluctantly, because he's still making a choice and having his own way. In fact you get to thinking that maybe it's you who is being conned and he was after the pork chop all the time. It's a very worrying game, the Menu game, with no clear winners.

******

Mr Emm likes to play games. Mr Emm is a big man, both physically and in business. He is a Managing Director in his late forties, slightly over six feet tall with fat jowls on a wine stained face. He probably weighs in at around sixteen stone.

He stays with us for two nights every week and with the passage of time and a growing familiarity, has come to believe that the Rules of the House don't apply to him.

Dinner is served from 7.30pm to 9.30pm? Right then, he wants to eat at 7.10 because he 'has work to do'. Or, knowing that we have no room service, he wants three courses served in his room because he 'has work to do'. Or he walks into the restaurant at 9.50, explains that he has been working in his room, orders his dinner and then when the first course comes out, he goes off to telephone Penang or Guatamala. He comes back at 10.15.

We always warm our potted shrimps before we serve them so Mr Emm wants his cold. He never sits through a meal without summoning one of us to his table; could he have a better pepper-mill and white bread instead of brown? Could he have another piece of lemon and would someone please take the head off his trout?

The red wine is rather cold, the white wine quite tepid, have we changed our shipper? None of the wines on our list taste as well as they did. Incidentally, the toast is a little limp or practically charred, the butter must have come straight from the fridge or from near a hotplate, it's salted or it's unsalted. Fetch me this and take that away. Is there a window open somewhere? he can feel a draught. And that's in the restaurant.

In the hotel, he tells the receptionist that he should have said he didn't want a room on the ground floor because of the noise of the residents above him nor, in the absence of a lift should she have put him on the first floor, at the front where the noise of the fountain and its flood lights keep him awake or at the back, where a neighbour keeps a barking dog. He knows we are full but we must move him for tomorrow. No thank you, he wouldn't like the same room each week, he fears that would become too monotonous.

As he says all this, he smiles and boyishly runs his fingers through his hair. "I *quite* like the food here," he says, "but last week I had two nights in a *really* first class place, the food was outstanding." And so on.

But I've discovered his Achilles heel. This spoiled and overgrown ex-public school boy hates choices. He hates making decisions. So he is given plenty of options.

"The rabbit is good but perhaps you don't like rabbit in which case I suggest the grouse, assuming that you are fond of gamey game and the roasted beef is almost as good as the roasted duckling, except that you can only have the beef rare or well done, with or without gravy or Yorkshire pudding whereas you can have the duckling served on or off the bone, without a fingerbowl and with or without orange or cherry sauce or gravy, that is unless you prefer the sole 'meuniere', or grilled on the bone then filleted or filleted and served 'bonne femme', 'Veronique' or 'Caprice' with a choice of vegetables or a mixed or green salad with or without new potatoes. Just name your choice, Mr Emm."

He looks hunted, his face crumples, his pouting lips tremble. A long pause then he says "Well actually, I'm not really very hungry. I lunched today at *Langan's* before taking the shuttle. I think an omelette would be as much as I can cope with."

"An omelette it shall be. Now then two or three eggs, fines herbes, Spanish, mushroom, cheese, onion, prawn, ham, smoked salmon omelette? Fluffy or flat, sweet or savoury? Come on, Mr Emm, up to you to decide."

Tonight, he eats quietly, never lifts his summoning finger once and goes off to his room because he has work to do.

You win one, you lose one, you win one.

******

We are certainly made aware of our faults when we are on the losing side.

Mr Exe is a health fanatic, not a jogger nor a chest expander type of nut but deeply into health food. He brings his own Hag coffee to the table where he pops vitamin pills, stirs wheat germ into his soup, sprinkles ginseng over his goulash. At breakfast, he likes plain yoghurt. Reasonable enough. Then sadly there comes a day when, through an oversight, we have no plain yoghurt. Informed of this, Mr Exe falls back in his chair, lips quivering, oh my Gawd, no plain yoghurt.

"Tell Mr Chadwick" he tells the waitress piteously, "that in future, I'll supply my own." So there, sucks to you, you wotter. My only consolation is that all this health food kick hasn't seemed to work. Mr Exe is still a great, dumb, ugly bastard.

******

By comparison, Mr Wye is quite good looking. Another six footer, in the last war he reached the Royal Navy rank of Lieutenant Commander and was several times decorated. I was walking through the restaurant on the way to the market one day as he was breakfasting. He called me to his table.

"I've been coming here now for six months and not once have you changed the breakfast cereals," he said. "All Bran, Alpen, Cornflakes, Weetabix, Shredded Wheat or Porridge."

"I'm awfully sorry," I said. "If there's some other cereal you fancy we'll certainly get it for you."

"Coco Pops," he said. "I'd love some Coco Pops." He didn't even blush when he said it.

******

Mr Zed grabs at my arm and whines. "I've told you before, I can only sleep on a feather pillow. I must have a feather pillow. Two feather pillows."

I can't have many more active years left to me, my double crown and my double chin are daily more obvious. I'm overweight, varicosed, cyanosed and generally knackered. Any harem eunuch has a higher virility rating. I think the caps on my teeth and one of my eyes are working loose. Certainly my ears are, me having to wear these heavy glasses to read the bills and the demand notes and the threatening letters I get. I'd be quite ready to lay down and die except that just now we couldn't afford a funeral and the walk-in freezer is full of unsold grub.

Plain yoghurt! Coco Pops! Feather bloody pillows!

"Feather pillows, Mr Zed? Certainly, sir, I'll see to it right away."

******

Still, I'm not as badly off as Mr Vee, another regular guest. Mr Vee is a softly spoken, round-faced, pink-cheeked chap, very appreciative and undemanding.

The time came when he was joined for just one night by his wife and his daughter. His wife turned out to be a huge imperious woman with grey hair — all over her chin — a Duke of Wellington hooter, heavy tweeds and polished chestnut brogues, three strings of pearls draped over the Pringle encasing her bolster-like bosom.

She kept up a booming denigratory commentary on the menu then finally roared, with an air of desperation "I SUPPOSE I'LL HAVE TO SETTLE FOR THE FISH."

At the table she shouted on about their neighbours, the Prendergasts, and their GHASTLY daughter Hilary in those terribly OUTRE dresses knocked up by that GROTTY little woman round the corner.

Mr Vee hid behind a fixed, dazed smile and pushed the food about on his plate. His daughter toyed with her salad and stared out into the garden.

"DO YOU HAVE A PEPPERMILL?" her mother bellowed at the quailing waitress. "I FIND READY GROUND PEPPER QUITE INTOLERABLE ESPECIALLY THIS PREPOSTEROUS WHITE SORT." And she scattered some from the pepper pot on to the carpet to prove her point.

She has a daughter? How on earth could she ever have been impregnated? It could only have been by artificial insemination. No way, the other way.

******

We leave it all to you

Happily our best customers are usually the most co-operative. As in the case of Mr Digby Thrutch. Digby is the Managing Director of the family firm of which his father is the Chairman. Digby and his wife Helen eat in our restaurant regularly and at least once a week.

"We're giving the old man a family party to celebrate his seventieth birthday and we'd like to have it here. There'll be thirty-six of us." Digby said.

"Love to have you," I replied, "but you do know that for thirty-six covers we will have to agree a fixed menu with no alternatives? It won't work any other way."

"No choices? No problem," he said. "We'll leave the whole thing to you. Food, wine, the lot. You know the sort of thing we like and we can't think of anyone more capable of giving us a good dinner. Surprise us."

I was deeply touched. This is what it's really all about, I thought. Not aggro, not hassle. More than peeling carrots, scouring pans, emptying grease traps, sweeping the car park, clearing blocked lavatory pans. There are people who trust and respect your judgement, people who have confidence in your expertise. There are those who want to repay you for your years spent dedicated to the enrichment of their life style. There comes a time, I thought, when a man can walk tall and look the world squarely in the face with his head held high.

A couple of nights later, Digby and Helen came to dinner with brother Harold and his wife Bette.

"I believe you're doing Dad's birthday dinner," Bette said.

"That I am, mam," I said, proudly.

"We *were* going to go into town, you know, to one of the

227

leading restaurants," she replied, "but then Manchester has become so expensive these days."

"Not that money matters," Harold put in quickly, "not for Dad's birthday party. No, it's quality that counts, not the cost."

"Not within reason, that is. One can't just go mad, can one, not these days."

"Oh, it's reasonable enough here," Digby said. "In fact, I don't know how he does it. We can rely on him."

"Well, I've always found your food quite tasty. Quite enjoyable really and remarkable when one remembers that you have never had any professional training."

"No training," Digby said, nervously. "I didn't know you've had no training. Nobody told me that."

"That's why my prices are so reasonable," I said. "I only charge for unskilled labour. Self taught but cheap."

"Well. Only three weeks to go. Getting geared up for it, eh? Girding up the old loins, what!"

"We're leaving it all to you," Helen said. "Food, wines. Something special. Something out of the ordinary."

"Not *too* much out of the ordinary. Not way out." Harold objected. "The choice is yours but nothing way out, old boy."

"Self taught, eh?" Digby said, reflectively as they were leaving. "Still, I suppose he's got some books of recipes and so on. And his prices *are* very reasonable.

"Well, if you're untrained, you've got to be competitive," Helen told him.

******

Digby was back on the phone a few days later.
'Had any ideas about the menu?"
"Yes a few."
"Well, you must know what you can take on, what you do best. And you know what we like. Any hints?"

"I thought it was to be a surprise."

"Well, I don't think game would be a good idea."

"No?"

"It would suit me, of course, but game isn't everyone's choice. What about that Greek thing you do? The one with the aubergines?"

"Moussaka?"

"That's it, moussaka. Never did much care for that. Moussaka's out."

"Fine, no moussaka."

"Hope you don't mind, old chap. Not interfering am I?"

"Not at all."

"Helen says please, no duck. Duck can be very fatty."

"Very hard on the digestion," I agreed, "and there are no fresh Seville oranges about at the moment."

"We can talk about the dessert later. Agreed no duck then. In fact, I'd say no poultry at all. Poultry's pretty run of the mill. Except pheasants. Any pheasants to be had? Well hung pheasants?"

"Not even well shot. Out of season, and anyway you said no game."

"Well, I don't call pheasants *game*. I mean, they're not like grouse or venison or wild boar."

"Nor like bison, bear or yak."

"Now, now, don't get tetchy, old chap. Only trying to be helpful. We're leaving it all to you."

A few days later I was in the kitchen when reception told me that Helen wanted a word.

"Has Digby spoken to you?" she asked.

"Oh yes, several times."

"I mean about fish. I've been sounding people out. No one seems very keen on fish. Digby and I just love your fish, of course, but most of the others don't seem to be at all fond."

"Even a little sole fillet with grapes or a piece of monkfish

229

under a bearnaise sauce? As a light fish course?"

"No fish course pleae," she said. "We will all have eaten breakfast and lunch that day. Please don't overface us. The ball's in your court. We're relying on you to come up trumps."

A day or so later, they came in for dinner again. "There won't be thirty-six of us. More like twenty-eight, as it now stands, but we'll give you the exact figure a couple of days before. There'll be three vegetarians and cousin Timothy is on a fat free diet, isn't he, Helen?"

"Fat free, salt free and nothing in wine sauce. Or with herbs or spices."

"Oh, and by the way," said Digby, "there are three of the family — I don't think you have ever met them — but they are very allergic to mushrooms."

"Just to complicate matters," Helen laughed. "Still plenty of scope though. I'm sure you have plenty of ideas."

"Not too plain. Not too way out, either," said Digby. "Steady on the garlic and the chili powder and that, what!"

"We should also mention that whatever you decide on should be pretty easy to eat. After all, Dad is seventy, you know, so nothing on the bone. Just something tender and easy to eat."

"A sort of spoon and fork job," I said. "How about gravy and mashed potatoes to stick the peas onto your fork?"

"You've got the idea," Digby said. "I knew we could safely leave it all to you."

Over the next few days they phoned once or twice and twice they dropped in, in passing, just for a run down on the run up.

On the big night, they were not thirty-six, nor twenty-eight in number. Just half an hour before they were due to go in, Digby told me they were twenty-two all told and we rushed around altering the table layout and settings but he must have got it wrong because when they sat down there were just seventeen of them.

No choices, No alternatives, so they all started with the watercress soup except the eight who had prawn cocktail and the five who had insisted on a mixed hors d'oeuvre.

Then they all had the roast sirloin with Yorkshire pudding and gravy except the vegetarians and those who were dieting and didn't want the Yorkshire puddings and those who made us strain the gravy off and blot their meat. Timothy, on his special fat free diet had a three egg, unseasoned omelette simmered in dry cider and six others said the beef was too rare and opted for Dover Soles.

The dessert was alright though, fresh cream sherry trifle, without sherry for the two members of Alcoholics Anonymous, without cream for the weight watchers and without fresh cream sherry trifle for the five who had Blue Stilton, excepting two of the five who had Brie with or without celery, chicory, radishes, wholemeal bread or crackers or any combination thereof.

Our coffee, black or with cream or in one case, with hot milk, went down well with those who didn't have tea with lemon or with milk.

They drank a Burgundy with their meat, if they hadn't chosen a Claret, that is, and a Sauterne with their desserts, except those on cheese who had port and except those who had Coke with or without Bacardi or vodka or lager, bitter or Guinness.

"I think we are all agreed," Digby said, as he was paying the bill, that we did the right thing in leaving the menu to you. You chose just what we like. It makes me wonder what heights you could have attained with proper professional training."

I was glad they were satisfied. I've got my eye on the old man's funeral party. From the look of him, I won't have too long to wait.

******

Out for dinner

One of the problems of being in the restaurant trade is that someone or other is always asking you to their house for dinner. They are obviously kind and they mean well and it would be churlish to refuse the invitation. Even so, we delay the evil day by dodging and ducking the invitation as long as possible, because quite frankly, to a restaurateur, dining at another restaurant is only bearable as a professional visit to assess the competiton. Dining privately *'chez la pratique'* is a chore.

"Look here, you've fed us often enough, it's high time we returned the compliment," says *la bonne femme*. "You must come and have dinner with us." "Have dinner with us," that dreaded phrase.

Admittedly, our particular job tends to make us a little anti-social. When you have spent the whole week chatting to and being chatted by a hundred and fifty different people for whom you have cooked barrow loads of food and whose mouths you have seen open to the rim of tilted glasses or the approach of loaded forks, it is not your idea of the best way to spend a precious night off, repeating your work-scene in miniature in someone else's house. Perhaps, it would be just about bearable if your hostess would refrain from trying to impress you with her own Cordon Bleu culinary skills and would be content to offer you real food, egg and chips or beans on toast, a rare-beef sandwich or sausage and mash, something sensible that you could enjoy. But no.

In her kitchen out will come the cookery books, the bouquet garni, the brandy bottle and a quart of double cream. You can bet your life that your hostess will spend days preparing the feast. For a whole week, the immediate environs of her house will resound to the whirr of her blender as she scrapes, chops, grates, slices and finally opens up that tiny tin of truffles.

Each fearsome course, from the soup liberally laced with sherry and topped with floating islands of cream, from the creamy fish mousse, the stroganoff with brandy and floating cream, the buttered vegetables, the liqueur-drenched pudding garlanded with whipped cream, each course will be presented with the appropriate wine, chilled or chambré, served in the correct glasses. All accompanied with abject apologies for the inadequacy of the food and wine upon both of which you will be eagerly invited to give 'your expert opinion' before hardly anything has passed your lips. "I'm afraid you'll find it all a complete disaster, but I do want you to be honest and tell me where I've gone wrong. I can always learn from a professional."

"Perfect," you murmur, "absolutely perfect. You make me quite envious. Superb." And smothering a belch laden with cholesterol, you wonder if you dare ask for some bicarbonate of soda with your coffee instead of sugar and after dinner mints.

If we made shoes for a living instead of cooking food, no one would ask us round to their home to try on their shoes. If we sold lampshades or garden gnomes or fancy door knobs, they wouldn't ask us round to comment on those they had at home. Why do they feel that because we cook food, they have to prove that they can do it too?

I sometimes think we're in the wrong business. But then, so did Albert Einstein towards the end.

******

It's not always cream, brandy and truffles. Sometimes it's just pretention. We were once inveigled out to dine with a couple of customers we called 'Giggle and Squeak', because that was just what they did, giggle and squeak. No harm in them really, just that they lived some sort of Noel Coward type fantasy.

233

He played the ex-Army officer part relentlessly, with a heavy wizard prang moustache and tweed jacket, cavalry twill trousers and chukka boots and, of course, a regimental tie. In the summer, the tie gave place to a regimental silk scarf worn in the approved Desert Rat style together with belted safari jacket.

She wore her hair in a braided bun, brogues on her feet and a brassiere two sizes too small for her best features, just as she wore a smile two sizes too large for her impressive expanse of predatory teeth.

Flo and I had put up a prolonged and spirited resistance but eventually we had to concede defeat and accept the invitation.

When their door was opened to us at the beginning of what was to be a very long night, I thought with some surprise that they had gone to the expense of hiring a waiter or that perhaps they kept a butler, until I realised that the man was not either but was our host in a dinner jacket. His face fell and he was covered in almost as much confusion as I was.

"I'm sure I said 'black tie', old boy," he said.

"You did and I know I have one somewhere, I wear it at funerals, but I couldn't find it. Still," I said, "this one is a very dark grey, in a way it's almost a light sort of black." He was too much of an ex-officer and a gentleman to turn us away. "Well, I suppose you'd better come in," he said reluctantly, the bottom falling out of his night.

His wife, in a long crinoline type of dress with what was either some of her or a bustle at the back, came clanking and clattering forwards, festooned in chains and jewellery and wearing — I thought — her husband's after-shave. It was when we were in the hall and the front door was closed behind us that I realised it wasn't after-shave and she wasn't wearing it. The door of the downstairs loo had been left ajar by whichever of them had just used it and guiltily half emptied an air-freshening aerosol.

I must confess that the disparity of our dress in that first, brief, air-freshened domestic moment rather dampened the persiflage over the stuffed olives, the salted peanuts and a glass of Cyprus sherry. We moved into what our hostess referred to as 'our little dinette', which our host, who was something of a handyman — perhaps he'd been in the Pioneers or Allie Slopers Cavalry — had created with shopfitter's bamboo poles, wood-grained Formica and banquette seating, upholstered in blood-red vinyl.

We started with a glass of chilled V8 vegetable juice and then a very hot Madras curry. Ambrosia tinned rice pudding was followed by a wedge of processed cheese, brought to the table on a tiled cheese board but still in its cryovac wrapper. We finished with instant coffee and yes, you've guessed it, 'After Eight' mints. Then we settled down to a litre of lukewarm Hirondelle while our host, still immaculate in his dinner jacket, regaled us with an interminably long and tedious series of singularly, unfunny, smutty stories.

It was a great pity really. If they had just cut out the crap and let themselves be the people I'm sure they were, we could have had a very nice time.

Instead of which it was a very long night. Old boy. For the good lady wife and yours truly.

******

Getting away from it all

Just ever so occasionally, we decide of our own freewill, to go out for dinner to someone else's restaurant. When we *are* going out for dinner, I like to have a few large whiskies before we have anything to eat as I find it loosens me up. It gets rid of my natural reserve and helps me to start in on that endless flow of anecdotes, jokes and witticisms that make Flo's nights out with me so enjoyable to her. Over the years, I've realised that she is rather reserved and undemonstrative really, so she never lets herself laugh out aloud at my jokes, but I am sure that behind her rather set expression, she is laughing away like crazy, only deep down inside herself where it doesn't show.

I always let her drive us there and back and on the way, in between jokes and telling her how nice it is to get away from business for a night, I always give her a chance to brush up on her driving by correcting her and telling her what she is doing wrong.

On just one such occasion, we had reserved a table for nine o'clock and we arrived in the restaurant bar at eight-thirty pm. Whilst we were waiting to be given the menus, I occupied myself in my usual manner when relaxing away from it all, by counting the staff and the customers and dividing the one into the other, then checking on how many tables and seats there were and slipping outside to take a second look at the car park in order to estimate its total capacity and count the cars that were actually on it.

I like to keep Flo entertained — she doesn't have a lot of fun so I then had a guess at the size of the spirit optics used in the bar and by referring to the list of bar prices and by relating their charges to estimated optic capacity, I worked out the house percentage of profit on the drinks. Well, it's a change from just telling jokes.

I kept our jolly interesting conversation going by next having a stab at what the weekly pay roll must be and roughly how many covers a week and what spend per cover would be needed in order to make a reasonable profit on the capital employed, assuming in the first instance that the property was freehold and also free from any incumbrance or, in the second instance, that if the property was leasehold, assuming that the sum I had mentally set aside for rental was reasonably accurate.

Passing on these brief calculations to Flo, I summed up by making a snap comparison of their operation with our own. I pointed out that the bar furniture was obviously supplied by X and Company and that the drinking glasses were the French ones made by Igrec et Cie, that the door closers and Emergency Exit signs were the same as our own and, something that Flo could never have ascertained for herself, that the urinals in the men's lavatories were by Shanks.

"Quite remarkable," Flo said. "Now, do you think we might order our dinner?" The menu covers were the quality leather ones made by Grotte at £12.00 each for quantities from one to twenty five, but the menu itself was a bit of a disappointment. It was printed, not hand-written or typed and far too expensive. Pages of it, always a bad sign. I was instantly on my guard.

"Moules mariniere," I commented, acidly. "If they have any at this time of the year, they'll be from the freezer; fresh mussels in mid-July indeed. And if that's the sort of place this is, then the paté will come in triangular slices and the soups will be out of the packet or a tin. Keep off the soups, you know how monosodium glutimate makes you flatulant and, oh, my God, I was right, look there, *'chicken and mushroom vol-au-vent'* and *'savoury seafood pancake',* you can imagaine what recycled gunge has gone into them. If you have to put it in a vol-au-vent or a pancake or under a pastry lid, it really is desperate."

"You should know," Flo said. "I'll start with egg mayonnaise."

"I'm warning you. It'll be bottled mayonnaise, probably salad cream more likely."

"Yes," she said, "And I've no doubt that the eggs won't be free range eggs with brown shells but battery hen eggs laid by miserable battery hens. Dingy white shells all streaked with poultry poo. That's what I want. Egg mayonnaise and the roasted poussin."

"Is the poussin frozen?" I asked the waiter. "No sir," he said, "not now it's been in the oven."

I can't face main courses, that's why I like a meal of Chinese *dim-sum* or of Greek or Turkish *meze*. I explained I wanted only starters and I ordered hot artichoke with hollandaise sauce, an avocado vinaigrette, whitebait and half a dozen snails. It was now 9.30pm. Whilst waiting to be called to our table, I captured and held Flo's interest — I think — with succinct criticism of the bar, the bar lighting and lay out, the barmaid, the wine list and the cost of the wines I had ordered. I mentioned that I didn't think a lot of the pattern of the carpet nor indeed of the decor in general. Neither was I particularly taken with the size and shape of the ashtrays; in short I kept up my flow of jolly interesting, informed and informative opinion. No idle chatter but an in-depth analysis of the whole damn thing.

The service was very slow. Four large Camparis later, I told the head waiter that if we couldn't start our dinner in the next ten minutes, he could forget it. I ordered a cheese and onion sandwich to put us on an bit while we were waiting, but, typical of the place, it never came.

When we eventually got our dinner, the wine was so thin I had to drink a second bottle before the taste of the grape broke through. When we came to the coffee, the cup was so large and the brandy measure so small that it took four large brandies to balance one cup of coffee. And after that, the port, although vintage, was not one of the best and they only had one bottle decanted and a couple of measures had gone out of that so it didn't last long.

I was not at all gruntled.

"How was your meal?" Flo asked me as the waiter left the bill on our table.

I told her. "The artichoke was grossly overcooked and soggy with tepid water and the hollandaise was more of an eggy vinaigrette; the avocado was hard and unripe and the vinaigrette was more of a sugar with vinegar; the whitebait were welded together and were cold and the snails, which I am sure had died of malnutrition, were devoid of parsley, garlic and butter. However, the cutlery and the plates were clean, as was the table linen and I *was* sitting comfortably even if I was in a draught."

The head waiter came up to our table.

"How was your meal, sir?" he asked.

"Absolutely first rate," I said, smiling ingratiatingly whilst I paid the bill and gave him an extra pound on top of the service charge. "Well really," I said to Flo, on the way out. "I don't see any point in having a go at people who can't answer back and upsetting them just because the food's bloody awful. Not every chef is in my class. It's not the waiter's fault, is it?"

"You're a creep," Flo said. "A phoney creep."

"Me a creep?" I said. Then I fell down their ill-lit but fortunately, thickly carpeted staircase.

She drove us home. I don't know how she did it, the way that centre white line kept turning into two lines and criss-crossing about all over the bloody place.

"I'm glad I've been able to give you such a terrific night out," I told her. "It must do you a power of good to get away from the business once in a while and I think you deserve a break, despite what you've just cost me."

"What *I've* just cost *you*?" She's not got much of a grasp of finance. Never had.

"You probably don't realise that for little more than the cost of that dinner, I could have stayed by myself in a self-catering apartment in Greece for a week."

"If, by yourself, you'd like to make it a fortnight, no, a month even," Flo said, "I'll gladly pay the difference." Whatever faults Flo has — and I must admit, she's not perfect — when I want to go away by myself, she never stands in my way, even although she must miss me terribly. She's incredibly unselfish, my wife is, and generous to a fault.

******

Ask a silly question

It seems likely that everyone engaged in the hotel and restaurant business eventually becomes a little quirky. Certain things are only minor irritants, others become major hang-ups. There can not be a restaurateur who hasn't bridled when someone has telephoned to ask what is on the menu for that day. It's somehow an insulting question inferring that the caller might not find the food on offer to be worth coming out for.

Late one Saturday afternoon, the telephone rang and I answered it. "Good afternoon, Old Rectory, here," I said. A woman's voice in terribly haughty tones asked "Can you tell me what you have on your menu tonight?"

"Yes, of course I can," I replied.

There was a long pause then she snapped "Well?"

"Yes, quite well, thank you. And how are you?"

"I asked you can you tell me what is on ......" I butted in "You asked me *can* I tell you. I think you meant *will* I tell you. The short answer is I *can* but I won't."

"What did you say?" Her voice was now positively imperious.

"I said I *can* tell you but I won't."

"Who is that speaking?" she snarled.

"It's me."

"And who is me?"

"I don't know who you is. I don't think we've ever met."

She slammed the phone down but rang back some five minutes later. I was half expecting the call and I answered in a strangulated far-back voice. "This is the Old Rectory. Can I help you?"

"Who is that?"

"This is the manager."

"I've just spoken to an incredibly rude member of your staff."

"Oh Lord, the phone must have been left through to the kitchen. That would be my chef, madam. Was the wretched man abusive?"

"No, just terribly rude."

"Thank heaven for that. It's obvious that he's been at the cooking wine again. If he was only rude and not abusive he's not yet stoned. When he's abusive he really is Brahms and Liszt. Sings Rugby club songs in Welsh.

"What on earth are you talking about. Am I speaking to a restaurant or a mad house?"

"A good question madam," I say, "and one I frequently ask myself. What with the chef permanently Oliver Twist and singing in Welsh, a head waiter who hears voices and a stone deaf bartender, I ......" but I was wasting my time. She had hung up.

*****

Hooked on fish

A major hang-up concerns fish.

I am dedicated to buying and cooking superb fish, from the simple but succulent eel, herring and mackerel, plaice, haddock and cod to monkfish and turbot, halibut and bass. I am close to the Manchester Fish Market and two or three times a week, I am down there, sorting through the boxes, feeling fish for flesh or for excess roe.

There is not a place in the world where I have been that I have not sought out the fish market, open air sales straight from the boats on the beaches of the Algarve or Penang or Cape Cormoran in India, the vibrant and clamorous indoor markets of Funchal, Athens, Paris. Fish fascinates me. But not the British diner. Surrounded by seas bearing some of the finest fish in the world, he quails if you suggest he should eat some of it. He doesn't even have the guts to say "Stuff your fish" but stammers pathetic excuses for insisting on meat. "I had fish for lunch," or if it is lunch time, "We're having fish at home tonight." Can you imagine the scene just before he leaves home in the morning? As he taps the barometer in the hall, his wife says, "If you're having lunch at the Old Rectory, don't be talked into having fish." "But he's so insistent, darling." "Well, tell him we're having fish at home tonight."
"Oh Lord, we're not, are we?" "Of course not, don't be ridiculous. Just tell him that."

I've got the plumpest, sweetest freshest fish in England for his lunch, poached to order in wine or butter-grilled on the bone, skate-wing with black butter or caper sauce, sole with prawns, or fillets of fresh halibut baked under a masking of grated Gruyere, cream and French mustard.

"We're having fish at home tonight," he babbles. The prick.

******

I'm the only member of my family who cares about fish. Flo doesn't, Lee and Margaret don't. I've bought the fish that morning. Now, if they are taking the orders I say "Sell the fish. It's magnificent." "As you hand 'em the menus, tell them about the fish. Picked by an expert. This morning. Sell the fish." I've seen them at it.

"If you like fish," Flo says, making liking fish sound like a perversion, "it's very nice."

"Fish," Lee says, pink with embarrassment at 'selling' something, "the fish is fresh but there's plenty of choice, beef, lamb, pigeons. The game pie is superb."

My approach is more positive and much more persuasive. I have these thick-soled wooden clogs and I come in out of the kitchens carrying a boning knife. I stand in front of the cutomer like Frankenstein's monster on my three inch platforms. Red in the face from opening oven doors, eyes bloodshot and leaking whisky and water, I loom over the seated diner and using the knife just under his throat to punctuate my simple, direct appeal with slashes and jabs, I fix him with one of my masterfully dominant looks and say "While you were in bed this morning, enjoying a bit of leg over, I was down in that goddam freezing cold …..ing fish market choosing those goddam …ing herrings. Have the fish."

"We're having fish at home tonight," he says and I fall sideways off those goddam ….ing platform soles. Not Dover soles. Not even lemon soles. Wooden platform soles.

Mark you, I'm usually sorry when they do order the fish. I've prayed for years that someone, somewhere, someday would open a How to Eat Fish Training School.

"My approach is more positive and much more persuasive."

"This fish you recommend. Does it have any bones in it?"
"No, sir. It's crossed with a jellyfish."

There's not one in ten who knows how to slide the knife along the spine from the tail to the head to lift off the fillet. The other nine attack the fish as if it were a two-inch thick steak straight in there with a knife and fork, hacking and chopping away. By the time they've finished, they would have better enjoyed chewing on a nylon pan scrubber stuffed with a fish finger. What comes back on their plate makes you think the fish have swum into the trawler's propeller instead of its nets. You also wonder, now that nanny has gone and perhaps mummy too, who combed their hair and tied their tie before they came out this morning and who's going to give them a helping hand if they need to go for a wee-wee.

******

On one occasion Lee was away so I said to Flo, "I'll take the orders until I've sold the fish then you can take over and I'll go back into the kitchen."

We were quite busy and at the end of my order taking I'd managed to shift a fair amount of tackle. I'd managed to sell all the steak and kidney pie, the roast beef and the pork chops flamande. The fish? Oh yes, I'd sold two herrings to a man who was thinking of doing an Open University course and wanted to feed his brain and a brace of mackerel to a Japanese who understood no English.

Suddenly the dishwasher went manic. I rushed into the kitchen just as a new hand, Ethel, so terrified at the sound of the Denby ware being ground up that she opened the front of the machine in full cycle, and showered with hot soapy water and pellets of pottery, fell back heavily into old Annie who emerged through a cloud of steam mumbling "Me teeth, I've lost me teeth."

"This isn't the time for fooling about," I cried. "We'll find

246

your teeth later" and I came off my platform soles again. In a desperate effort not to fall into the stockpot, I put one hand firmly into a freshly made bowl of trifle and thrust the other, quite inadvertently I assure you, down the open-necked blouse of an astonished waitress. It was something of a *contretemps*. Half an hour later, the waitress brought a plate back from the restaurant bearing an ominous amount of uneaten Fritto Misto di Mare.

"Mr Faulkner said the monkfish bits were very nice but there's something wrong with the squid."

"Cooked to perfection," I said, prodding it with a fork. "Dry, crisp, golden brown. Oh dear — oh dear. We've found your teeth Annie."

Annie, just back from a week's holiday, popped them back in, batter and all, just in time to grin nervously at Flo, who had come into the kitchen.

"My word Annie, you do look well," Flo said, "been sleeping in a deckchair with your mouth open, have you? You must have had good weather, even your teeth are tanned."

******

What exactly is ......?

Monkfish never appears on the menu without someone saying "Monkfish? What exactly is monkfish?" This customer says just that.

"Goujons of monkfish on a bed of chopped mushrooms in a pastry case, masked with bearnaise sauce. That sounds interesting. What exactly is monkfish?"

"Well, it's more or less exactly that, sir. It's a Monkfish. That's what it is. I could joke that it's a male fish that's taken Holy Orders, but I am sure you would rather I didn't."

"Well then, what exactly is it?"

"It's not easy to define monkfish, sir, not with any exactitude."

"Please do try."

"Well, a monkfish is a deep-water, firm-fleshed, white-fleshed, very edible fish which swims about in the salt-water depths of the North Sea. At least, one must assume that whilst alive it swims about. All the monkfish I have ever seen have but recently died and in consequence, have ceased any type of movement and are just laying there, deceased. Swimming not. Neither about nor hither and thither."

"I'm still no wiser. What is a monkfish like?"

"Oh, I imagine very much like another monkfish. In fact when you see a number of them together, some big, some small, but all deceased, they bear a remarkable resemblance to each other. A little bit as we find the Chinese. In that sense. They all look alike to me."

"Well what does it taste like then? Does it taste like plaice? Like sole or cod? They're white-fleshed fish."

"You know your fish, sir, you certainly know your fish. No, it doesn't taste like any of those except in the sense that they all taste of fish. It's much easier to eliminate what it doesn't taste like than to define what it does. If I may draw an analogy?"

"Please do."

"Suppose that someone asked you what an egg tastes like?"

"What sort of an egg?"

"A boiled egg, for instance. You could truthfully say that a boiled egg tastes a little like a poached egg, not much like a fried egg and not at all like a scrambled egg. But they all taste of egg."

"You are speaking, of course, of a hen's egg."

"With respect sir, all eggs laid by birds are hen's eggs in that the cockerel or cock of the species is not equipped for laying eggs. I imagine that what you are asking is, are we discussing the egg of the common, domestic fowl we refer to as a hen?"

"Quite so."

"Well then, assuming that we are trying to describe the taste of what we call a 'hen's egg, we could say that a duck's egg tastes stronger than a hen's egg, that pigeon's, quail's and seagull's eggs taste a bit different from a hen's egg and that there would be no point in bringing an ostrich egg into the discussion as very few of us have ever eaten one, or joined others sharing one, boiled, poached, scrambled or fried."

"Agreed. But I think that the line of your thinking is directed to the argument that the very terms of reference, boiled, poached or fried, or duck, pigeon, quail or seagull eggs, would only have meaning to those already conversant with the end result of the cooking method employed and the actual egg being cooked."

"Absolutely."

"So it follows that anyone already so experienced in different types of egg and the methods of cooking them would not need to ask the question in the first place as he would already know the answer."

"Well reasoned sir. The converse being as you have inferred, that if he were not so experienced in eating cooked eggs, whatever comparisons were made would be meaningless without a remembered criteria of previous experience."

"Good. Now let's be done with eggs and get back to the monkfish? I do have remembered experience of other fish, poached, grilled and baked."

"Other fish, sir, such as the Moray eel, the tiger shark, the great white whale?"

"Well, no, not to my knowledge."

"So if I say that monkfish doesn't taste like a Moray eel, a tiger shark or a great white whale, you would have to accept the validity of the statement without it adding anything to your knowledge of the monkfish. You have eaten herring, mackerel, cod, plaice, sole and mullet?"

"All of them. And whitebait and skate."

"Monkfish tastes like none of them. Nor does it taste like trout, turbot, hake, halibut, salmon, swordfish or tunny all of which I have no doubt you have eaten at some time or other."

"Yes I have. All of them."

"Well then, let us now look at the question from another angle. Let us take plaice, flounder, dabs, skate and even halibut and sole, which are all built horizontally, flatfish, as opposed for instance, to conger and cod, hake and bass, built more in the vertical plane ...... "

"Enough. You've convinced me. Even these sketchy observations have aroused anticipation of a new taste experience. We're not having fish at home tonight. I'll have the monkfish."

"With pleasure, sir, but it must be some other time. I'm afraid that the monkfish is finished."

"What a pity, just when I felt I was about to learn something. To be quite honest, before I asked you about the monkfish, I was *torn* between the lamb's sweetbreads and the tripe a la mode. Tell me, what exactly is a sweetbread ...... ? What does a sweetbread taste like?"

******

Coupez
the bull merde

There is a commonly held belief that the French are the greatest cooks in the world and that French citizens are gourmets to the last man or woman. Don't believe a word of it. It's a load of codswallop. As proof of that, go into any French supermarket and watch those gourmet French housewives queuing at the check-outs, their baskets loaded with exactly the same chemical, processed and pre-packaged garbage that you would find in supermarkets anywhere else in the world. Well, perhaps not quite. Where the British housewife may be carting off a tin of Heinz beans, the French housewife may have a tin of an appalling mush labelled Ratatouille. Try spreading the tinned Ratatouille on toast or eating it with sausages and grilled bacon. I'll take the Heinz beans every time.

Obviously some French chefs are very good at their job and those whose dishes are sold at the cost of two days income are usually the best. Obviously some French housewives are superb cooks and their husbands are appreciative of what they get, but exactly the same statement is true of the chefs and citizens of almost any other country you could name.

This myth of French supremacy in the kitchen has been so slavishly absorbed in our hotel and catering industry that any British chef with aspirations to be recognised as accomplished, would be brave or foolish to offer Carrot Soup instead of Creme de Crecy, Braised Oxtail for Ragout de Queue de Boeuf or even Cheeses in place of Le Plat des Fromages.

Take this menu, for instance:-

Chartreuse d'oie aux framboise a l'ecarlate
Krupnic royale
Filets de saumon Lennexlove
Souffle de sorbet de cacao blanc et la menthe
Cotelettes d'agneau a la Belle Cara
Legumes parisienne
Haricots verts en paquet
Pommes Rob Roy
Compote de poires a l'Edimbourg

How many members of the Royal Zoological Society of Scotland sitting down to this dinner at the Scottish National Zoological Park in Edinburgh would have learned anything from the menu except that the vegetables came from Paris and the green beans were still in their packet? *Aussi bien, un tour de force pour le chef de cuisine, un monsieur Brian Kennedy.*

You could fill a book with this sort of nonsense. And what nonsense it is, what chi-chi bullshit!

It is all part and parcel of the same pretentious and flatulent piffle you will read in the writings of cookery columnists, the Foodies or the pages of The Good Food Guide, not quite as daft under Drew Smith as it used to be when edited by Chris Driver but still daft enough.

Full of verbal diarrhoea, penned by self-appointed gourmets, who pose then prance through the Guides' pages with idiot phrases like *'A silky fish soup poised between clarity and gravity and a partridge deliciously roast (sic) in a slightly too sweet but voluptuous sauce.'* Hey-nonny-no!

Somewhere else, *'With piquant but very courteous spicy sauce.'* *'Courteous'* sauce? What meaningless poppycock. Or try *'A nicely understated hollandaise'* or *'mushroom soup of the correct graphite colour.'* Did you know the British Standards Institute have a number for the 'correct' graphite colour of mushroom soup? And what must you think of whomever wrote *'...... the creme caramel is not to be compared with that in the grill of the Addis Ababa Hilton'* or *'Tarte Tatin would have been classically made but for the wrong apples'.* Have you ever in your life come across such pompous, witless drivel?

******

Let me finish with two long quotes.

Under the heading — pinched from Priestley, no doubt, 'An Inspector Calls', I read a detailed account of how an A.A. Inspector marks up a hotel restaurant. *'Are the butter pats too soft? Is the soup hot enough? Is it served in the right kind of dish? Is the consommé, already flavoured with lemon and sherry, slightly overflavoured as the result of an additional wedge of lemon? Should the wine waiter return to replenish the glasses? Was the cream added too soon to the mille feuilles so that the pastry became soft? Should there be a prompter offer of more coffee?*

There is a maximum mark for each section. Rolls and butter, for example, can get a maximum of three marks. The hotel, which makes its own rolls and serves them warm, received between 2¼ and 2½ marks, being marked down because the butter was slightly soft and there was no white alternative to the excellent brown wholemeal rolls.'

The mark between 2¼ and 2½ really got through to me. That's got to be really keen marking, however you see it.

Then I read that British Petroleum, at their Sullom Voe terminal, laid on a buffet for a delegation from the Chinese Petroleum Corporation.

There was 'Smoked Scottish salmon, paté maison, Iranian caviare, Parma ham with ogen melon, melon au porto, roast Norfolk turkey, smoked trout, decorated Spey salmon, loin of Danish pork, roast Highland pheasant, Shetland lobster, Wiltshire ham, dressed crab, saddle of lamb, decorated ox-tongue, mallard duck, roast sirloin of beef, Norwegian prawns, soused herrings, roast French quail, North Sea mackerel, Waldorf salad, American salad, coleslaw, Indian salad, Hungarian salad, Spanish salad, charlotte royal, pineapple Drambuie, croquembouche, fresh fruit salad, lemon meringue tart, English trifle, strawberry gateau, banana Chartreuse and English and Continental cheese'.

And this for a total of twenty-four people! Don't you find that quite disgusting?

******

Gourmets,

at home ~

~ and abroad

A look at the shelves of your local bookseller will convince you that the one over-riding interest of the British is food. Strange it is that a people internationally thought to live on a diet of fish and chips are captivated by glossily expensive cookery books. Each year and especially in time for the Christmas trade, they thud off the presses; books on meat, fish, vegetables, how to compose breakfast, lunch and dinner menus, menus for picnics, barbeques, Glyndebourne supper parties. There are writers whose names are better known and whose works are more widely read than those of Homer, Horace or Seneca; Milton, Dr. Johnson, or William Blake, simply because they write about cooking with eggs or how to put together an interesting sauce or a different salad.

When does a perfectly healthy interest in good food become obsessive and, in a world where two thirds of the people are starving, when does the obsession of the fat and well fed become obscene?

*****

In my time at the Old Rectory, I've arranged special 'gourmet' evenings for this or that Wine and Food club and invariably found the membership to be composed of the same smug, self-satisfied, well-breeched, pains in the arse as could have written the comments just quoted.

I'll give you an example.

A group of English people, finding that they shared similar appetites, those of the tapeworm, the hyena and the barracuda, declared themselves to be an eating club. They even chose an aptly suitable imprint for their notepaper, a boar's head, which after all, is the head of a hog.

Their secretary asked me to arrange dinner for forty of their members.

I first doubted the accuracy of their self-proclaimed status when the twenty-odd year old wife of one of the committee members, after a luncheon before the big night, complimented me on one of the vegetables served and asked me what it was. It was a leek. I showed her one trimmed for steaming and one washed but complete as grown. "Oh yes," she said of the one with roots, "I've often seen those in the greengrocer's and wondered what you do with them." "Well, now you know," her loving husband commented sagely.

Later, when a committee of four turned up to arrange the menu for the blow-out, my doubts gave way to certainties. I was dealing with the demented. Each man had firmly fixed ideas of what dishes he wanted included, most of them heavy concoctions of cream and brandy drawn from the Cordon Bleu cookery pages in the glossy magazines.

But it was the fillers that they wanted which shocked me, dishes scattered with croutons or served 'en brioche' or with melba toast, or noodles or potato dumplings on the side. The Potato Marketing Board would have been overjoyed to hear of their choice of vegetables; potato croquettes, pommes vapeur, pommes duchesse, pommes lyonnaise, pommes boulangère or Anna.

I fought them every inch of the way. "Have you thought," I

asked, "that if you have mushroom soup with cream in it, you don't really want your fish course in a cream and mushroom sauce, it's rather much of the same thing, albeit fishier. Again if you follow that with Beef Stroganoff, you've got cream and mushrooms in there once again, even if the mushrooms *are* thinly sliced and the cream soured. You have still chosen to finish with a dessert admittedly without mushrooms, but with egg yolks and cream?" It was all to no avail and they forced me to make one concession after another.

On the chosen night, my barmaids were astonished at the esoteric, the arcane choice of aperitifs ranging from Pernod and orange, through strange uses of the vermouths. These people hadn't been to Torremolinos and Benidorm for nothing. Each vermouth became a *'vair-moot'* in the 'chintz-arno' style and our sherries got their proper pronunciation, 'a-monty-yard-o' and 'man-than-eel-yah'. The choice of wines was left to individuals at the table and that night, we sold more sweet or sweet and fizzy than throughout the rest of the year.

Each time they ordered, they said 'At room temperature' or 'Nicely warm' for the reds or 'chilled' or 'cold please' for the whites. One man told me that with his food he and his wife always drank Chateau d'Yquem. "I first came across it at our lodge meeting. The queen of wines," he said. He also smoked a cigarette between courses and a pipe with his coffee, his petits fours and his V.S.O.P. brandy.

After the event, I had a letter from the prime organiser to say that although, in general, his members had enjoyed the meal which he described as 'quite tasty and very filling', they had been disappointed with the *'boeuf a la bourguignonne'.* There had been no dishes of cubed beef and other ingredients for the *'gourmets'* to spear and cook for themselves in dishes of hot oil on the tables. It appeared that we at the Old Rectory had little idea of what *'boeuf a la bourguignonne'* was and the whole thing had been 'cooked in the kitchen as a kind of beef, onion and mushroom wine stew'.

I waited until his cheque had been cleared and then I wrote to him saying that what his committee had ordered and committed themselves to in writing was what they had got, a winey stew of beef, onions and mushrooms, *boeuf a la bourguignonne,* beef in the fashion of the houswives of Burgundy.

Apparently what they had been expecting was that laughable dish known as *'fondue de bourguignon',* a deplorable dish invented by the manufacturer's of those little copper fondue sets, originally meant for cheese, but eventually selling so slowly as to drive their makers to new but desperate sales promotion measures. Of which the creation of the most unhygienic dish *'fondue de bourguignon'* was one. *'Fondue de bourguignon'* was the sort of miserable dish that normally would be eaten only by drunken package-deal holidaymakers wearing large straw hats or by people trying to upstage their friends' sausage and kebab barbeque parties. Or perhaps by the members of the (Such and Such) Gourmet Club. I also pointed out that their boar's head symbol was well chosen.

Strangely enough, I never again had the pleasure of feeding them but some years after this solitary occasion, I read in a local newspaper a detailed report of another of their banquets held at an Italian restaurant. I quote the report headed *'How to make a meal of it'.* (The italics are mine.)

"Do you fancy making a true *gourmet's* meal at home? I am able to pass on the menu chosen by the (Such and Such) Gourmet Club at the (What d'you call it) Restaurant. Here you are: the memorable meal beginning with caviare served in *barquettes* garnished with thin slices of Parma ham wrapped around *grissine sticks.* Then came another Italian dish of roast sea trout with stuffed artichoke hearts and bearnaise sauce.

The main dish was a haunch of venison which had been steeped for five weeks in a claret based marinade and served with a sauce made from gooseberries and a reduction of the marinade. It was garnished with *barquettes* filled with puree of spinach topped with Parisienne cut balls of Bramley apples and served with red cabbage and a selection of root vegetables.

And so, creaking to pud — based on an Italian *sweetbread, panetoni,* which was hollowed, filled with a puree of chestnuts, ice cream and fresh cream, frozen, covered in meringue and baked. It was presented flamed with the Italian liqueur Sambuca."

Well, how's that then? A delicately balanced, elegantly chosen, pigging it, that's got your old corned beef buttie with HP sauce skinned to death. The newspaper columnist I have quoted failed to mention the follow-up but I understand that before leaving the restaurant, each *'gourmet'* was given a peacock's feather and a vomit bag and two hog's head, hand-carved, jacket-baked potatoes lying on a bed of porridge, layered with crushed potato crisps and chopped fried bread in a *barquette* hollowed out of a cottage loaf and stuffed with whipped cream and Weetabix, flamed in sweet stout. In case they got peckish on the way home.

******

An extreme case of 'mangare vulgaris'. But any more vulgar than 'Le Tour Gastronomique' organised some years ago by one Anthony Docherty in association with the Observer?

The all-in, package blow-out included a return flight from London to Lyons, three days hire of car with unlimited mileage, three nights with Continental breakfast, VAT or its French equivalent, and service charges at one of four nominated hotels and three other standard *table d'hote* meals at any of six chosen shrines to gastronomy listed in the prospectus.

The price? Well, it's not much use quoting it now some years after the event, but believe me, it was more than enough. Think of the Third World, all those pictures you watch or switch off on television, the starving mums with emaciated babies sucking on withered, milkless paps. Then wrap your mind round this piece of purple prose. '*Alain Chapel, at Mionnay, is perhaps the purest of the great chefs in the Lyons area. There is a certain single mindedness about the man; and this is reflected, not only in the simplicity of his menu, but even in the austerely elegant surroundings of his dining room.*' Well, the austerely elegant surroundings of his dining room, perhaps with those Louis Quinze and Benvenuto Cellini bits and pieces, Sisley's and Pissaros, we can only guess at, not having been there, but the simplicity of his menu is apparent.

Petite gelee de pigeonneaux
a l'anis etoile sot-l'y-laisse
et jeunes legumes
***
Une bouchee de coquillages praires,
parlourdes petoncles, vernis et gravettes
et sauvages aux chicons
***
Oreille de veaue farcie
comme en Bugey, persil frit
ou
Ventre et dos de dorades roses
de petits bateaux, en infusion
de vin rouge, fondue de
jeune poireaux
***
Quelque fromages fermiers
***
Glaces a la creme et sorbets
aux fruits, Migardises et bugnes
***

Patisserie maison
***
Tout avec aperitif, vins, cafe
et servis compris.

******

Well, for Chrissakes, you can't get simpler than that, can you? It's positively stark that menu is, not to say spartan.

After reading how simple it was, I thought we could do the same thing a l'Anglais.

I got together with a few nearby restaurateur neighbours and we cobbled 'le Tour Gastro-Enteric' which exploited the outstanding local cooking of the area bounded by Haughton Green, Boggart Hole Clough, Diggle, Daisy Nook and Blubberhouses.

Local delicacies included Le Cowheel Pie avec ou sans Les Mushee pois, Doigts de Cod, cuit en parte in savoury, vieux grease de friteux, et le pouding Wet Nellie.

Our package deal included three nights at the Old Rectory with unlimited use of a calor gas ring for self catering breakfasts, forged Senior Citizens' bus passes and three other standard *'table d'hote'* meals to be taken as wished at the 'Chukki Tup Layta Tandoori', the 'Yellow Peril and Farting Dragon Takeaway' or 'Le Perroquet Constipè avec Une Patte dans Le Pissoir Bistro'.

Guests could drink what passes locally for beer, and elsewhere for camel piss, in pubs with historical connections such as 'The Stripper and Grinder' or the 'Clogger and Cap Nebber', whilst delighting in a range of potato crisps including the new 'Smokers Pyorrhoea' and the ever-popular 'Salt and Cheesey Armpit'.

We also produced a menu, which was even simpler than Alain Chapel's simple one, and was also in French.

Le choix trés limité de tinned potages
***

Le best piece de tinned saumon John West
con legume misto de congeleur deep, chambreéed
***

Formaggio con brot vieux
***

Le poudin blanc de cold sago
***

Le plat de bread et butter pour two
***

Le pot du Tea
***

Le sac hygienique. (Sur request)
***

Voila, mesdames et herren!
***

We must be in the wrong area for such an exciting, total experience.

We never sold a ....ing one. So we ....ing jacked it in. Incidentally, I don't remember the Observer repeating the experience either. Although I may well be wrong. I frequently am. Losing my marbles, it is said.

******

Well, all this is a far cry from what I refer to as *real* food. In the Hungry Thirties, my Mum never bothered with *Mousseline de Fruite au Coulis d'Ecrivisse* or *Poulet du Montardier with Sauce Diable.* Now I know you'll find this hard to believe, but I swear that it is true, not once do I remember her cooking *Cuisse de Canetons au Bouzy, Escalopes de Veau Brillat-Savarin, Coeur de Filets de Boeuf en Chevreuil with Sauce Grand Veneur* nor even the more commonplace and, in the smoky environs of Levenshulme, Manchester, extremely popular *Clafoutis.*

No, my Mum scorned such run-of-the-mill, reach-me-down recipes. In our back parlour you ate soup made out of anything you could do nowt else with. You ate potato hash, a delicious amalgam of rough cut chunks of taters with shin or skirt beef, sweated down with onions and a pig's foot or two, or a whole cowheel, stewed slowly under the seal of a heavy lid until the gravy was a succulent, lip-sticking glue and the potato melted on the tongue like the finest *quenelles.*

The cold lamb left over from our summer Sunday lunches — or Sunday dinners, as in our appalling ignorance, we called our mid-day meal — or the cold beef from Sundays in the winter, were minced with onions and parsley and God knows what else and served up on a washday Monday as the most savoury and plump, fried rissoles ever tasted, and better to a hungry mouth than anything La Gavroche has ever served.

Isn't that the truth of it? That hunger is the best sauce, that there can be no better food than that of the *'cuisine du proletaire'* because it is eaten with hunger?

Like my mother's Elysian suet puddings stuffed with meat or served as a sweet pudding, smothered with melting golden syrup and eaten either way, lying lighter on the stomach than the finest swansdown duvet?

******

Flo and I sat with the wife of one of France's greatest restaurateurs in the courtyard of their elegant restaurant on the Cote d'Azur. Together, we watched the chauffeur-driven Mercedes, Cadillacs, and Rollers disgorge their bored and jaded owners and their enamelled females. We watched their faces through the restaurant's plate glass as one lacquered woman stubbed her cigarette out in one of monsieur's incomparable souffles.

Nay, it were never like that in our house. We ate up t'lot, had seconds if there were owt going and wiped plate clean wi' us bread. We ate because we were hungry. It's always been the best reason for eating and the best way of eating. You don't need those 'paintings on plates' when there's a rat nibbling away at your stomach lining.

******

Still on the same theme, I passed a Civil Service examination when I was sixteen and I was posted to London as a clerk in the Post Office Savings Bank.

My first landlady — five pounds a month, half-board, handed over on pay-day — was an aged crone from Shropshire, living in a seedy terraced house in the still seedier street, Sterndale Road, just off Blythe Road, behind Olympia. There was a broken and unhinged front gate, two dirty, dispirited and separate privets, both in their dotage, leaning against a low stone wall, stained by generations of pissing dogs and spitting pedestrians and the slow passage of time.

The house could actually be *seen* to smell of boiled cabbage and dry rot, and, of course, it did.

Mrs Pattenden looked a little like a female Mr Punch. She was rounded of shoulder and stooped and wrapped around in blouses and jerseys, cardigans and voluminous skirts and like her house, she smelled of dry rot and cabbage water.

She was one of life's survivors but for me, the worst part of her survival programme was the food she served us. I was always convinced that she bought it second hand.

It was the cheapest food, the nastiest food, bought in the dingy back streets of Shepherd's Bush and Hammersmith. It was food bought from cut-price shops, water-damaged, fire-salvaged food, bankrupt stock food, import and export reject food, seconds and thirds. She gave us soggy bread made from wet, white sawdust gone grey from old age, brown bread made from stale, ground-up blood clots, mysterious eggs which, when boiled and opened up, revealed to the shocked eye, whites more marbled and mottled than a cardinal's nose and ochrous yolks streaked with the blood of their laborious breeches birth.

She fried bacon rashers taken from pigs that had died of malnutrition. She cooked indescribable minced meat made from incurable dogs and cats that had been put down, or old, tubercular donkeys that had failed to survive their prostatectomy.

Most of this malevolent, crusted sludge came from blown, rusting tins or mouldering cardboard packets. To help us get it down, she always served a sauce, no not hollandaise nor bearnaise, not even HP or Tiger, Daddies or OK Sauce.

No, her sauce would be especially imported from Hong Kong, a sauce whose garishly printed label would warn rather than cajole. "Open only in a well ventilated room. Protect the eyes. Wash the skin after handling. Dangerous to pets, goldfish and children. Avoid spillage in inhabited areas."

Yet, we ate it. We ate Mrs Pattenden's food. With all its dangers, I can tell you that after a few pints in the Brook Green pub and a walk back for bread and cheese, followed by a near midnight philosophical stroll across the Hammersmith Bridge and down the towpath, seventeen years old and all the stars above you and all of life before you, it wasn't at all bad. Youth is a hunger and hunger is the best sauce.

Come to think of it, the best meals I have ever had have been the simplest. All the beans on toast, egg and chips, fish and chips, I ever ate when I was hungry. All the food my Mum cooked for us when we were all young or younger. The coarse hard bread, rubbed with garlic, dribbled with olive oil and dusted with salt, I ate once with the vineyard workers, sitting under a hedge in the Chateau Neuf du Pape Vineyards on the other side of the Rhone from Avignon, and the same bread and oil, salt and garlic eaten outside an impoverished bistro in a near derelict village high in the Corsican mountains, watching the rain blot out the villages far below. *'Vegetables are perfection without pretention and new potatoes were boiled exactly as an egg',* simpers the Good Food Guide. *'A salmon with shrimp sauce responded dramatically to an infusion of squirted lemon'.* Well, it would, wouldn't it? It was probably cooked 'al dente' and still half alive.

".... me," it responded dramatically. "That infusion of squirted lemon has gone straight up my ....ing vent."

You don't have any 'dramatic responses' with a piece of real bread, salt, olive oil and garlic. Except from people coming later within range of your breath.

******

"The salmon responded dramatically to an infusion of squirted lemon ..."

Chewed up bread

There are eminent leaders in our trade about whose kitchen expertise epic stories have been written. Their confident and powerful facial exressions of immense self-satisfaction confront us, not only in our trade papers, but in all the would-be up-market but popular publications. Great artists dedicated to the elevation of good grub to the level of an Old Master, a Beethoven symphony, a Michelangelo sculpture or painting. They devote their entire fleeting lives to 'paintings on plates', to tonal compositions of colour, texture, and tingle-tongue taste, completed and then, with a knife and fork, an open mouth, a set of teeth and a working jaw, destroyed, devoured and, in no time at all, converted into posh pooh for the wealthy patrons who can afford better, richer turds for tomorrow.

Would Beethoven have composed the 'Kreutzer' sonata if it had to be inscribed on toilet paper and used the next day? Would Michelangelo have spent four years on his back painting the ceiling of the Sistine Chapel if, the day after it was completed, the Pope had consigned it to be flushed down the Tiber?

******

A very old man once told me about his life as a plumber. "When I was about twelve," he said, "I was apprenticed to this master plumber. He was called Owd Bob because he was about sixty then. In those days, when the sewers got blocked, we used to dig down until we found the blockage, then Owd Bob would get a heavy stick and thrust it in and out there, and bash away at the stuff and it would all fly about, some of it landing on his bowler hat and hanging off it and dripping all over. I were nobbut

268

a lad and it used to make me feel poorly, quite faint like. He'd seen that I weren't much taken with what was going on and he'd say "What's the matter with thi lad? It's nobbut chewed-up bread."

That's just what it all is. Tomorrow, all that wonderful food is just chewed-up bread.

Today it's caviare or lobster, or a pheasant stuffed with partridge. Or it could be a Berni steak, a MacDonald or some of *your* mum's potato hash. Whatever it is today, it will be just *'chewed-up bread'* tomorrow. They used to ask, 'Can you tell Stork from butter?' Well then, could you tell, the next time you saw them, *'Mousselines de volaille a la florentine'* from a couple of cheese and onion sandwiches and a packet of pork scratchings. Not the next time you saw them, I'll bet you couldn't.

******

I started by asking when does a perfectly healthy interest in good food become obsessive and, in a world where half the people are starving, when do the eating obsessions of the fat and the well fed become obscene. I question whether it is proper for men of great talent and imagination to dedicate their lives to pandering to the jaded palates of the wealthy, producing great culinary works of such fleeting transience. No doubt merely to ask the question will arouse angry response amongst those so doing. But perhaps, in time, we will come to have a more moral view.

The argument is not whether the perfectly sound leg of lamb my mother roasted was as good as is a boned leg of pré-salé stuffed with salmon or fresh peaches and cooked in a pastry case. The argument is where do you draw the line?

It's not the whole story, but when we see those pot-bellied, fly-encrusted, stick-armed and legged kids all over the Third

World, some of us should feel more than a little guilty at the quality of our ordure.

******

You gotter larf

So what else is there to say?

Not a lot.

I hope that you have been amused by what you have read and, at the same time, I want to assure you that, apart from the obvious bits of nonsense such as Annie's teeth in batter, it's all true. With next to no exaggeration.

I *did* cock up the Sunday morning breakfast and I did forget that the clocks went back late one Saturday night or early one Sunday morning.

When Fawlty Towers was on the box and the rest of the nation watched and fell about laughing, it was not so with the hoteliers and restaurateurs, for whom all that they saw was agonising because it could and did happen to them.

Pushed to the extreme limits, Basil plunged his hands into the large meringue or souffle looking for the roast duck. My wedding soup did go off but turned out alright in the end.

******

A man once asked me how I made the sauce which he had found delicious with his cider baked ham. "With parsley," I replied. "It tasted different and looked a different colour from the parsley sauce my wife makes," he said. "We use chopped, *fresh* parsley," I said, smart-arse wise. I gave him a bunch of fresh parsley. "Give that to your wife and then she'll make you proper sauce."

Back in the kitchen I told my chef that his parsley sauce had been much appreciated. "We haven't got any parsley sauce," he said. "That's cheese sauce, made with Lancashire." "Keep it up," I said, turning pale. "They really like it."

******

In passing a table, we hear the female textile buyer say to her salesman host, apropos of something or other, "Oh, is your wife Jewish then?" "Oh no," says the man, "we come from Birmingham."

******

A bit like the blue and white plaque on the wall of the restaurant housed in a protected Tudor building. I read 'On this site on the fifth of January 1763, nothing happened'.

It's all part of the human comedy and as the old comics used to say "You gotter larf 'aven't you?"

Laugh then, but please, if you are a diner out, the next time you sit down to food that other people have prepared and served from the most appalling work conditions and during the most unsociable of hours, remember, they only do it for the money. Be kind. Please give generously.

Or if you are one of those wage slaves in the kitchen or sliding about in the restaurant on your flat feet, don't let the customer get you down. You always have the upper hand, the last laugh, by secretly doing indescribable things to his food before he eats it.

Come on! I'm only joking, really! I think.

Bon appetit, mes amis.

******

Scenic Touring
VERMONT

Scenic Driving

VERMONT

Exploring the State's Most Spectacular
Byways and Back Roads

STEWART M. GREEN

Globe
Pequot

Guilford, Connecticut

Globe Pequot

An imprint of Rowman & Littlefield

Distributed by NATIONAL BOOK NETWORK

Copyright © 2016 by Rowman and Littlefield

Photography by Stewart M. Green

Excerpted from *Scenic Routes & Byways New England* (Globe Pequot, 978-0-7627-7955-0)

British Library Cataloguing in Publication Information Available

Library of Congress Cataloging-in-Publication Data
Green, Stewart M.
  Scenic driving Vermont : exploring the state's most spectacular byways and back roads / Stewart M. Green.
      pages cm
  "Excerpted from Scenic routes & byways New England (Globe Pequot Press)"—Title page verso.
  Includes index.
  ISBN 978-1-4930-2241-0 (paparback : alkaline paper) — ISBN 978-1-4930-2242-7 (e-book) 1. Vermont—Tours. 2. Scenic byways—Vermont—Guidebooks. 3. Roads—Vermont—Guidebooks. 4. Automobile travel—Vermont—Guidebooks. I. Green, Stewart M. Scenic routes & byways New England. II. Title.
  F47.3.G74 2016
  917.4304—dc23

                                                    2015036368

∞™ The paper used in this publication meets the minimum requirements of American National Standard for Information Sciences—Permanence of Paper for Printed Library Materials, ANSI/NISO Z39.48-1992.

TABLE OF CONTENTS

Vermont

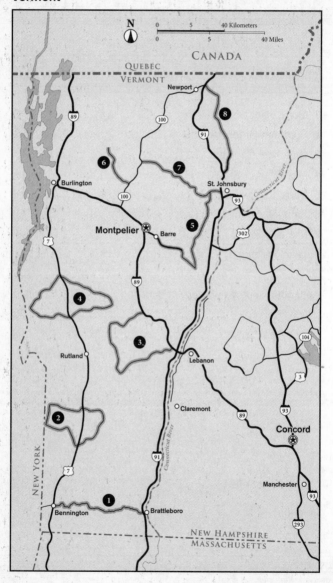

INTRODUCTION

Vermont offers travelers a spectacular assortment of natural and scenic wonders, historic sites, and varied recreational opportunities. Numerous state parks, forests, beaches, and recreation areas preserve slices of superlative landscapes. In addition to these gems, thousands of lakes and ponds and numerous rivers and brooks offer boating, swimming, canoeing, and angling choices for outdoor enthusiasts. The cities, towns, and villages, from the urban center of Burlington, to myriad tiny villages dotting the hills of Vermont, are filled with culture and steeped in history.

Scenic Driving Vermont, an indispensable mile-by-mile highway companion, explores and discovers the wonders of this compact region. The drives follow miles of highways and back roads, sampling the region's colorful history, beauty spots, hidden wonders, and scenic jewels. Drivers will wind through the valleys and hills of Vermont, marvel at classic villages set between mountains, pass rural birthplaces and burial sites of the notable and the notorious, and wander among enchanting forests. Most of the drives leave the urban sprawl and interstate highways behind, setting off into the beautiful heart of the region.

Vermont is laced with highways and roads, some dating back to the earliest paths that once connected colonial settlements. Area natives will undoubtedly wonder why some roads are included and others omitted. These routes were chosen for their beauty, unique natural history, and historical implications. Omitted are worthy roads for one reason or another, but mostly due to the development along those asphalt corridors in an amazing labyrinth of highway possibilities.

Use these described drives to win a new appreciation and understanding of this marvelous land. Take them as a starting point to embark on new adventures by seeking out other back-road gems among the rolling hills and historic towns of Vermont.

Travel Advice

Be prepared for changing weather when traveling these scenic highways, especially in winter when snow and ice encase the roadways. Most of the drives, except for bits and pieces, are paved, two-lane highways that are regularly maintained. Services are available on almost all the drives, and every little village offers at least some basics during daylight hours. Use caution when driving. Many of the roads twist and wind through valleys and over mountains, with blind corners. Follow the posted speed limits and stay in your lane. Use occasional pullouts to allow faster traffic to safely pass. Watch for heavy traffic on some roads, particularly during summer vacation season and on fall-foliage weekends. Be extremely alert for animals crossing the asphalt. Take care at dusk, just after darkness falls, and in the early morning.

The region's fickle weather creates changeable and dangerous driving conditions. Make sure your windshield wipers are in good shape. Heavy rain can impair highway vision and cause your vehicle to hydroplane. Snow and ice slicken mountain highways. Slow down, carry chains and a shovel, and have spare clothes and a sleeping bag when traveling in winter. Watch for fog and poor visibility. Know your vehicle and its limits when traveling and, above all, use common sense.

Travelers are, unfortunately, potential crime victims. Use caution when driving in urban areas or popular tourist destinations. Keep all valuables, including wallets, purses, cameras, and

The Stowe Community Church towers above the Little River in Stowe.

video cameras, out of sight in a parked car. Better yet, take them with you when leaving the vehicle.

These drives cross a complex mosaic of private and public land. Respect private property rights by not trespassing or crossing fences.

Remember also that all archaeological and historic sites are protected by federal law. Campers should try to use established campgrounds or campsites whenever possible to avoid adverse environmental impacts. Remember to douse your campfires and to pack all your trash out with you to the nearest refuse container.

Every road and byway we travel offers its own promise and special rewards. Remember Walt Whitman's poetic proclamation as you drive along these scenic highways: "Afoot, light-hearted, I take to the open road. Healthy, free, the world before me."

Legend

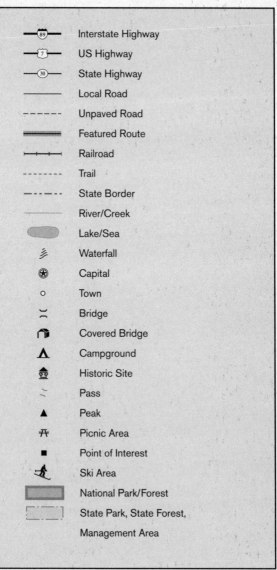

──⟨89⟩──	Interstate Highway
──⟨7⟩──	US Highway
──⟨30⟩──	State Highway
──────	Local Road
------	Unpaved Road
━━━━━	Featured Route
├─┼─┼─┤	Railroad
········	Trail
─ ─ · ─ ─	State Border
──────	River/Creek
⬭	Lake/Sea
≋	Waterfall
✪	Capital
○	Town
⌣	Bridge
⌂	Covered Bridge
▲	Campground
⛩	Historic Site
≍	Pass
▲	Peak
⊼	Picnic Area
■	Point of Interest
🎿	Ski Area
▬	National Park/Forest
▢	State Park, State Forest, Management Area

1 Molly Stark Scenic Byway

General description: The Molly Stark Scenic Byway travels 48 miles across the southern Green Mountains from Brattleboro to Bennington in southern Vermont.

Special attractions: Brattleboro historic district, Brattleboro Museum and Arts Center, West Brattleboro, Creamery Covered Bridge, Marlboro, Hogback Mountain Scenic Overlook, Molly Stark State Park, Wilmington, Woodford State Park, Bennington historic districts, Old First Church, Bennington Monument, Bennington Museum.

Location: Southern Vermont.

Drive route numbers: VT 9.

Travel season: Year-round.

Camping: Molly Stark State Park has 23 tent/trailer sites and 11 lean-to sites. Woodford State Park has 103 campsites. Both are fee areas open in summer and autumn.

Services: All services in Brattleboro and Bennington at each end of the drive. Limited services at Marlboro and Wilmington.

Nearby attractions: Mount Equinox Sky Line Drive, Connecticut River Valley, Mount Snow Resort, Lake Shaftsbury State Park, Townshend State Park, Mount Ascutney State Park, Berkshires (MA), Mount Greylock (MA), Williamstown (MA).

The Route

The 48-mile-long Molly Stark Scenic Byway, an official Vermont Scenic Byway, meanders across southern Vermont between two of the state's leading towns—Brattleboro on the east and Bennington on the west. The highway twists across the rolling Green Mountains, passing rumpled farms, horse pastures, scenic viewpoints, and historic country villages like Wilmington and Marlboro.

Molly Stark Scenic Byway

The character of the drive, traversing Vermont from its eastern border with New Hampshire to its western border with New York, is defined by its mountainous geography and rich history. The Green Mountains, while less pronounced than mountains farther north, still rise well above 2,000 feet. Thick forests of leafy deciduous trees blanket the hillsides, broken by farms and fields lined with old stone walls.

Much of New England's rich history began in southern Vermont after the town of Bennington, the western anchor of the Molly Stark Scenic Byway, was chartered in 1749. Brattleboro, Vermont's oldest town, sprang from Fort Drummer, a stockade built in 1724 to protect the western frontier from Indians and French Canadians.

Molly Stark

The drive, also known by the more pedestrian name VT 9, follows an old road that dates back to the Revolutionary War. The track was used in August 1777 by General John Stark and his army of New Hampshire colonials after the decisive Battle of Bennington, one of the last battles in the northern colonies, on their victorious march home.

The first question most travelers ask about the drive is not "What's to see?" or "Where's the best scenery?" but "Who the heck is **Molly Stark**?" Molly Stark, more properly Elizabeth Paige Stark, was the wife of **General John Stark,** a Bunker Hill hero who was called to lead the 1,500-man New Hampshire militia against part of General John Burgoyne's army, 800 British troops including German Hessians, Loyalist turncoats, and British redcoats commanded by German Lieutenant Colonel Friedrich Baum, on the remote Vermont frontier.

General Stark was an inspirational fellow, and before the battle on August 16, he told his troops, "Now, my men, yonder lie the Redcoats and the Tories. Tonight the American flag flies over yonder hill or Molly Stark sleeps a widow!" The pep talk

apparently worked, and the Americans won the engagement. The battle actually took place in today's New York State, but 10 miles from the site, the Bennington Monument in Vermont commemorates the victory.

Molly Stark herself, despite having a road, a mountain in northern Vermont, and schools, parks, and streets named after her, never set foot in Vermont. She did raise 10 children at their New Hampshire home, recruited soldiers for the war effort, and converted a barn into a makeshift hospital to tend wounded men from both sides.

Brattleboro

The drive unceremoniously begins on the north side of Brattleboro at I-91's junction with VT 9. Take exit 2, 9 miles north of the Massachusetts border, off the freeway and head west on the byway. The road passes through a residential area in Brattleboro, north of the town center.

Brattleboro, a hilly hamlet lying on the edge of the Connecticut River Valley just north of the Massachusetts border, is a busy and personable town that seems bigger than its population of 12,046 (2010 census). Brattleboro, or "Brat" as it's sometimes called, is an old industrial center that began as rustic Fort Drummer in 1724 at a strategic location at the confluence of the Connecticut and West Rivers. After King George's War ended in 1748, the garrison of troops was disbanded, and the town was chartered in 1753 and named for Colonel William Brattle Jr., a major land owner.

After the Revolution, Brattleboro prospered as the gateway to Vermont. The first United States postage stamps were issued here in 1846, and the town thrived as a health resort with its pure spring water, which attracted tourists. That same water at

Center Cemetery near Marlboro is an old burying ground with graves of Civil War and Revolutionary War soldiers.

Autumn-colored trees frame Lake Harriman, the largest lake in Vermont.

Whetstone Falls fueled industry with abundant hydroelectric power. By 1859 the town boasted a sawmill, gristmill, textile mill, paper mill, flour mill, as well as factories that made machinery, parlor organs, and carriages.

Besides being a historic town, Brattleboro also has its own quirks and oddities. The first Social Security check ever issued went to Ida May Fuller, Social Security number 00-000-001, on January 31, 1940, for the grand sum of $22.54. Until July 17, 2007, Brattleboro allowed public nudity, but that summer a group of naturists descended on town and shed their fig leaves. After complaints by clothed citizens, a quick law was passed that banned "nudity on the main roads and within 250 feet of any school or place of worship." Brattleboro is the only town in Vermont with three interstate exits, and it likes to brag that it's the only Brattleboro in the world. One of the town's printers issued the first Bible printed in Vermont in 1812, and later another made the first American printing of the first Harry Potter book.

Before heading west on the Molly Stark drive, take an hour to stroll around the old downtown area with its eclectic shops along Main and Elliot Streets. The area is part of the **Brattleboro Downtown Historic District.** Nearby is the **Brattleboro Museum and Art Center** in an old railroad station. Exhibits include local memorabilia, railroad history, and an exhibit detailing Brattleboro's fame as the parlor organ capital of the world. Also close to town is the bright red **Creamery Covered Bridge,** built of spruce lumber in 1879, spanning Whetstone Brook. The perfectly preserved bridge is the only one near the drive.

Brattleboro to Marlboro

The drive heads west from north Brattleboro and I-91, quickly passing residences, a left turn to the covered bridge, and West Brattleboro before climbing up Whetstone Brook into the Green Mountains. As you drive the scenic byway, keep an eye out for eight obelisks with interesting information about local history. The first two obelisks are between the interstate and West Brattleboro.

The suburb of **West Brattleboro,** a couple miles west of Brattleboro, is protected as a National Historic District with numerous 19th-century buildings erected around a town green. The drive passes several Colonial and neo–Gothic Revival homes and a whitewashed Congregational Church in the district as it heads west.

The highway curves upward in a creased valley alongside **Whetstone Brook.** The brook's tumbling waters, now riffling over rock ledges and boulders, powered Brattleboro's mills in the 19th century. The brook begins at Hidden Lake, just north of Marlboro and the drive, and drops 1,500 feet in 7 miles to Brattleboro where it empties into the Connecticut River at 250 feet above sea level.

Whetstone Brook, usually a placid, well-behaved stream, became a raging flood on August 29, 2011, when the moist remnants of Hurricane Irene dumped torrential rains on Vermont, flooding rivers and creeks like Whetstone Brook, erasing roads, and swamping Brattleboro's streets with 3 feet of water. West Brattleboro endured the worst of Whetstone Brook's fury. The drive alongside the creek was washed away as the floodwaters undermined the roadbed and reoriented the creek's course. As you drive up this road section, note how the flood scoured the valley floor, washing away trees and vegetation and leaving only cobbles and boulders in the course.

Marlboro

After 6 miles, the Molly Stark drive emerges from the hills and reaches a high road junction at **Center Cemetery.** Before making a left turn to Marlboro, pull off here and take a stroll through the cemetery. Low stone walls, simply piles of field rocks removed from the cemetery, separate the road and cemetery. Step through the entrance, an old wooden gate hitched to granite posts. Old gravestones, mostly from the 1800s, tilt across the hilltop beneath spreading maples. Some remember Civil War veterans as well as a few Revolutionary War soldiers.

From the cemetery, continue west on a country lane to **Marlboro.** The town, chartered in 1761, is quiet and historic, with a handful of buildings that were built along the original turnpike road through here. A white Congregational Church, organized in 1776, sits next to an 1882 meetinghouse, with daylilies spilling over its stone steps, and the town hall.

Continue down the road to **Marlboro College,** one of the nation's smallest colleges with less than 400 students. Buckminster Fuller built one of his first geodesic domes here. Marlboro is also well known for the famous **Marlboro Music Festival,** founded by famed pianist Rudolf Serkin. The concerts, every summer weekend from late June through August, sell out early, so make plans in advance.

Hogback Mountain Scenic Overlook

Drive out of Marlboro and get back onto VT 9, heading west. This highway partly follows the old **Great Albany Road,** a wilderness track that was built in 1746 between Fort Drummer, outside today's Brattleboro, and Fort Massachusetts, in North Adams in Massachusetts, to move soldiers and supplies. The road's Western Extension, the first road passage over the Green Mountains, was built in 1762 to connect Wilmington to Bennington. John Wallace, a soldier, noted in his diary in 1777, "the worst road I ever traveled, through mire and ruts." In 1802 the track became the Windham County Turnpike, a toll road.

In 1836 the road became public, freely allowing the passage of freight from Brattleboro to Bennington and on to the Erie Canal in New York through the 1800s. In the 1920s, locals began calling the road the Molly Stark Trail. It became a state highway in 1931, was officially named the Molly Stark Trail in 1967, and was designated a Vermont Scenic Byway in 2003.

The highway continues climbing and reaches lofty **Hogback Mountain Scenic Overlook** with its famous "100-mile views" on a clear day. This is the high point of the drive. Pull over on the south side of the road and park. On prime leaf-peeper weekends in October, as many as 10,000 visitors stop here.

The stunning view spreads south from the overlook, with ridge upon ridge of wooded mountains stretching to a hazy horizon. Here lies the southern terminus of the Green Mountains, a 160-mile range of billion-year-old bedrock that reaches north to the Canadian border and forms the spine of Vermont. Beyond rises bulky 3,489-foot Mount Greylock, high point of the Commonwealth of Massachusetts, flanked by the Taconic and Hoosac Ranges.

An elevated boardwalk leaves the car park and goes to the **Hogback Mountain Gift Shop** where you can buy ice-cream cones, Vermont maple syrup and cheese, fudge, T-shirts, coffee mugs, shot glasses, and any other souvenir that your kids desire.

Or you can get off easy by dropping a quarter in one of the standing binoculars. Remember to "Remove your eyeglasses and focus with the red knob." Also check out the four interpretive panels of Obelisk 3 on the deck.

Next door to the gift shop is the **Southern Vermont Natural History Museum,** housed in a white clapboard building. Step inside to view the huge Vermont wildlife collection amassed by taxidermist Luman Nelson in the early 1900s. The exhibits include over 600 native animals and birds mounted in 100 dioramas. The museum also offers other natural history programs.

Wilmington to Woodford

Get back in the car and head west on VT 9. The highway rolls downhill and in 3 miles (15 miles from Brattleboro) reaches **Molly Stark State Park** to the south. If you brought a picnic lunch, the park makes a great stop with tables and a group pavilion. Two camping loops with 23 sites and 11 lean-to sites welcome campers. A good hike follows a trail up to a steel fire tower on the summit of 2,415-foot Mount Olga. The park was originally cleared for agriculture and sheep in the 19th century. The Civilian Conservation Corps built a picnic area here in 1932.

The drive continues downhill and briefly links up with VT 100, a long Vermont highway that runs from the Massachusetts border to Canada, before entering the village of **Wilmington.** This old town, chartered in 1751, sits squarely at the junction of VT 9 and 100 in the broad Deerfield River Valley. Long a crossroads, Wilmington is one of those classic Vermont country towns with over 60 historic buildings and houses, preserved in a National Historic District, some dating back to the early 1800s. The town, like others along the drive, was severely damaged by flooding from Hurricane Irene in 2011.

Wilmington is also popular with the outdoor crowd with easy access to lakes and rivers, to hiking trails, and to skiing. Nine miles north of town is **Mount Snow Ski Area,** one of

New England's oldest winter resorts. Walter Schoenknecht bought a farm on Mount Pisgah here in 1953, cut some runs, and renamed it Mount Snow. Today the resort offers 467 acres of ski terrain, 1,700 feet of vertical drop from the 3,600-foot mountain summit, 20 lifts, and an average of 156 inches of snow annually.

Past Wilmington, the drive swings along the northern shore of **Lake Harriman,** the largest lake in Vermont, for a mile. The reservoir, also called Lake Whitingham, is 8 miles long and boasts 28 miles of shoreline. A dam, built in the 1920s to generate hydroelectricity, blocks the Deerfield River, forming the man-made lake. The lake drowned an old lumber town called Mountain Mills. Anglers hunt for bass, walleye, crappie, and catfish in the lake's still waters. Stop at a pullout on the north shore for a look at the lake, its glassy surface reflecting clouds and sky. Obelisk 5 is at the parking area.

The highway runs northwest along the Deerfield River, passing a farm with a gorgeous painting of an American flag on a giant boulder of Vermont granite, before bending west to **Searsburg,** a small town with 100 residents, and **Woodford State Park.** The park, on the south side of the road, has the highest park campground in Vermont at 2,400 feet. The 398-acre park is covered in a dense mixed forest of spruce, fir, and birch. It offers 103 campsites and Adams Reservoir, with a beach, rental boats, picnic area, and a 2.7-mile trail that encircles the lake.

To the south spreads 5,060-acre **George D. Aiken Wilderness Area,** a rough land named for the late Vermont senator who strongly advocated wilderness preservation in New England. The highway continues west and passes **Woodford.** A small village chartered in 1753, Woodford is known as the highest town in Vermont at the lofty elevation of 2,215 feet. The township also includes over 14,000 acres of Green Mountain National Forest as well as sections of the Appalachian Trail, which runs 2,181 miles from Georgia to Maine, and the Long Trail, a 273-mile trail along the crest of the Green Mountains. A good hike on the AT begins

on the byway and climbs 1.8 miles to the summit of Harmon Hill to the south.

Bennington

Past Woodford and the Appalachian Trail, the drive descends down a valley and enters **Bennington,** one of New England's most historic towns. Bennington is quintessential Vermont, a livable town of 15,764 (2010 census) tucked in the wooded folds of the Vermont Valley between the Green Mountains on the east, which you've just driven over, and the Taconic Mountains along the New York border. The town, Vermont's first, was chartered in 1749 but wasn't settled until 1761 because of Indian troubles.

Bennington is Vermont's counterpart to Boston. It's a place steeped in the American Revolution, a place of revolt and defiance to the British crown, a place that quelled any British hopes of colonial victory. The drive itself, named for General John Stark's wife (see "Molly Stark"), was the supply road for this frontier outpost in the 1770s.

The Battle of Bennington, fought on August 16, 1777, occurred 10 miles west of town in North Hoosick, New York, when the British force was surprised by Stark's army while marching east to Bennington to capture munitions and supplies. Stark's men held off the Brits until Colonel Seth Warner, commander of Vermont's famous Green Mountain Boys, arrived with a 350-man company to complete the rout. Stark's men captured 600 prisoners, killed almost 200, and suffered only 30 deaths. This victory by what was really a rag-tag group of farmers and woodsmen over the well-trained British and German soldiers inspired American morale.

The great battle is commemorated by the **Bennington Battle Memorial,** which should be your first stop in Bennington. The

An American flag adorns a granite boulder at a farm alongside the Deerfield River.

giant granite obelisk, rising from the site of the old Yankee supply dump, towers 306 feet above a hilltop west of downtown in Old Bennington. The 306-foot monument, the tallest structure in Vermont, was built between 1887 and 1889 from dolomite stone for $112,000. The monument, three-fifths the size of the Washington Monument, has 7-foot-thick walls at its base. Take an elevator to the viewing observatory 200 feet up for an eagle's view of Bennington and parts of three states. The stairway with 412 stairs is closed.

From the obelisk, drive or walk south on broad, maple-lined Monument Avenue to another prominent Bennington landmark, the **Old First Congregational Church.** This gorgeous church, the oldest in Vermont, was designed by Lavius Fillmore and built in 1805 on the site of an older church organized in 1762. The Old First Church, the most photographed church in Vermont with its classic lines, is listed on the National Register of Historic Places.

Surrounding the church is the **Old Burying Ground,** a plot designated as "Vermont's Sacred Acre." The cemetery contains the graves of five Vermont governors, early settlers, Revolutionary War soldiers (each marked with a flag), and Robert Frost, New England's beloved poet.

Robert Frost, interred with his wife, Elinor Miriam White, and children, was buried here after his death on January 29, 1963. His epitaph, inscribed on a flat slab of Vermont granite littered with coins and oak leaves, is "I had a lover's quarrel with the world," while his wife's is "Together wing to wing and oar to oar." She died in 1938 while the Frost family lived in Shaftsbury just north of Bennington. The gravesite is on the hillside east of the church.

Lots of well-preserved houses dating from the late 1700s line the streets around the Old First Church. Across from the church is the **Walloomsac Inn,** which opened in 1766. Two future

A flag marks the grave of a Revolutionary War soldier at the Old Burying Ground in Bennington.

Famed poet Robert Frost and his Elinor rest beneath a granite slab behind the Old First Congregational Church.

presidents—Thomas Jefferson and James Madison—slept there in 1791. Nearby is the Old Bennington Country Store in a building that has been a store continuously since 1793.

Down the hill from the monument and church is the **Bennington Museum**—another must-see attraction here. The museum highlights, details, and explains the crafts, arts, and history of Bennington and Vermont. The galleries include a collection of glassware and Bennington pottery and porcelain; a display of New England furniture; the Bennington Battle Flag from 1776, the oldest known Stars and Stripes in existence and reputedly flown at the battle; a Wasp touring car, built in 1925 in Bennington and one of 16 made; and a spectacular collection of paintings.

The most famous artist represented is **"Grandma" Anne Mary Robertson Moses,** whose folk art paintings from the first half of the 20th century illustrate with a naïve primitivism and bright colors the life of rural New England. Grandma Moses, born in 1860 just over the border in New York, took up painting at age 76 and achieved critical acclaim and success. She painted until her death at age 101 in 1961. Looking at her paintings allows you to see the landscape of this drive through the eyes of someone who lived there when life was simpler but harder.

After seeing the main sights, head back downtown and roam around the **Bennington National Historic District.** You'll find lots of shops to poke around in as well as restaurants like the famed Blue Benn Diner and points of interest including the Old Stone Mill and Potters Barn. If you want to do more driving, there is a covered bridge tour that discovers five bridges in the area. Ask at the chamber of commerce office for details. Afterwards, return east to Brattleboro on the drive, head south to the Mohawk Trail Scenic Route in Massachusetts, or north to the Southern Green Mountains Scenic Route.

2 Southern Green Mountains

General description: This 69-mile drive explores the southern Green Mountains, the northern Taconic Mountains, and the Vermont Valley.

Special attractions: Green Mountain National Forest, Big Branch Wilderness Area, Hapgood Pond Recreation Area, Batten Kill River, Long Trail, Bromley Ski Area, Manchester villages, Hildene, American Museum of Fly Fishing, Southern Vermont Arts Center, Dorset, Dorset Playhouse, Merck Forest and Farmland Center, Pawlet, Danby, fly fishing, hiking, camping, bicycling, downhill skiing, cross-country skiing, picnicking.

Location: West-central Vermont.

Drive route numbers: US 7, FR 10, VT 11, 30, 315, 153, and 133.

Travel season: The lower-elevation roads are open year-round. Expect snow and icy conditions in winter. Most of FR 10 is closed in winter. Avoid during the spring mud season.

Camping: Emerald Lake State Park off US 7 between Manchester and Danby offers 67 campsites and 37 lean-tos. Hapgood Pond Campground north of Peru has 28 campsites. Several private campgrounds are found along the drive.

Services: All services in Danby, Manchester area, Dorset, and Pawlet. Limited and seasonal services are found in other towns along the drive.

Nearby attractions: Emerald Lake State Park, Mount Equinox Sky Line Drive, Bennington, Shaftsbury State Park, Coolidge Homestead, Middlebury, Middlebury Gap, Lake Champlain, Stephen Douglas birthplace, Quechee Gorge, Mount Ascutney State Park, Gifford Woods State Park, Woodstock.

The Route

The two-part, 69-mile Southern Green Mountains Scenic Route explores a remote slice of the Green Mountains before dipping

Southern Green Mountains

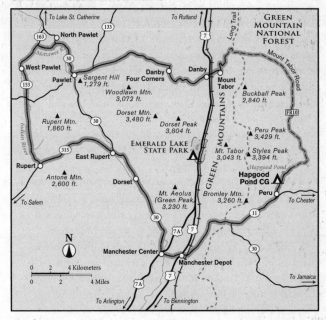

across the Vermont Valley at Manchester and driving a series of pastoral back roads through the northern Taconic Mountains along the New York border. The roads traverse a wide variety of topography, including broad valleys, intimate vales, and densely wooded mountains. Foliage season is excellent along this drive. The first drive segment, a narrow dirt road in Green Mountain National Forest, is passable only during the summer and autumn months. The rest of the drive is open year-round.

Danby to Devil's Den

The drive begins at **Danby,** a crossroads village between Manchester and Rutland. This quaint village nestles at the northern end of the Vermont Valley along US 7 and offers antiques stores, an inn, and a general store. Settled by Quakers in the 1760s, Danby prospered with the dairy industry, lumbering, and marble quarrying, but now relies on tourists for its trade. The town boasts Vermont's first home-grown millionaire. Native son Silas Griffith, born here in 1837, amassed a fortune as a lumber baron after selling his Danby store. His sprawling empire included more than 55,000 acres of timber, 12 sawmills, and holdings in Kansas, Washington, and California. Part of Griffith's local legacy still includes Christmas gifts for town children. Nobel Prize–winning novelist Pearl S. Buck settled here in the 1960s, buying local properties and renovating them after US 7 bypassed the town center.

The drive begins by turning east from US 7 at Danby onto Forest Road 10. The road bumps across railroad tracks, crosses Otter Creek, and after 0.5 mile passes a few homes in the tiny village of **Mount Tabor** at the base of the Green Mountains. This town, the story goes, was called Griffith for wealthy landholder Silas Griffith between 1891 and 1905 after mail coming to town listed its name as Griffith. It was originally a center for Griffith's charcoal industry before becoming a marble center. Even today, Vermont's largest marble quarry operates at nearby Mount Tabor.

The drive's first segment traverses 19 miles along FR 10 (Mount Tabor Road), a narrow paved and dirt track that climbs to the crest of the Green Mountains before dropping south along rounded ridges to Peru and VT 11. This scenic road, flanked by Big Branch and Peru wilderness areas, runs through some of Vermont's most rugged and remote landscapes. The still-paved road exits Mount Tabor at the base of the mountain range and begins a long uphill ascent. Signs warn motorists to be alert for logging trucks. After a mile the road enters 36,400-acre **Robert T. Stafford White Rocks National Recreation Area,** where a roadside kiosk offers information and a locator map.

The road swings across **Big Branch Creek,** a rushing stream that tumbles over worn boulders and cobbles, then begins a

Looking down into Big Branch Valley near the crest of the Green Mountains.

steady switchbacking ascent up a steep hillside blanketed with birch trees. Eventually the road bends onto the northern flank of Big Branch's deep gorge and edges northeast above abrupt dropoffs. Big Branch Overlook perches on the hillside at 2.7 miles. The area offers stunning views of Big Branch Valley below and the high peaks of the southern Green Mountains, as well as a picnic area. Big Branch Trail drops south for 0.1 mile into the canyon from here, enticing anglers with some of Vermont's best trout-fishing opportunities.

The narrow paved road continues to climb above the gorge before beginning to flatten at 3 miles. The Appalachian/Long Trail crosses the road here, and a small parking area for hikers lies just past the trail crossing. At 3.4 miles the pavement ends and the narrow road becomes dirt and gravel. Watch for mud and slippery sections during wet weather for the road's duration. The road rises over rounded ridges dense with conifers and hardwoods and dips through shallow valleys filled with beaver ponds, trickling brooks, swamps, and moose stomps. An abandoned apple orchard that gave fruit to some early homesteader sits alongside the road at 6.4 miles. Early Vermont was heavily populated with hill farmers who decimated the state's original forests for building material, firewood, and arable land. Foresters say 75 percent of Vermont's forests were cut then. Today, 78 percent of the state is forest again. Steep, bouldery slopes and roadcuts rear above the road as it slowly descends southeastward. One of the best is **Devil's Den**—broken rocky outcrops in a narrow saddle just past the 8-mile mark. Occasional views of surrounding knolls are seen from open valleys.

Hapgood Pond & Peru

The drive leaves the national recreation area at 8.4 miles and drops south alongside Mount Tabor Brook, a small brook riffling over boulders. The road leaves Green Mountain National Forest at 13.1 miles, passes some beaver ponds, then reaches homes and open fields. Beyond a right turn and an old cemetery, the drive swings through the small, picturesque village of 1,300-foot-high **North Landgrove.** The town site was originally settled by William Utley in 1769. At 14.8 miles the road makes a sharp right turn, crosses Utley and Griffith Brooks in a shallow, open valley, and rises into a dense forest.

The road becomes paved again at 16 miles, near where **Hapgood Pond Recreation Area** sits off to the right in the woods. This area, acquired in 1931 for the infant Green Mountain National Forest, offers swimming, boating, and fishing on 7-acre Hapgood Pond. A picnic area and 28-site campground also accommodate visitors. A couple of miles north of here is **Wild Wings Ski Touring Center,** a small, family-centered area with plentiful snow atop the range crest and more than 25 kilometers of ski trails.

The road runs southwest into **Peru,** a serene and graceful town on the eastern flank of 3,260-foot Bromley Mountain. The town was established in 1773. Neat white houses line the road here. Peru's square-towered Congregational Church was built in 1846. Another point of interest is the J. J. Hapgood Store, built in 1827. The first drive section ends at FR 10's junction with VT 11. Turn west (right) on VT 11 toward Manchester for the next 8-mile segment of this drive.

The highway rolls southwest, traversing rounded ridges to **Bromley Ski Area.** Begun in 1937, the ski area is one of New England's oldest ski resorts. Its mountain offers 43 trails with a vertical drop of 1,334 feet, snowmaking capabilities, and lots of amenities. **Hapgood State Forest** perches atop Bromley Mountain north of the ski area and highway. Allowing far-reaching views to the south, the drive climbs west to the crest of the Green Mountains before beginning a long, steep descent into the Vermont Valley and Manchester. A scenic viewpoint partway down yields great views of the valley below. The highway quickly drops to cross US 7 and enters Manchester.

Manchester

Manchester has long been Vermont's most exclusive and trendy resort. The town is itself a collection of several villages, including Manchester Center, Manchester Depot, and Manchester Village. The area's gorgeous mountain scenery, sparkling rivers and brooks, winter snowfalls, clear air, and mineral springs began attracting visitors in the mid-19th century, although the town was chartered in 1761. Urbanites flocked to Manchester to bathe in the salubrious, sulfuric waters for good health and long life. The posh, white-pillared **Equinox House** hotel became one of the East's fashionable spas in the 19th century and today is the refurbished centerpiece of the **Manchester Village Historic District** on the town's southern outskirts.

This genteel, historic town with Colonial mansions and marble sidewalks is also a booming, upscale shopping center with dozens of outlet shops for shrewd bargain hunters. Visitors flock

The village of Manchester nestles against Vermont's Green Mountains.

here to dine in trendy restaurants and cruise designer stores for labels such as Ralph Lauren, Izod, Timberland, and Calvin Klein. Northshire Bookstore, a complete bookshop, offers plenty of printed material to peruse.

The Manchester area is renowned for its superb trout streams. The town itself is the home of the **Orvis Company,** a famed manufacturer of fly-fishing rods and tackle begun in the 1850s by Charles Orvis, whose brother Franklin founded Equinox House. The store, located on US 7A, offers split bamboo rods, reels, flies, and other equipment. Buyers can test gear in a pool out back. The shop also offers the **Orvis Fly Fishing School** from April through August. Manchester is also home to the **American Museum of Fly Fishing,** displaying historic rods and reels from famed Americans including President Dwight D. Eisenhower, Daniel Webster, Ernest Hemingway, and Bing Crosby, as well as colorful hand-tied flies. The **Batten Kill River,** considered by many anglers to be Vermont's and perhaps New England's prime trout stream, meanders south through the Vermont Valley through Manchester and Arlington.

Manchester's many other attractions include **Hildene,** the spacious estate of Robert Todd Lincoln, Abraham Lincoln's only surviving son, and the **Southern Vermont Arts Center.** Hildene is an impressive, 24-room Georgian Revival manor on 412 valley acres. The historic mansion was bought after Mary Lincoln Beckwith's death in 1975 and preserved as a museum. Visitors can tour the house and its formal gardens, and perhaps hear a demonstration of its thousand-pipe organ. Robert Todd Lincoln first came here as a boy before the president's death and later returned to build this splendid summer retreat during his career as an attorney, diplomat, and Cabinet member. He died here in 1926.

An excellent side-trip from Manchester is the 5-mile Sky Line Drive toll road up 3,825-foot **Mount Equinox** in the Taconic Mountains southeast of town. The summit offers stunning views of southern Vermont, New Hampshire, Massachusetts, and New York.

Dorset & Rupert

The main drive route winds through **Manchester,** turns north on VT 30, then quickly leaves homes, churches, and outlet stores behind. The highway runs northwest along the West Branch of the Batten Kill River up a broad valley past pastures filled with grazing sheep, horses, and geese. High, wooded mountains flank the valley, with 2,535-foot Owls Head looming to the east and 3,290-foot Mother Myrick Mountain and Bear Mountain rising to the west in the main Taconic Range.

The road runs through South Dorset before entering **Dorset,** a charming village at an elevation of 962 feet that could be rightly called the birthplace of Vermont. Originally settled in 1768, the town was the meeting place of the Green Mountain Boys in 1776 when they declared their independence from New York, the New Hampshire Grants, and England. Meeting at Cephas

Kent's tavern, these founding fathers of the state agreed at their first convention "to defend by arms the United American States against the hostile attempts of the British fleets and armies until the present unhappy controversy between the two countries shall be settled."

Mount Aeolus above the town is the site of the first commercial marble quarry in the United States, established by Isaac Underhill in 1785. Dorset is a picturesque, well-preserved village with an affluent population. The **Dorset Inn,** a National Historic Site, is reputed to be Vermont's oldest operating hostelry, and the Dorset Playhouse is one of New England's most popular summer theaters. The drive quickly swings through town, passing large homes, the town center, and a golf course.

Outside town the road crosses the wide, flat valley to East Rupert. Turn west (left) off VT 30 here onto VT 315. The next 6-mile leg of your route heads west up a narrowing valley flanked by wooded hills. Slowly the road narrows and climbs through dense forest past occasional houses. After 3 miles it crests a ridge. The turnoff to the **Merck Forest and Farmland Center** is here. This pristine 3,130-acre nature center offers trails, picnic sites, a spring-fed swimming hole, interpretive talks, a visitor center, a farming museum, and a working sugarhouse. The visitor center lies 0.5 mile south of the highway. The center's mission is "to teach and demonstrate the benefits of innovative, sustainable management of forest and farmland."

From the ridge the highway drops steeply. Antone Mountain, a 2,600-foot wooded knoll, looms to the south above open fields. Slowly the degree of descent lessens. A couple of miles later, the road enters the town of **Rupert.** Lying in a peaceful valley near the New York border, Rupert is famed as the site of Vermont's first and only mint. When Vermont was still an independent republic before joining the United States, the legislature

Ferns grow in a moist glade in Mill Brook's narrow gorge.

gave Ruben Harmon exclusive permission to mint copper coins. The mint, built on Mill Brook, smelted copper, rolled, cut, and stamped the new coins. The first coins were pressed with the words *Vermontensium Res Publica,* the date 1786, and images of a plow and a mountain sunrise. Rupert remains a tidy town with old white homes and the simple Congregational Church.

Rupert to Danby

Turn north (right) on VT 153 in Rupert. The highway runs north for 7 miles up the Indian River in a shallow valley. The broad valley floor holds open pastures and cornfields flanked by low wooded hills. After a few miles the road winds into the hills and through farmland to **West Pawlet,** a small village perched on the New York border. The town center is marked by a flagpole atop a granite marker. Deep slate quarries lie in the hills just east of town, surrounded by slag heaps or filled with water. The highway bends northeast out of West Pawlet and crosses open pastures before dropping down to the lovely Mettawee Valley where, 2.5 miles later, it rejoins VT 30.

Turn right on VT 30 and drive south up the valley past prosperous farms. Hills embrace the valley. Among these is rugged 1,919-foot Haystack Mountain with dark cliffs banding its flank. A few miles later the drive reaches **Pawlet.** This village nestles in **Flower Brook**'s narrow valley at its confluence with the Mettawee River. Town Hill (to the north) and Sargent Hill (to the south) hem the town and valley. This now quiet town once rivaled Rutland as an industrial center. As far back as 1830, Pawlet bustled with mills and factories, including Vermont's first cheese factory. Before that the town was a hive of rebellion in the Revolution. Herrick's Rangers, the "Terror of the Tories," were organized here in 1777. Stop in at the General Store for a look through a glass-topped counter at Flower Brook beneath the floorboards. The brook is harnessed to a turbine to generate the store's electricity.

Follow the last 11 miles of this drive by heading east from Pawlet on VT 133. The highway heads up a broadening valley floored by dairy farms, hayfields, and pastures. At an intersection reached a mile east of Pawlet, continue straight on a narrow road instead of turning left on VT 133. The road climbs gently eastward on the south side of the Flower Brook valley. Lofty 3,072-`foot Woodlawn Mountain, a northern outpost of the Taconic Mountains, rises to the southeast, while low wooded knolls block the northern horizon. The road dips and rolls over low ridges, running alternately through forest and field to the residential village of **Danby Four Corners.** This small settlement lies on a sloping plateau studded with farms. The village churchyard keeps many interesting old tombstones dating back to the American Revolution.

Turn right in town and follow the road southeast through thick woods for a mile into Mill Brook's narrow canyon. The high, rounded knob of 3,804-foot Dorset Peak towers to the south. The drive's last 2 miles wind down the steep narrow gorge before entering Danby. The road then drops through town to US 7 and the drive's terminus. **Emerald Lake State Park,** with 105 campsites, lies a few miles south.

3 Quechee–Coolidge

General description: A 61-mile open loop that passes through picturesque villages and hilly countryside in the Piedmont of central Vermont.

Special attractions: Quechee Gorge State Park, Woodstock, Billings Farm and Museum, Coolidge State Park, Calvin Coolidge Homestead and Birthplace, Plymouth Notch Historic District, Plymouth Cheese Corporation, Killington Ski Area, Gifford Woods State Park, White River National Fish Hatchery, historic sites, shopping, hiking, old-growth forests, downhill skiing, cross-country skiing, camping, autumn foliage.

Location: East-central Vermont.

Drive route numbers: US 4, VT 100A, 100, and 107.

Travel season: Year-round.

Camping: Mid-May to Columbus Day only. Quechee Gorge State Park on US 4 has 45 campsites and 7 lean-to sites. Coolidge State Park offers 26 campsites and 36 lean-to sites. Gifford Woods State Park has 22 campsites and 20 lean-to sites. Silver Lake State Park, 10 miles north of Woodstock off VT 12, has 40 campsites and 7 lean-to sites mid-May through Labor Day.

Services: All services in White River Junction, Quechee, Woodstock, and Sherburne Center. Limited and seasonal services in other towns along the drive.

Nearby attractions: Green Mountain National Forest, Batten Kill River, Manchester Center, Hildene, Mount Ascutney State Park, Saint-Gaudens National Historic Site (NH), Middlebury, Middlebury Gap, Joseph Smith Monument, Thetford Hill State Park, Connecticut River.

The Route

The 61-mile Quechee–Coolidge Scenic Route passes through some of Vermont's finest landscapes. This land, part of the New England

Quechee–Coolidge

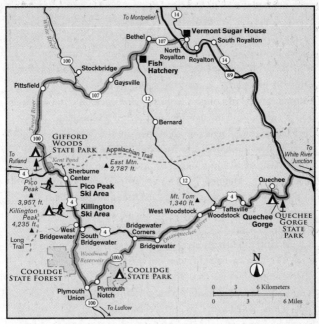

Uplands or Piedmont, is a plateaulike region of low, rolling hills incised by river valleys. The drive offers not only superb scenic views but also a good look at rural Vermont and its sleepy country villages, the abrupt Quechee Gorge, gentrified Woodstock, historic Plymouth and the birthplace of President Calvin Coolidge, and the central Green Mountains.

Quechee Gorge

The drive begins off I-89 in the **White River Valley** just upriver from White River Junction and the Connecticut River. Take US 4 at exit 1 on the interstate 3 miles west of I-91. US 4, running west from here to Rutland, is Vermont's principal east–west thoroughfare and one of its busiest highways. Semi-trucks laden with goods, skiers' cars topped with gear, leaf-peeper buses, and local farm traffic all conspire to overload the narrow highway. Use care and caution on the US 4 section of this drive. The highway closely follows the old right-of-way of the Woodstock Railroad between White River and Woodstock. Operating from 1875 to 1933, the railroad carried vacationers to posh Woodstock until diminishing traffic, a flood, and the new highway forced its closure.

The highway bends south away from the White River Valley and after 4 miles reaches **Quechee Gorge State Park,** one of Vermont's best-loved natural wonders. The abrupt 165-foot-deep gorge, nicknamed "Vermont's Little Grand Canyon," is a mile-long chasm excavated by the **Ottauquechee River.** The gorge's cliffs and slabs, densely blanketed with trees and foliage, are formed by green schist and quartzite in the Devonian-age Gile Mountain Formation. Quechee Gorge began forming a mere 13,000 years ago at the end of the Wisconsin glaciation when an immense ice sheet that covered New England began to melt. As the ice melted, the water drained into Lake Hitchcock, a long lake formed by a gravel moraine-dam near today's Hartford, Connecticut. Later the gravel dam was breached and the lake drained. The Ottauquechee River, instead of following its ancestral course to the east, began cutting through soft lake bottom sediments and soon became entrenched in the erosion-resistant metamorphic bedrock. The trapped river slowly gnawed away at the formidable bedrock with the powerful rush of meltwater, excavating Vermont's deepest and most spectacular river gorge. The gorge's present level was reached about 6,000 years ago.

The gorge is protected in Quechee Gorge State Park. An overlook lies near a parking area at the **Quechee Gorge Bridge,** a 1911 steel railway bridge that spans the ravine. A popular and airy view can be seen by walking out to the bridge's center. Another lookout and picnic area sit on the gorge's west rim. A

A country road runs by the cemetery at Plymouth Notch, home of President Calvin Coolidge.

pleasant 1.25-mile trail threads along the gorge's east rim and descends to the canyon floor to the south. A variety of plants and trees are seen in the gorge, including beech, red maple, sugar maple, white pine, and hemlock, the dominant tree that thrives in this cool, wet climate. A series of small waterfalls and scoured potholes lie south of the bridge. Hikers entering the gorge should be very careful since the riverbank rocks can be slick and treacherous. Anglers often trek into the gorge seeking rainbow and brown trout in the river's furious whitewater. A pleasant state-run campground sits among towering white pines just east of the bridge.

The highway bends northwest away from the gorge and runs through strip development—houses, antiques shops, motels, and gas stations—outside the village of **Quechee.** The village is now mostly a mish-mash of condos and vacation homes in the Quechee Lakes resort. The best attraction here is the **Simon Pearce Glass Works** in an old mill run by hydroelectric power. Stop by and watch a glassblower shape the vases, jugs, goblets,

and other functional glassware sold in the showroom. Look for "seconds," sold at a discount.

Woodstock

Past Quechee, US 4 meanders west through green hills along the south bank of the river for 6 miles to Woodstock. Along the way, at the small village of Taftsville, lies the red Taftsville Covered Bridge spanning the Ottauquechee River at a small waterfall and dam. The picturesque bridge, with two spans totaling 190 feet, was built in 1836 by Solomon Emmons. The drive arcs around Blake Hill and almost 3 miles later enters the famed town of Woodstock.

Woodstock is a genteel and elegant town that straddles the river valley between the rounded knobs of Mount Tom and Mount Peg. It's a sophisticated, almost aristocratic place that works hard at preserving and protecting its storied past from the onslaught of unrefined 21st-century businesses, and as a result remains one of New England's prettiest towns. This charm comes with a price of course; the town attracts droves of tourists and celebrities who come to eye Woodstock's pristine Colonial architecture.

The town site was granted in 1761 by Benning Wentworth and settled 4 years later by Timothy Knox. It became the Windsor County seat, or shire town, in 1786 and a leading publishing center in the 1800s with bookbinders, publishers, and five newspapers. The town attracted many prosperous bankers, merchants, scholars, and craftsmen who built the handsome Federal-style homes that encase the elliptical village green. In 1818 more than 10,000 Vermonters gathered on the green to watch the hanging execution of Samuel Godfrey, convicted of killing the state prison warden. The state's first medical school was housed here between 1827 and 1856.

Clearing mist after a rainstorm fills Quechee Gorge, Vermont's deepest river gorge.

Many of Vermont's most distinguished residents and native sons lived in Woodstock. These luminaries include Jacob Collamer, postmaster general and US senator who was a close confidant and advisor to President Lincoln. Collamer once remarked, "The good people of Woodstock have less incentive than others to yearn for heaven." George Perkins Marsh, a European diplomat, congressman, scholar, and scientist who helped found the Smithsonian Institution, lived on a farm outside town. Marsh's 1864 pioneering book *Man and Nature,* regarded as the ecologist's bible, detailed man's destruction of natural habitats and called for efforts to mitigate and curb further damage.

Frederick Billings, born in 1823 up the road in Royalton, was one of the town's most influential residents. Billings trekked out to California with his sister and her husband and set up the first law office in San Francisco. He prospered, made a fortune, and returned to Woodstock in 1869 where he bought the 270-acre Charles Marsh farm. He also invested in the Northern Pacific Railroad and took charge of its transcontinental construction. One of the towns along its route through Montana was named for him. Billings also ordered more than 10,000 trees planted on Woodstock hillsides denuded by timber cutting. Billings's influence continues today through his granddaughter Mary French's marriage to Laurance S. Rockefeller. The Rockefellers' generosity has included opening the Billings Farm and Museum to the public and burying the town powerlines.

Park the car in central Woodstock near the town green and roam around a bit. Most of the town is listed on the National Register of Historic Places, with almost all of its buildings dating from the 19th century. The chamber of commerce booth at the green offers daily walking tours. Highlights of any tour should include the Woodstock Historical Society's 1807 **Dana House** with its collection of antiques and resident ghost; the Romanesque **Norman Williams Public Library;** and the

1806 **First Congregational Church.** The **Vermont Institute of Natural Science,** lying 1.5 miles southwest of town, offers nature exhibits, a rare herb collection, nature trails, and a raptor center with more than 40 raptors on display.

Two covered bridges are in town. The Middle Covered Bridge near the town center was built in 1969. Its lattice structure spans 125 feet. The 1865 Lincoln Covered Bridge in West Woodstock extends 136 feet across the Ottauquechee River. The **Billings Farm and Museum,** north of town off VT 12, is a restored, living museum that details Frederick Billings's 1890s farm where even today workers plant and harvest crops, make cheese and butter, and run a dairy with prize-winning Jersey cows. The farm, Woodstock's most popular attraction, is open daily from May through October.

The drive leaves Woodstock along a strip of houses and motels on US 4 and heads west along the north bank of the Ottauquechee River for 7 miles to the junction of US 4 and VT 100A. Just before the turn is the old mill town of Bridgewater. The **Long Trail Brewing Company,** located in the Marketplace at the renovated 3-story Bridgewater Mill, brews small but tasty batches of Long Trail beers. Stop by for tours and tasting in their pub. Turn south or left onto VT 100A a mile past town.

The next lovely 7-mile road segment, running from US 4 to Plymouth Union, offers marvelous mountain scenery and a slice of real Americana. The road crosses the river on an old girder bridge and runs southwest up a broad valley filled with farms. After 1.4 miles the highway bends west up a side valley. The narrow road winds up a verdant hollow alongside Pinney Hollow Brook. After a short distance it passes the turnoff for Coolidge State Park, a 500-acre parkland located within **Coolidge State Forest.** The park includes 62 campsites and lean-tos, hiking trails, a small museum, and trout fishing. The drive continues to wind up the valley and after 6 miles reaches Plymouth Notch National Historic District, the birthplace and burial site of Calvin Coolidge, the 30th US president.

Plymouth Notch

The tiny, white-clapboard village of **Plymouth Notch,** still a functioning community, forms a cluster on a grassy hillside on the eastern edge of the Green Mountains. This quiet, off-the-beaten-track hamlet gave the nation Calvin Coolidge, a stoic, laconic, and reserved Yankee president who helped maintain a national sense of decorum and simplicity during the boisterous Roaring Twenties. Casual visitors, unacquainted with Coolidge, will wonder if they should bother stopping here. But those who do make the effort to visit Plymouth Notch find not only a fascinating glimpse into the late president's life, but also a nostalgic look back at New England's rural history.

Plymouth Notch was originally settled in 1771 as Saltash, but changed its name in 1797. The area, like so much of New England, prospered with industry in the early 19th century, with iron foundry work and stove manufacturing. A gold boomlet occurred in the 1850s, but things quieted down and the area reverted to its agrarian roots. It was from these roots that **Calvin Coolidge** was born on July 4, 1872, to John and Victoria Coolidge, Yankees from way back. John Coolidge's English ancestors landed in America about 1630.

Cal grew up, went to school, and launched his political career from this austere, no-frills town. His father, a state representative and senator, passed a sense of public service, political shrewdness, and self-restraint on to Calvin. After graduating from Amherst College, Coolidge entered the law profession and was elected to the city council of Northhampton, Massachusetts, in 1898. He went on to become city solicitor, a state representative and senator, mayor of Northhampton, lieutenant governor, and governor of Massachusetts. In 1920 Coolidge received the Republican vice-presidential nomination to run with Senator Warren

President Calvin Coolidge is buried at his hometown cemetery in Plymouth Notch.

G. Harding. The pair was elected easily, and Coolidge, at Harding's invitation, regularly attended Cabinet meetings, the first vice president to do so.

History was made at Plymouth Notch on the night of August 3, 1923. The vice president, in Vermont to help his father with haying, was awakened from a sound sleep and given the news of Harding's death. Coolidge telegraphed Washington for the oath of office, and at 2:47 a.m. was sworn in as president of the United States by his own father, a notary public, by the light of a kerosene lamp. Afterward, Coolidge went back upstairs to bed. The Coolidges' simple family room, now called the Oath of Office Room, remains much as it did that August night with a Bible, stacks of papers, a pen, and a lamp.

As president, Coolidge tidied up the mess left by Harding's Teapot Dome scandal, presided over a booming economy, established a summer White House at Plymouth Notch, and was easily re-elected in 1924 with the slogan "Keep Cool with Coolidge." After five years in Washington, he decided against running in 1928, citing the heavy strain on First Lady Grace Coolidge. Perhaps, some pundits conjecture, he foresaw the ruinous 1929 stock market crash. On leaving the capital, he told reporters, "Goodbye. I have had a very enjoyable time in Washington."

Coolidge retired to an estate in Northhampton, where he wrote his autobiography and a series of newspaper columns entitled "Thinking Things Over with Calvin Coolidge." He died suddenly of a heart attack at age 60 and was buried beside six generations of the Coolidge family in the Plymouth Notch cemetery, only a few hundred yards from his birthplace. His tombstone on a terraced hillside differs from those of his relatives only by the Great Seal of the United States above his name. The cemetery sits just south of VT 100A past the entrance to the town parking area.

Plymouth Notch remains a 19th-century village, touched only by preservationists. Its centerpiece is the Coolidge family compound with its houses and barns. The president's birthplace and boyhood home is a modest, five-room frame house attached to the back of the general store operated by his father. Displays in a small stone visitor center detail Coolidge's life history and achievements. Other buildings include the Wilder Barn with farm exhibits; the yellow 1830 **Wilder House;** the **Union Christian Church,** built in 1849; the **Plymouth Cheese Factory,** owned by the president's son John Coolidge; and the nostalgic **General Store** with lots of old-fashioned things for sale. Visit the cemetery on the south side of town. Other interesting graves in addition to those of the Coolidge family are found here, including 24-year-old Barton Billings's stone. Engraved on it is his dying request in Kansas: "Carry me back to old Vermont, Where the rills trickle down the hills. There is where I want to lie when I die."

When strolling around Plymouth, remember President Coolidge's words from a 1928 speech:

> I love Vermont because of her hills and valleys, her scenery and invigorating climate, but most of all because of her indomitable people. They are a race of pioneers who almost beggared them-selves for others. If the spirit of liberty should vanish in other parts of the union and support of our institutions should languish, it could all be replaced from the generous store held by the people of this brave little state of Vermont.

The historic district and museum is open daily from late May through mid-October.

Plymouth Union to Sherburne Center

Past Plymouth Notch, the highway climbs sharply to a ridge and drops down a steep wooded valley to VT 100 in Plymouth Union. Turn right (north) on VT 100. The drive runs north for 5.5 miles alongside the Black River below the Green Mountains. Northan Road turns west from the highway to a large section of Coolidge State Forest a couple of miles up the highway, just before Wood-ward Reservoir. The 21,500-acre forest is composed of several irregularly shaped blocks encompassing several high peaks and a wide swath of pristine hills.

This forest section protects a pair of natural sites—Tinker Brook Natural Area and Shrewsbury Peak Natural Area. The 45-acre **Tinker Brook Natural Area,** lying about a mile up and just south of rough Northan Road, is a small and lovely preserve blanketed by an undisturbed, old-growth stand of tall red spruce and hemlock. The brook tumbles down a steep, narrow ravine lined with virgin forest. The 150-year-old trees here reach heights of 100 feet and have trunks more than 20 inches in diameter. Mosses, ferns, painted trillium, starflower, lily of the valley, and violet grow along the moist sides of the ravine. Bug repellent is handy when visiting in summer.

Continue up Northan Road (1.9 miles from the highway) to the **Shrewsbury Peak** trailhead. The 1.8-mile trail winds north through an excellent spruce-fir boreal forest to the lofty summit of 3,720-foot Shrewsbury Peak, one of the forest's highest points.

The drive continues on the highway past Woodward Reservoir. A fishing boat access area can be found on the lake's west shore. Past the lake, the valley narrows. **Killington Peak** towers to the west, its 4,235-foot summit wreathed in clouds. The peak, the second highest in Vermont, offers a superb view of the surrounding mountains and valleys. It was this view that supposedly gave Vermont its name—Reverend Samuel Peters from Connecticut surveyed the surrounding countryside below Killington Peak in 1763 and called it Verd Mont, or Green Mountain in French. Sunrise Ski Area, part of the famed Killington Ski Resort, is reached just before the junction of VT 100 and US 4 at West Bridgewater.

US 4 climbs north from the small village up the Ottauquechee River Valley. Bear Mountain at Killington Ski Area is a mile up the road on the left. The drive continues up the rounded glacial valley, its flat, marshy floor densely matted with willows. After 4 miles the highway reaches Sherburne Center and begins steeply climbing out of the valley and bending west. Pico Peak looms to the west, its sides creased with ski runs. At 6.4 miles VT 100 (your route) turns right, while US 4 continues straight to Rutland.

Killington Ski Area, the East's largest ski resort, lies a few miles south of this junction. With seven mountains, including Pico, the resort encompasses the longest ski run and ski season in New England, the longest gondola in the United States, and the world's largest snowmaking facilities. The area opened in 1958 with three lifts on Snowden Peak. Today it boasts 141 runs and slopes with a vertical drop of 3,050 feet on 752 skiable acres. Snowfall averages 250 inches each winter. Numerous ski lodges line the highways and back roads around these ski areas, with accommodations for more than 11,000 visitors. Killington also offers four-season activities with an alpine slide, mountain bike rentals and trails, an 18-hole golf course, and tennis courts and schools. In summer you can ride the Killington Peak chairlift to the mountain summit and a restaurant. Many riders elect to hike back down.

Gifford Woods to Bethel

To continue the drive, turn north (right) on VT 100, which drops down a hill into **Gifford Woods State Park.** This 114-acre park offers 42 wooded campsites and lean-tos, picnic areas, and hiking trails, including the Appalachian Trail, which crosses the park. The park, built in the 1930s, houses some impressive northern hardwoods in its developed area, but a hidden stand across the highway from the campground on the western shore of Kent Pond is even more thrilling. Somehow this virgin forest, today a state natural area, escaped the wholesale clearing of timber for firewood and construction that stripped 75 percent of Vermont by 1850 as well as today's rampant ski development to the south.

This climax forest alongside Kent Brook is one of the few remaining, untouched sugar maple–beech forests in the north-eastern United States. The maples tower as high as 300 feet, while the trunks of eastern hemlocks are as thick as 3 feet. The understory of this small, primeval, forest remnant counts 19 fern species and 64 species of flowering plants. This small forest is vulnerable to human impact and damage, so use care when hiking not to leave any sign of your passage. Ask at the park headquarters for directions to the old-growth forest.

VT 100 next runs north from the woods down a widening, glacier-carved valley on the eastern slope of the Green Mountains. The Tweed River riffles over boulders and hides behind woods alongside the asphalt. **Pittsfield,** 7 miles from Gifford Woods, was established in 1791 by settlers from Pittsfield, Massachusetts. The road runs through town past a private covered bridge (signed do not enter) and the long village green bordered by the town hall and immaculate white houses. Nearby are several ski lodges.

Past the village, the drive and river bend east and run past farms and cornfields on the river bottomlands. Almost 3 miles from Pittsfield, VT 100 intersects VT 107. Turn right on VT 107. For a side-trip to historic Stockbridge, go a mile farther north on VT 100.

The main drive's last 13 miles follow VT 107 and the White River northeast to I-89. The road reaches the wide river's south bank after a mile and traverses the long, narrow valley. Dense woods line the highway. The road dashes through Gaysville, passes the White River National Fish Hatchery, and continues to Bethel at the confluence of the White River and the Third Branch. **Bethel** was the first town chartered by the State of Vermont in 1778. The small village once thrived as a cutting and shipping center for granite quarried from area hills. Today's town of Bethel sits on the site of old **Fort Fortitude,** erected in 1780 to protect Bethel's early settlers from hostile Indian war parties that traveled down the White River Valley from Canada. Two months later nearby Royalton was burned by Indians, but Bethel was ignored because of its armed fort.

At Bethel the highway crosses an old girder bridge to the river's north bank and climbs onto terraces above. In 2 miles the highway reaches I-89 and the end of this drive. Continue straight past the interstate to North Royalton, Royalton, and South Royalton. At the junction of VT 107 and VT 14 is the **Eaton's Sugarhouse,** a maple sugar–theme restaurant and gift shop decorated with chain-saw wood carvings. Try their excellent pancakes smothered in Vermont maple syrup, and pancakes will never taste the same again. Interstate travelers can quickly reach Barre and Montpelier by driving north, and southbound travelers can head down the four-lane highway back to White River Junction.

4 Middlebury Loop

General description: An 81-mile loop drive through Middlebury and Brandon Gaps in the Green Mountains and across open farmland in the Champlain Valley.

Special attractions: Middlebury College Center for the Arts, Sheldon Museum, Vermont Folklife Center, Middlebury College Snow Bowl, Robert Frost Wayside Area and Trail, Middlebury Gap, Texas Falls Recreation Area, Green Mountain National Forest, Long Trail, Chittenden Brook Recreation Area, Brandon Brook Recreation Area, Brandon Gap, Vermont Ski Museum, Lake Champlain, apple picking, bicycle touring, fishing, hiking, downhill and cross-country skiing.

Location: North-central Vermont.

Drive route numbers: VT 30, 74, 73, 100, and 125, and US 7.

Travel season: Year-round. Expect snow and icy conditions in winter.

Camping: Branbury State Park offers 37 campsites and 7 lean-to sites from Memorial Day weekend through Columbus Day. Chittenden Brook Campground, with 16 sites, lies 2.5 miles south of VT 73 on the east side of Brandon Gap.

Services: All services in Middlebury and Brandon. Limited and seasonal services in other towns along the drive.

Nearby attractions: DAR State Park, Fort Ticonderoga (NY), Mount Independence State Historic Site, Crown Point State Historic Site (NY), Chimney Point State Historic Site, Branbury State Park, Silver Lake Recreation Area, Lincoln Gap.

The Route

The 81-mile Middlebury Loop Scenic Route, beginning in the college town of Middlebury, crosses the Green Mountains via Middlebury and Brandon Gaps, then runs across rolling farmland on the eastern side of the Champlain Valley. This drive incorporates two of Vermont's geographic regions—the state's rugged spine formed

Middlebury Loop

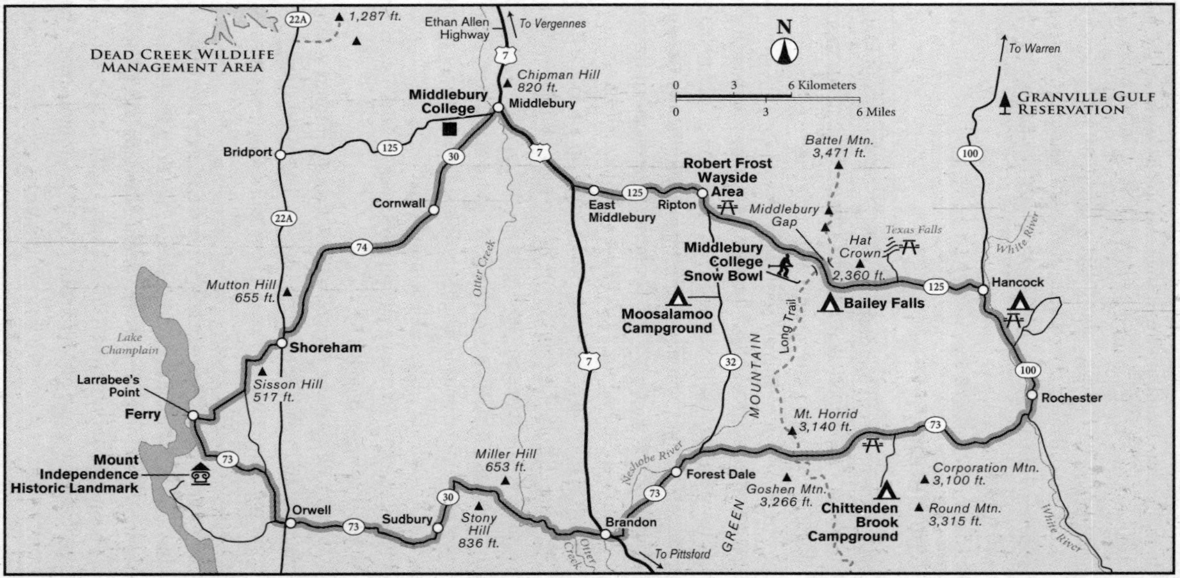

by the Green Mountains, and the Champlain lowland, the broad basin holding Lake Champlain that separates the Green Mountains from New York's Adirondacks. The drive's diverse scenery samples farmland and orchards, the Lake Champlain waterfront, superb mountain views, and a host of picturesque country villages and towns.

Middlebury

The drive begins in **Middlebury,** a classic New England town of just over 8,000 people that straddles Otter Creek in the morning shade of the Green Mountains. Although chartered in 1761, the town was not permanently settled for almost 20 years until the local Indians were subdued. It received its name because it sat midway between Salisbury and New Haven on an old military road. Middlebury is home to prestigious **Middlebury College.** Founded in 1800, the college contains many excellent historic buildings, including the 1815 Painter Hall made from locally excavated marble. A college office is in the Emma Willard House National Historic Landmark, site of the 1814 Middlebury Female Seminary. The **Johnson Gallery** at Middlebury offers a collection of Vermont artists as well as work by Rodin and Rosso. Despite its more-famous marble neighbors Rutland and Proctor to the south, Middlebury boasted Vermont's first large marble quarry, opened in 1803. The town sits on a bedrock of Ordovician limestone, marble, and quartzite.

To really see and appreciate Middlebury, it's best to park your car and walk the tree-lined streets. The Middlebury Common sits in the town center. A pretty white Congregational Church, completed in 1809, dominates the green. The church's tall Ionic columns were each hewn from a single tree trunk. Just down from the town common spreads the **Frog Hollow Historic District,** along tumbling **Otter Creek.** The waterfalls along Otter Creek powered numerous 19th-century textile mills when wool processing was one of Middlebury's dominant industries. The district's buildings date from the 1700s and 1800s and have been renovated into shops and galleries.

One of the best stores here is the Frog Hollow **Vermont State Craft Center,** with exhibitions, classes, and lots of Vermont crafts for sale, including stained glass, jewelry, and pottery. The **Vermont Folklife Center** in the Gamaliel Painter House near the green promotes folk art and traditions through special events and revolving exhibitions. The **Henry Sheldon Museum,** located on Park Street in an 1829 house, displays everyday 19th-century artifacts including furniture, tools, and household utensils, in period settings.

Through the Champlain Valley

The drive starts at the Middlebury Common at the junction of US 7 and VT 30. Turn southwest on VT 30, dropping past Frog Hollow Historic District, and pass Middlebury College on the outskirts of town. In less than a mile, the two-lane highway has left Middlebury far behind and entered a bucolic, rolling land. Good views of the lofty Green Mountains along the eastern horizon are to the highway's left. After 4 miles the road passes a church and cemetery and enters Cornwall. Turn west here onto VT 74.

The drive follows VT 74 for the next 13 miles to Larrabee's Point on the eastern shore of Lake Champlain. This rural highway stretch yields pleasant views west to the Adirondack Mountains in New York as it meanders past cornfields, apple orchards, silos, barns, and white farmhouses on the gently tilted plain. Occasional hillocks poke above the farmland. Among these is 655-foot Mutton Hill and 517-foot Sisson Hill near the small village of Shoreham. Most of these hills are streamlined, elongated knobs called "sheepbacks," oriented north-to-south by thick ice sheets that scoured the land during long episodes of glaciation.

The lowland topography here in the **Champlain Valley** was first excavated by the glaciers and later filled by thick sediment deposits beneath the ancient Lake Vermont and Champlain Sea

The broad Champlain Valley and the Adirondack Mountains are seen from the summit of Middlebury Gap.

waterways. Lake Vermont was a huge inland lake that covered all of the Champlain basin when the drainage to the St. Lawrence River to the north was icebound during glacial melting at the end of the Pleistocene Epoch. The lake also featured fjordlike fingers that poked east through the Green Mountains into today's Winooski, Lamoille, and Missisquoi River Valleys. The numerous hills in today's Champlain Valley were islands in the ancient lakes. Terraces of wave-deposited sediments are still visible on some hills here.

A few miles north of **Shoreham,** just off the drive, is **Dead Creek Wildlife Management Area,** at 2,858 acres the largest state waterfowl refuge in Vermont. The Dead Creek wetlands, created by water-control dams, offer excellent birding opportunities. Canada and snow geese, various species of ducks, wading birds such as bitterns and herons, and songbirds bring flocks of bird-watchers, particularly in spring and fall. Northeast of the wildlife area is the landmark promontory of 1,287-foot **Snake**

Mountain, with a fine hiking trail up its long ridge to good summit viewpoints.

Past Shoreham, VT 74 zigzags south and west to **Larrabee's Point.** This quiet village named for John Larrabee, who built a warehouse on the shore here in 1823, was once a busy commercial port and center for shipping quarried stone, lumber, and textiles. The railroad network that spread across the Northeast by the mid-1800s reduced the point's attractiveness as a shipping hub. Historic structures here include not only Larrabee's original warehouse but also the town's ferry dock, still in use.

The Fort Ticonderoga Ferry runs from Larrabee's Point to **Fort Ticonderoga** in New York from May through October. The fort was originally built by the French and later captured by the British. In 1775 Vermonter Ethan Allen and his Green Mountain Boys surprised the then-British garrison, capturing the fort and its guns. These weapons were eventually used to free Boston. British General Burgoyne recaptured the fort from the colonials in 1777, but lost it again with independence. The restored stone fort, open mid-May through mid-October, displays weapons, uniforms, and artifacts in its museum.

Mount Independence, just south of Larrabee's Point, is another Revolutionary War site, Vermont State Historic Site, and National Historic Landmark. The 400-acre site on a peninsula jutting into Lake Champlain was largely ignored by preservationists until 1975 when restoration, archaeological, and interpretative work was undertaken. Four trails lace this key military complex that faced Fort Ticonderoga. The fort, linked to Ticonderoga by a floating bridge, was built in 1776 to house 12,000 soldiers intended to protect the northwestern flank of the American colonies. It was captured by the British in July 1777 along with Fort Ticonderoga. The Continental Army, after abandoning the two forts, retreated southeast to Hubbardton where the army's rear guard, including Seth Warner and the Green Mountain Boys, fought the British army to a standstill on July 7 in the only Revolutionary War battle fought on Vermont soil. The 1,200

Vermonters held the select British units off for 2 hours before scattering when Hessian reinforcements arrived. Their action, however, delayed the British enough so that the main American column was able to escape southward. The battlefield, 12 miles south of Sudbury off VT 30, is commemorated by a marble spire.

Larrabee's Point to Brandon

The second segment of the drive runs 20 miles from Larrabee's Point to Brandon on VT 73. Head southwest from the lake and pass a picturesque barn painted with a large-scale imitation of Grant Wood's *American Gothic.* The road dips and rolls past hilly farms and the turnoff to Mount Independence State Historic Site. After 5 miles it crosses VT 22A and enters the hamlet of Orwell. The highway then heads east toward the Green Mountain wall, crossing beautiful farmland broken by wooded hills. About 5 miles from Orwell, the drive intersects VT 30. Turn north here on VT 30/73 to enter **Sudbury.** This small town perches atop a hill and offers good views of the Champlain Valley and the rounded Adirondack Mountains to the west. Continue north on VT 30 for a couple of miles to its junction with VT 73. Turn east (right) here.

A marker designating the Crown Point Military Road is found by going west for a mile from the crossroads. This 85-mile road reached the farthest outposts of the American colonies when it was built in 1759. The road connected the Connecticut River Valley with the Lake Champlain region and eased travel for British army units and early settlers.

The drive route runs southeast from VT 30 through low hills and along Otter Creek for 6 miles to Brandon. VT 73 climbs sharply up through a gap between Miller Hill on the left and 836-foot Stony Hill on the right before it drops to meandering Otter Creek, the longest river entirely within Vermont. The highway runs along the flat valley floor through swampy 278-acre Brandon Swamp Wildlife Management Area, passing fields of corn punctuated by dense woodlands. After turning away from the creek at last, the asphalt enters Brandon.

A busy town of 4,000, **Brandon** sits on low hills between Otter Creek and the Neshobe River. It offers two village greens, an 1861 town hall, and a good selection of 19th-century Federal and Victorian homes. The town, chartered in 1761 as Neshobe, was rechristened Brandon in 1784 after the Revolution. It flourished after iron deposits were discovered nearby in 1810. John Conant's furnace cast Vermont's first cookstoves. The Forestdale Iron Furnace, dating from 1810, preserves this heritage. Other industries included the Howe Scale Company, which moved to Rutland in the late 1860s, and marble-cutting mills powered by the Neshobe River. Thomas Davenport invented the electric motor here in 1834 and used his new invention to operate a newspaper press in New York City. In an editorial he foretold the future when he wrote that electricity "must and will triumphantly succeed."

Brandon was also the 1813 birthplace and childhood home of Stephen A. Douglas, the "Little Giant" who became a powerful Democratic senator from Illinois. Regarded as a potential president, he debated Abraham Lincoln in the famed Lincoln–Douglas debates during the 1858 Senate race in Illinois and was elected. The tables turned 2 years later when Lincoln, the Republican nominee, defeated Douglas for the presidency. Douglas, Vermont's native son, received only 19 percent of the state's vote and died shortly afterward in 1861.

Over the Green Mountains

The drive meets US 7 in downtown Brandon. Drive past the intersection and the 1785 Baptist Church and turn east (left) on VT 73 after 0.25 mile. The road runs past stately houses and exits Brandon in 0.5 mile. Two miles later the highway passes through modest Forest Dale and climbs eastward into the Green Mountains in a narrow valley alongside the Neshobe River. This meager river, hemmed in by dense woods, tumbles over a rocky streambed. As the highway steepens, glimpses of high ridges and peaks, including 3,266-foot Goshen Mountain on the right and 3,140-foot Mount Horrid on the left, stretch ahead. The drive enters 416,000-acre Green Mountain National Forest 6.5 miles from Brandon and climbs more steeply up the final grade to **Brandon Gap,** a pass between the two peaks. A picnic area, the Long Trail crossing, and Brandon Gap trailhead all lie near the gap's summit.

Marvelous views unfold upon cresting the gap. Mount Horrid and its precipitous Great Cliff loom dramatically above a roadside overlook and reflective beaver ponds on the valley floor. The top of the granite cliff lies 700 vertical feet above Brandon Gap and is reached by a spectacular 0.6-mile trail (part of the Long Trail traversing Vermont's Green Mountain crest). The hike begins in a small pullout near the gap summit. The short, steep, 45-minute hike leads to a superb viewpoint atop the cliffs. The Champlain Valley lies below, floored by the glistening lake, and the rugged Adirondacks stretch to the western horizon. The forested spine of the Green Mountains, punctuated by lofty peaks, stretches to the north and south, and a maze of hills lies to the east. Besides hiking, the Great Cliff area offers some of Vermont's rare rock-climbing opportunities and wildlife watching. Peregrine falcons, re-established by the Forest Service, are slowly making a comeback here. They can be seen soaring high above the cirque.

The **Mount Horrid Great Cliff** and the deep U-shaped valley of **Brandon Brook** east of the gap clearly illustrate the effects of glaciers on the Green Mountains. The cliff itself was formed by a glacial process that geologists call "quarrying" or "plucking." This occurs on the leeward side of the mountain, away from the direction in which the glacier came. As the ponderous glacial ice slowly crept across the exposed rock surfaces, it froze to the rocks then "plucked" them out along fracture lines as it moved downslope. Many thousands of years of glacial activity sculpted these lofty cliffs and excavated the deep valley below.

The drive drops eastward alongside Brandon Brook, passing Brandon Brook Picnic Ground and, a few miles later, the turnoff for **Chittenden Brook Campground.** This 17-site campground, open Memorial Day through Labor Day, lies 2.5 miles south up a dirt road and offers fishing and several good hiking trails. The highway and brook join the broad valley of the West Branch of the White River a mile later, and follow it east past cornfields and farms for 4 miles to the White River and the junction of VT 73 and VT 100. Turn north (left) on VT 100 and enter Rochester 0.1 mile later.

Rochester is a pleasant village that once thrived with logging, talc mining, and dairying but now offers a diverse business base that includes a New Age book publisher, a greeting card company, and **Liberty Hill Farm,** a working guest farm. Rochester is a good place to stop, sit back on the village green, and watch the world go by. Visit the Rochester Ranger Station on the south side of town for hiking, camping, and fishing information and maps of Green Mountain National Forest.

From Rochester the highway runs north across corn-covered, flat bottomlands along the White River, passing a small picnic area 0.5 mile north of town. The drive enters the lumber village of Hancock 4.5 miles from Rochester, turning west in Hancock on VT 125. An excellent side-trip continues north a few miles on VT 100 to 1,171-acre **Granville Gulf Reservation.** Dense forest lines the road as it ascends into Granville Gulf, an immense rock-lined cirque. **Moss Glen Falls State Natural Area** includes a marvelous waterfall that plummets over abrupt cliffs.

Middlebury Gap

The main drive route heads west up VT 125 alongside the Hancock Branch of the White River. This last drive segment over **Middlebury Gap** is a designated Vermont Scenic Highway. The highway leaves Hancock and runs west up the narrowing valley. The turnoff to **Texas Falls Recreation Area** is reached after

3.1 miles. Turn right and drive a short distance north to the falls parking lot and small picnic area with 13 sites. **Texas Falls** is a spectacular series of waterfalls sharply sliced into ancient metamorphic bedrock. The walls of the small gorge here are festooned with dense mats of moss and ferns. A short footbridge spans the gorge and gives a great view of the dashing water. Texas Falls Nature Trail, an easy 1.2-mile hike, begins at the bridge and explores Texas Brook.

The highway continues westward up the glacier-carved valley through a thick forest of hardwoods, pine, and spruce. After a couple of upward miles, the road climbs steeply into leafy 2,149-foot Middlebury Gap. Like the other east–west passes in the Green Mountains, Middlebury Gap was initially excavated by streams before the Wisconsin glaciation completed the final sculpting. The Long Trail, a 265-mile pathway along the main crest of the Green Mountains between Massachusetts and Canada, crosses the highway atop the gap.

Past Middlebury Gap, the drive begins a steep descent down a broad valley flanked by mountain ridges. Less than a mile from the summit, the road passes **Middlebury College Snow Bowl Ski Area,** a popular winter destination. The ski area has 3 chairlifts, 17 trails, a ski school, a rental shop, and a restaurant. The highway descends more gradually below the ski area and, in a mile, reaches the rolling bottomland along the South Branch of the Middlebury River.

The drive dips and rolls north of the river, past occasional cleared fields, before cutting through the campus of Middlebury College's famed Bread Loaf School of English. This collection of dun-colored buildings houses the college's esteemed summer writers' programs. Forest Road 59, which turns north just past the campus, leads to trailheads at the edge of **Bread Loaf Wilderness Area.**

Texas Falls, surrounded by moss and ferns, is a spectacular series of short leaps in a narrow gorge.

Past the campus, the drive enters Robert Frost country. The highway runs west through woods past an old cemetery to the **Robert Frost Wayside Area.** The area, offering picnic sites in an open red pine forest, is enclosed by a ragged stone fence. Robert Frost, the famed Poet Laureate of Vermont, summered in a farmhouse near here between 1939 and 1962. After his death in 1963, the Vermont Division of Historic Sites dedicated this wayside area and a nearby nature trail to the poet's memory. This highway section is the Robert Frost Memorial Drive. A small, unmarked dirt road just before the wayside area leads to the whitewashed Homer Noble Farm and Frost's small cabin there. Pilgrims can park in a designated lot and walk to the unassuming cabin, although it's not open to the public. The cabin, owned by Middlebury College, is maintained exactly as it was upon Frost's death in 1963. Just down the highway on the left side is the **Robert Frost Interpretative Trail.** The 1.2-mile-long path treks out along a boardwalk through a marsh and open fields. Some of Frost's famous poems are mounted on placards along the trail. Stop and linger at each one and feel the power of his interpretations.

Robert Frost is one of America's most beloved poets. Using simple language tempered by irony, this Yankee bard penned numerous stanzas about his adopted homeland. His poems evoke the character of this harsh countryside, reveling in its hard-won joys and stern sorrows and the plethora of emotions in between. Frost employed this powerful landscape to explore and delineate the relationships between poet, landscape, season, and fellow man. His poems speak to us not as New Englanders but as Americans. They look forward, toward the future, offering a promise of spring, a promise that miracles do happen amid the toil and grim overcast of winter. In plain English the poems show the land as we see it as well as the underlying landscape of our hearts and consciences.

It's important to remember that Frost was not a native of New England, but rather a traveling poet who came to love this land and people. He chose the intimate geography and humanity of New England for his life's work. Born and bred in California (of all places), Frost moved here at the age of 26 to live with his family on a small New Hampshire farm while he mastered the art of poetry. His most famous poem, "The Road Not Taken," tells of that choice:

> I shall be telling this with a sigh
> Somewhere ages and ages hence:
> Two roads diverged in a wood, and I—
> I took the one less traveled by,
> And that has made all the difference.

Beyond the trail site the drive bends northwest along the river. Forest Road 32 turns south here and runs 4 miles to 19-site Moosalamoo Campground in the national forest. The highway parallels the river's rocky streambed and enters the quiet town of **Ripton.** The town, chartered in 1781 and organized in 1828, is one of Vermont's largest townships with 31,599 acres and a population hovering at 550. Sights here include the usual white clapboard churches and the old Ripton Country Store.

The drive crosses the river upon leaving Ripton and twists along the rocky south bank. The river tucks into a small roadside canyon that quickly deepens and becomes **Middlebury Gorge,** an abrupt defile slicing through Precambrian layers of fine-grained gneiss and fractured quartzite. The highway drops steeply down the edge of the gorge, passes a good viewpoint, and crosses the river on a bridge 3 miles from Ripton. Look up-canyon from the bridge for a good view of the gorge.

At **East Middlebury** the road enters a more sedate country-side on the eastern fringe of the Champlain plain. Continue west through residential East Middlebury, taking care to angle right on VT 125 at its junction with VT 116. East Middlebury offers many bed-and-breakfasts, including the now famous **Waybury Inn,** open since 1810 and listed on the National Register of Historic Places. The exterior and front porch of the inn were used as the locale for the long-running television show *Newhart*. Even today fans of the series stop for a glance at the inn.

After leaving the village, the highway crosses farmland and joins US 7. Turn right on US 7 and head northwest across pastures dotted with grazing cattle and farms. Good views of the Green Mountain escarpment stretch across the eastern horizon. After a couple of miles, the highway passes Middlebury Ranger Station and enters the town of Middlebury. Continue on to the green at the town center, the end point of this drive.

5 Barre to Danville

General description: A 49-mile drive through rolling hills and picturesque country villages in Vermont's upland region.

Special attractions: Barre, Rock of Ages Quarry, Groton State Forest, Peacham, country churches, quaint villages, trout fishing, cross-country skiing, hiking.

Location: North-central Vermont.

Drive route numbers and name: US 302, VT 25, Minard Hill Road.

Travel season: Year-round. Expect snow and icy conditions in winter.

Camping: Groton State Forest, with 4 state park campgrounds (Ricker Pond, Stillwater, Big Deer, and New Discovery) and 223 sites, is open Memorial Day through Labor Day.

Services: All services in Montpelier, Barre, and St. Johnsbury. Limited services elsewhere along the drive.

Nearby attractions: Montpelier, Vermont Statehouse, Vermont Historical Society Museum, Stowe, Stowe Ski Area, Smugglers Notch, Mount Mansfield Toll Road, Mount Mansfield State Forest, Middlebury Gap, Green Mountain National Forest, St. Johnsbury attractions, Lake Willoughby, White Mountain National Forest (NH), Franconia Notch (NH).

The Route

Beginning in Barre, just east of Montpelier, this 49-mile drive runs southeast along US 302 and VT 25 before turning north along a back road to Danville. The route crosses rolling, wooded hills and dales and passes through picture-postcard villages. This area, encompassing Orange and southern Caledonia Counties, is quintessential Vermont. Its lovely landscape is a verdant tapestry broken by modest pastures and farmhouses tucked against hills clad in hardwoods and dark evergreens. Tidy, well-preserved villages

Barre to Danville

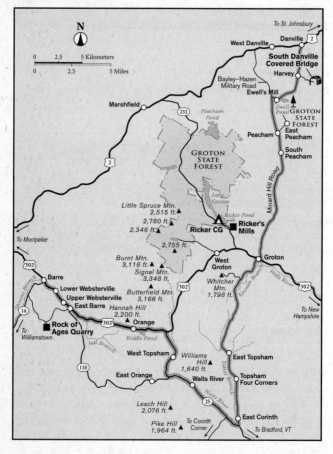

crowned by white-spired churches sit atop humped ridges and nestle in shallow valleys.

Although Vermont offers some wild, inspiring vistas of snowy mountains and rugged defiles, it is this peaceful corner of the state that attracts visitors and photographers with simple grace and beauty. The land and villages here are the image of a utopian rural America. While driving down these country lanes, it's easy to imagine the horse-and-buggy days, the mule-drawn plow, the backbreaking labor of clearing a field and building a stone fence. That's what this drive offers—a glimpse into the forgotten heart of agrarian America and the practical values that sprang from this simple countryside.

Barre to East Corinth

The drive begins in **Barre** (pronounced "berry"), a rough-edged town adjoining dignified Montpelier, the capital of Vermont. A 4-mile strip of stores and fast-food joints lines US 302 between the two rival cities. Barre is actually two cities—Barre City and Barre Town—with a combined population approaching 17,000. It sprawls along the banks of the Stevens Branch of the Winooski River in a shallow valley. Nicknamed the "Granite Center of the World," Barre was, like so many Vermont towns, famed for the excellent granite quarried from the surrounding hills.

The Barre towns were originally part of Wildersburgh, a village chartered in 1793. The first settlers held a town meeting to rename the village. Local legend says two Massachusetts emigrants, Thompson from Holden and Sherman from Barre, came to blows over the town's new name. Sherman battered his way to victory, then stood over his inert opponent and declared, "There, by God, the name is Barre." Historians dispute the colorful account but agree that the town was named after Barre, Massachusetts.

Granite quarrying began here in 1813 at the Wells-Lamson Quarry, America's first granite quarry. Other quarries on

Millstone and Cobble Hills southeast of Barre began excavating granite for millstones, foundations, window and door lintels, and fence posts. The granite vein here is as wide as 4 miles and as deep as 10 miles. The flawless light and dark granite from Millstone Hill was shipped by ox teams for use in the construction of the state capitol in Montpelier between 1833 and 1837. Barre's population and fortunes soared after 1880, when thousands of low-paid European stonecutters worked in the thriving quarries. This volatile mixture of immigrants from Scotland, England, Germany, Spain, Scandinavia, and Italy successfully struck for higher wages and benefits in the early 1900s. They also elected a socialist mayor, supported the Communist Party during the Great Depression, and built Socialist Hall to benefit workers.

Granite remains a mainstay of Barre's modern economy, with more than 1,000 workers excavating and milling the rock for use as monuments, sculptures, floors, and building exteriors. Visitors can view the nearly 600-foot-deep, 27-acre Rock of Ages Quarry and the adjoining Craftsmen Center in Graniteville, southeast of Barre.

The route travels east from Barre on US 302. The highway heads up the narrow, wooded valley of the Jail Branch River, passing a few homes and businesses in Lower Websterville and Upper Websterville. After 3 miles and the junction with VT 110, the road dashes through East Barre and climbs out of the valley into rolling, thickly forested hills. The town of **Orange,** spread along the roadside, is dominated by a white Congregational Church. Atop a rise just west of Orange, look back west for an impressive view of the Rock of Ages Quarry notched into a distant hillside.

The highway runs east for the next 4 miles through thick evergreen woods and past rounded, 2,000-foot hills. At Riddle Pond the asphalt drops into a narrow valley with a shallow, meandering creek to the junction of US 302 and VT 25. Turn south (right) onto VT 25 and head down the broad Waits River Valley.

A couple of miles down VT 25 lies **West Topsham,** a small hamlet perched above the river. Beyond the village the highway drops steeply down the picturesque valley, past green hayfields hemmed in by Sanborn Ridge to the east. The road bends southeast after the turn to East Orange and follows the broadening Waits River Valley downstream. After a short distance the drive passes through the tiny village of **Waits River.** The village and river, as well as the town of Waitsfield, were named for General Benjamin Wait, a veteran of both the French and Indian Wars and the American Revolution.

East Corinth to Groton

The highway continues down the pastoral valley another 4 miles to its junction with a narrow country lane that runs north. Turn north (left) at this intersection. The next 28-mile drive segment

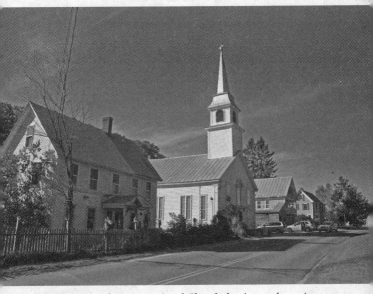

The East Cornith Congregational Church dominates the main street of East Cornith.

runs north from here to Danville through a lovely swatch of Vermont's Piedmont country, that area of rolling hills between the Green Mountains and the Connecticut River on the state's eastern border. The drive runs alongside trickling Tabor Branch through a scenic valley with hayfields, occasional cattle, and large farmhouses. In 0.5 mile the road climbs through **East Corinth,** a small village dominated by the lovely East Corinth Congregational Church. The road quickly passes through Topsham Four Corners, a small collection of houses, and continues up the valley to **East Topsham.** This quaint cluster of homes is set on grassy knolls above the creek. The town's whitewashed church lifts its steeple above tin roofs and wood piles.

The drive leaves East Topsham and the Tabor Branch to climb steeply along Powder Spring Creek in a densely wooded draw. Rolling hills, some as high as 1,900 feet, rise above the road. Beaver ponds in the forest reflect a sky of steely clouds. Occasional moose stomps, trampled mudflats, lie alongside the narrow roadway. After 4 miles the road tops a rise then begins a northward descent past stubblefields fenced in by thick woods. Bending northeast around 1,798-foot Whitcher Mountain, the asphalt meets Keenan Brook in a shallow vale before descending gently into the broad valley of Wells River. This section of road yields superb views eastward across rolling hills to the snowcapped Presidential Range in northern New Hampshire.

The road enters Groton and drops to another junction with US 302 and the town center. **Groton,** named by early Scottish settlers for Groton, Massachusetts, straddles the Wells River in a wide valley amid forested hills. **Groton State Forest,** Vermont's largest state recreation area, sprawls across 25,625 acres northwest of town. This immense swath of wild forest is topped by numerous peaks that reach higher than 2,500 feet. Signal Mountain, a 3,348-foot-high summit, lies just south of the park's boundary.

The drive bends through Topsham Four Corners, passing houses, barns, and a whitewashed church.

More than 40 miles of developed trails lace the forest, scaling the peaks and exploring lakes, ponds, and streams. **Lake Groton,** a 3-mile-long reservoir, and nearby **Ricker Pond** offer the bulk of the area's recreational opportunities. Most visitors come to fish and swim in the lakes, hike the trails, hunt in the forests, and ski-tour and snowmobile in winter snow. The state forest also offers four campgrounds in four state parks for summer campers.

Like most of New England's forests, Groton State Forest was heavily logged in the 19th century. **Ricker's Mills,** just outside of Groton, is one of the nation's oldest continuously operating saw-mills. The area is also rife with lumberjack history, including the Old Lake House, a boardinghouse that was the hangout of bank robber Bristol Bill Darlington from Bristol, England. The famed outlaw was finally captured here in 1850, and in a final desperate act during his sentencing at St. Johnsbury, he killed the prosecutor with a knife.

Peacham & Danville

On reaching Groton, turn east (right) on US 302 and drive 0.3 mile to Minard Hill Road. Turn north (left) here toward Peacham. The narrow, paved road climbs steeply out of Groton and drops into a broad swale. The drive runs north alongside Tannery Brook up the narrowing valley. Dense woods interrupted by occasional farms and hayfields line the blacktop. After a few miles the road crests an open ridge. Superb views of the distant White Mountains and the Vermont Piedmont unfold beyond the rise. The road gently descends into open farmland, crossing South Peacham Brook and sliding past a few houses in South Peacham. A mile later it enters Peacham.

Set among green hills at the relatively lofty elevation of 1,908 feet, **Peacham** is one of Vermont's most charming villages. This isolated community was chartered in 1776 by Deacon Jonathon Elkins and flourished after the Bayley–Hazen Military Road pushed through the region. This 55-mile route was begun in 1776

A farm nestles among green rolling hills south of Peacham.

for launching possible attacks on British Canada and opened northern Vermont to settlers after the Revolution. The Peacham Academy, founded in 1795 as the Caledonia County Grammar School, operated for well over 100 years until closing in the 1920s. A stone monument marks its former site. The impressive Congregational Church, recognized as one of America's most beautiful country churches, presides over the town, lifting its tapered white spire above surrounding trees, barns, and houses near the village green. The church was built in 1806 and moved to its present location in 1843.

Notable Americans who grew up in Peacham include the violent abolitionist Thaddeus Stevens and George Harvey, an influential journalist and editor of *Harper's Weekly* who was nicknamed "The President-Maker." Harvey engineered Woodrow Wilson's rise to political power as governor of New Jersey. He later pushed Warren G. Harding's nomination and supported fellow Vermonter Calvin Coolidge for vice president. Herbert Hoover also consulted with Harvey before his election.

Peacham is a good place to stop and stretch your legs. Walk west from the four corners up a side street past the village church to a cemetery with spacious views of the surrounding countryside. Lovely green hills punctuate the skyline, among them New Hampshire's White Mountains to the east. The town is also graced by several stately historical homes and the **Peacham Store,** which vends fresh croissants and Vermont crafts and quilts while at the same time serving as a bed-and-breakfast.

Leave Peacham and travel north out of the valley over rolling ridges and shallow vales. At Ewell Pond, a large lake hemmed in by trees, the road bends northeast and passes a detached section of Groton State Forest. Turning north again the road rolls through a small collection of houses at Harvey and 1.5 miles later enters **Danville.** The drive ends at the road's junction with US 2 in Danville. This lovely village, spread across a humped hill, was northern Vermont's largest town some 200 years ago. Today it is home to the American Society of Dowsers. I-91 and St. Johnsbury lie 7 miles east.

6 Smugglers Notch

General description: This 23-mile drive climbs to the summit of Mount Mansfield, Vermont's highest point, and threads through 2,162-foot-high Smugglers Notch, an abrupt cleft chiseled into the Green Mountains. Cars pulling trailers and recreational vehicles should not attempt the road section through Smugglers Notch.

Special attractions: Smugglers Notch State Park, Mount Mansfield State Forest, Mount Mansfield Toll Road, Bingham Falls, Mount Mansfield Ski Area, Smugglers Notch Ski Area, Stowe, hiking, rock climbing, ice climbing, downhill skiing, cross-country skiing, alpine tundra, Long Trail.

Location: Northern Vermont.

Drive route number and name: VT 108 and Mount Mansfield Toll Road.

Travel season: May through October. The highway usually opens sometime in May and closes by November, depending on snowfall.

Camping: Smugglers Notch State Park, open late May to mid-October, offers 20 sites with flush toilets, showers, phone, picnic tables, and lean-tos. A 100-site private campground is just south of Stowe off VT 100.

Services: All services in Stowe and Jeffersonville.

Nearby attractions: Elmore State Park, Little River State Park, Burlington, Shelburne Museum, Lake Champlain, Chester A. Arthur birthplace, Montpelier attractions.

The Route

Mount Mansfield, Vermont's highest point at 4,393 feet above sea level, towers above the surrounding Green Mountains and forms a distinctive landmark for travelers. The mountain's 5-mile-long summit ridge resembles a reclining human profile, with four fanciful bumps defining the forehead, nose, chin (actual summit), and Adam's apple. American Indians saw the peak's unique features

Smugglers Notch

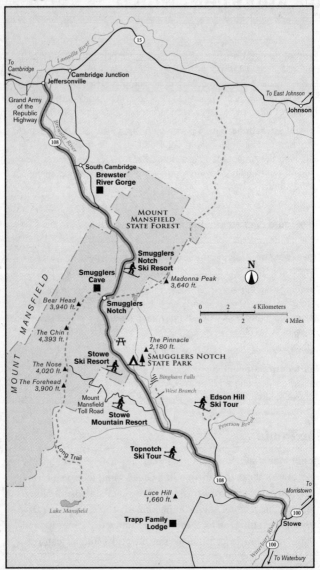

differently, calling Mansfield Moze-O-Be-Wadso or "mountain with a head like a moose." The mountain dominates northern Vermont, looming over the broad Stowe Valley and casting an alpine presence on the otherwise pastoral landscape.

The Smugglers Notch Scenic Route follows VT 108 for 18 miles on a short but spectacular outing that runs northwest from the Stowe Valley into the abrupt defile of Smuggler's Notch below Mount Mansfield. The road drops past the notch to Jeffersonville along the Lamoille River. An excellent side-trip is a 4-mile toll road that leaves the drive and climbs to the peak's windswept summit, Vermont's high point.

Stowe

The drive begins in downtown Stowe at the junction of VT 100 and 108. Head northwest on VT 108. **Stowe,** lying at an elevation of 723 feet along the Waterbury River in Stowe Valley, nestles between the Green Mountains to the west and the Worcester Range, a subsidiary range of the Greens, to the east. The town, the self-proclaimed "Ski Capital of the East," owes its ski fame to the prodigious amounts of snow that blanket the surrounding mountains. The town itself is old, with its charter granted by Governor Benning Wentworth of New Hampshire in 1763. It received its name from several early residents who hailed from Stow, Massachusetts. The e appeared in the name in 1838.

Despite its bustling resort atmosphere, Stowe retains a quiet and elegant charm. Before the ski boom, the town languished as a logging and farming center. Then southern New Englanders discovered its superb winter snow and snow sports in the mid-1800s. The town's history is preserved in its 1864 Stowe Community Church; a museum run by the local historical society; the Bloody Brook Schoolhouse, a restored 1828 one-room school that was moved here in 1909; and the **Helen Day Art Center,** a community arts and education nonprofit organization with exhibits by Vermont artists, housed in an 1861 high school. The town offers

travelers more than 5,000 beds in a wide range of accommodations, from rustic to elegant, including the **Trapp Family Lodge,** built on 2,000 acres by the real von Trapp family after their *Sound of Music* escape from Nazi Austria. Another famous spot is the Green Mountain Inn, one of the town's oldest hostelries with roots back to 1833.

Visitors will find a broad selection of fine restaurants in Stowe. The town and the immediate area also afford numerous recreational opportunities, including downhill skiing, cross-country skiing, hiking, horseback riding, golf, tennis, and fishing. A popular option is the **Stowe Recreation Path,** a scenic 5.5-mile trail through a greenway along the West Branch River.

Stowe to Mount Mansfield

The drive winds through Stowe and bends up the West Branch of the Waterbury River. After 4 miles the highway leaves most development behind and heads up the broad valley toward looming Mount Mansfield and its famed facial profile. The **Stowe Country Club** and its 18-hole golf course, open to the public, sit on the right just out of town. The **Trapp Family Lodge,** one of the area's more popular attractions, is still owned by the Trapp family. Reach the lodge by taking the well-marked left turn just past the golf course. The lodge, rebuilt after the original one burned in 1980, sits in the shadow of Luce Hill. The Baroness von Trapp, buried here after her 1987 death, settled with her family in Stowe because the Green Mountains resembled her beloved Austria.

The highway and valley bend northwest following a broad valley floored with gravel glacial deposits. After 7 miles the drive begins to climb. Two ski-touring centers lie along this stretch of highway: **Edson Hill Manor** (25 kilometers of trails) and **Stowe Mountain Resort** (45 kilometers of groomed trails and

Rock walls on the north flank of Mount Mansfield loom above the Smugglers Notch Scenic Route.

Stowe, the "Ski Capital of the East," lies along the Waterbury River in Stowe Valley.

30 kilometers of backcountry terrain). The signed turn for the **Mount Mansfield Toll Road** is on the left as the road climbs.

The 4.5-mile dirt toll road, open from late May through October, makes a spectacular scenic detour. This popular route finishing on Mansfield's summit ridge, and the roof of Vermont, offers spectacular views and Vermont's most extensive alpine tundra—the cold, windswept land above timberline. The road dates back to 1858 when a carriage road was hacked onto the peak's slopes and a modest hotel built in the saddle between The Nose and The Chin. The first 3 miles wind up through a forest of northern hardwoods, including beech, sugar maple, and paper and yellow birches. Above, the road steeply climbs and switch-backs through a life zone akin to that of northern Canada with its forest of balsam fir, mountain ash, and paper birch. The auto trip ends at a parking area below The Nose, a 4,020-foot promontory on Mansfield's long summit ridge.

A worthwhile hike treks northwest from here along the Long Trail for 1.4 miles to The Chin, Mount Mansfield's 4,393-foot high point. The trail wends through a pygmy forest of balsam fir krummholz, the crooked trees twisted and stunted by relentless high winds, and finishes atop 250 acres of tundra covered with rare and endangered plant species. The plants here are like those species found in the Arctic more than 1,000 miles to the north, including turflike Bigelow's sedge, alpine bilberry, crowberry, and mountain cranberry. These small but hardy plants, adapted to a frigid world of snow, high winds, and a 3-month growing season, occur on only a handful of New England summits. Despite the harsh conditions, life not only survives but flourishes here on this land above the trees.

The vegetation, however, forms a very delicate ecosystem that is easily damaged by thoughtless walkers. Tundra has almost no carrying capacity, and any human use quickly impacts the plants. Trampled areas take hundreds of years to recover. Stay on the rock-surfaced paths and boardwalks to preserve this unique alpine grassland from being loved to death.

Mount Mansfield's summits also yield some of Vermont's best far-reaching views on a clear day. Low hills roll westward to the glistening expanse of Lake Champlain. Farther west, New York's Adirondack Mountains recline above the lake. To the east loom the Worcester Mountains above the broad Stowe Valley. Beyond them stretch the high peaks of the White Mountains in New Hampshire, their lofty summits studding the distant horizon. Mount Ascutney's solitary summit looms to the south above the Connecticut River Valley, while the long crest of the Green Mountains marches southward past prominent 4,083-foot Camels Hump. The pleasant valley of the Lamoille River unwinds to the north, and in the hazy distance beyond it rise domed peaks in southern Québec, including Mont Royal overlooking Montréal.

Up to Smugglers Notch

Past the turnoff to Mount Mansfield, VT 108 steadily climbs upward through the narrowing U-shaped glacial valley. A roadside parking area on the right just past the toll road leads to a short trail that drops down to Bingham Falls, a cascade tucked into a shallow gorge. After 9 miles the road enters 34,000-acre **Mount Mansfield State Forest.** Only 0.25 mile later is the main turn to Stowe Ski Resort.

On the northeast slope of Mount Mansfield, **Stowe Mountain Resort** is one of America's oldest ski slopes and one of the largest east of the Rockies. Skiing began here as early as 1912. A ski jumping event at a winter carnival drew more than a thousand spectators in 1921. Albert Gottlieb designed and built, with the help of a Civilian Conservation Corps crew, one of America's first ski trails—the famed Nose Dive Trail—here in 1933. The mountain's and the East's first chairlift opened in 1940. The National Ski Patrol, a skier's rescue squad, was organized here in 1938. Today Stowe Ski Resort spreads over two mountains—Mount Mansfield and Spruce Peak. Its 39 miles of slopes and 116 trails are served by 13 lifts. Winter snowfall averages 333 inches. The gondola climbing Mount Mansfield's steep flank offers summer travelers a good alternative to a drive to the summit.

Smugglers Notch State Park sits across the highway from Stowe Ski Resort. The park offers 20 campsites, including 14 lean-tos, and hiking trails. The Spruce Peak section of the ski area is also accessed from here. An alpine slide, a popular summer attraction for kids, twists down the mountainside.

Past the state park and ski area, the highway climbs steeply upward for 2 miles to **Smugglers Notch.** A picnic area lies along a tumbling creek about a mile past the state park. Above here the valley funnels visitors toward the precipitous notch. Steep, forested slopes are littered with massive moss-covered boulders and broken by soaring moist cliffs. Small gurgling creeks tumble over cascades and boulders in the thick forest. The last 0.5 mile, a winding, narrow road of sharp hairpin turns, slows traffic to a

The twisting, narrow highway through Smugglers Notch, a glacier-carved valley, is great for bicycling and sightseeing.

crawl, and the shoulderless road gives scant room for oncoming cars to pass. Cars pulling trailers and recreational vehicles should not attempt to drive this road section.

Near the top the road threads through immense moss-covered boulders before leveling off and reaching a parking area atop the 2,162-foot pass. One huge boulder, **King Rock,** is designated by a plaque that notes the 6,000-ton block rolled from the cliffs above in 1910. Park at the rest area atop the notch and walk around. A trail climbs the opposite hillside to good viewpoints of the abrupt defile. Rock climbers enjoy scaling the scattered boulders at the notch summit.

Smugglers Notch is a narrow, leafy cleft filled with damp air. A canopy of trees encloses the road and summit parking area in a shroud of cool shadow, while sunlight glints off broken cliffs of metamorphic rock high above. The twisted rock, belonging to the Camels Hump group from the Cambrian Age some 550 million years ago, is green schist (colored by the mineral chlorite) interspersed with layers of erosion-resistant quartzite. The rocks were folded, faulted, then thrust westward from their original position and slowly uplifted. As the mountains rose, erosion, particularly glaciation, attacked and sculpted them into the mountain range seen today. As much as 6 miles of rock layers were stripped off the old peaks, leaving only stumps of the once-mighty range.

Periodic episodes of glaciation excavated the **Green Mountains** over the last 2 million years, but it was the last great advance, called the Wisconsin glaciation, that put the finishing touches on the scenery. This ice sheet surged across New England some 20,000 years ago, burying Vermont under mile-thick ice. During the early part of the Wisconsin glaciation, valley glaciers filled the valleys on either side of Smugglers Notch. Later the advancing ice sheet overrode Mount Mansfield and locked the land in an icy grip. The ice gouged deep U-shaped valleys and

Elephant Head Buttress, overlooking the scenic route, is the best rock climbing cliff in Smugglers Notch.

scraped their sides into cliffs and steep slopes. The ice further contoured the landscape, softening and smoothing its rough edges and erasing all traces of previous glacial periods.

The cliffs and forests of Smugglers Notch, like the summit of Mount Mansfield, harbor a selection of rare and hardy plants found almost nowhere else in New England. The cliffs host an arctic flora superbly adapted to harsh living conditions—cool, moist summer weather, deep winter snows, and frigid temperatures of spring and fall. Plants found here include mountain saxifrage and butterwort, a carnivorous plant that snares insects in its sticky leaves. Common trees found on the pass are sugar maple and yellow birch. The notch is famed for its numerous fern species, however. Vermont boasts more than 80 species of this graceful, shade-loving plant, including the rare green spleenwort. This beautiful fern was first discovered in the notch by botanist Cyrus Pringle in 1876.

Smugglers Notch received its colorful name in the tumultuous period just before the War of 1812 broke out between the fledgling American republic and the British Empire. Trade with Canada was prohibited at that time by President Thomas Jefferson's Embargo Act. Businessmen, however, were quick to see the opportunity to make a few dollars by smuggling goods along the old Indian trail through this notch in Vermont's remote backcountry. Contraband, including herds of cattle to feed hungry British soldiers, passed through the mountain fastness on its way to markets in Boston and Québec. A small, damp cave tucked into a cliff west of the notch is where the smugglers supposedly stashed their cargoes.

Down to Jeffersonville

The highway drops away from the pass, swings onto the northeast flank of a deep amphitheater drained by the Brewster River, and edges across steep, wooded slopes. The road plunges almost 1,700 feet in 8 miles from the notch to the drive's end in Jeffersonville.

The first 3 miles are the steepest. After 0.5 mile the highway sweeps past a roadside waterfall, its frothy water cascading over rock ledges. **Smugglers Notch Ski Resort,** nicknamed Smuggs, lies another mile downhill. This self-contained resort offers over 50 miles of ski trails on three mountains with a 2,610-foot vertical drop. The area also has accommodations, indoor tennis, a skating rink, a ski shop, and other resort amenities.

Past the resort, the road leaves Mount Mansfield State Forest and begins to flatten out, paralleling the Brewster River as it tumbles over worn cobbles and ponds behind beaver dams. A picnic area sits on the roadside at 16 miles. The **Brewster River Gorge,** with cascades and riffling rapids in a steep rocky canyon, lies off the road near here. The drive route descends along the riverbank, passes the small hamlet of South Cambridge, and swings onto a high gravel terrace west of the river in the broadening valley. It then runs along the terrace for 1.5 miles before dropping steeply into the river canyon. About 0.5 mile later the drive enters Jeffersonville and ends at the junction of VT 108 and VT 15.

At road's end **Jeffersonville** is a placid old town spread along the south bank of the Lamoille River, one of Vermont's few east–west-trending rivers. The town, named after Thomas Jefferson, once boasted a bustling lumber industry. Now it's a quiet place with a peaceful 19th-century ambience. Attractions include the **Mary and Alden Bryan Memorial Gallery** with its superb New England landscapes and the elegant **Le Cheval d'Or** French restaurant next door to the bakery. The local chamber of commerce on Main Street dispenses lodging, dining, and visitor advice. From here travelers can retrace their paths to Stowe via the drive for a second look at the spectacular scenery or head southwest on VT 15 to Burlington.

7 Lamoille River

General description: A 34-mile drive over rolling hills and along the placid Lamoille River between St. Johnsbury and Morrisville.

Special attractions: St. Johnsbury, Fairbanks Museum and Planetarium, Maple Grove Maple Museum and Factory, St. Johnsbury Athenaeum, American Society of Dowsers (Danville), Fisher Covered Railway Bridge, trout fishing.

Location: Northern Vermont.

Drive route numbers: US 2, VT 15.

Travel season: Year-round. Expect snow and icy conditions in winter.

Camping: Elmore State Park, south of the drive and southeast of Morrisville off VT 12, offers 45 tent sites and 15 lean-tos from late May to mid-October. Includes showers, toilets, phone, tables, but no hook-ups. A private campground is south of Hardwick.

Services: All services in St. Johnsbury, Danville, Hardwick, and Morrisville.

Nearby attractions: Lake Elmore State Park, Moss Glen Falls, Stowe attractions, Stowe Ski Resort, Mount Mansfield Toll Road, Smugglers Notch, Green Mountain National Forest, Lake Willoughby, Connecticut River Valley, Crawford Notch (NH), Franconia Notch (NH), White Mountain National Forest (NH).

The Route

The Lamoille River Scenic Route runs through pleasant countryside west of St. Johnsbury to the Lamoille River Valley. It continues along the river to Morrisville at the northern base of the Worcester Mountains.

The 34-mile drive begins at the intersection of I-91 (exit 21) and US 2 just west of St. Johnsbury. The town lies east of the junction on the other side of The Knob, a 1,120-foot-high bluff, among high hills at the confluence of the Sleepers, Passumpsic, and Moose

Lamoille River

Maple Grove Farm

Passumpsic River

Moose River

To Littleton, NH

18

93

St. Johnbury

91

To Barnet

To Canada

Passumpsic River

91

2

2B

Pumpkin Hill
1,380 ft.

South
Danville

To Peacham

Sleepers River

Danville

Harvey

West
Danville

To Peacham

To Glover

16

Lamoille River

Walden

15

Joe's Brook

Joe's Pond

Molly's Pond

2

Marshfield

South Walden

Bayley-Hazen
Military Road

Grand Army
of the Republic
Highway

To Montpelier

Hardwick

Hardwick Lake

15

Woodbury Mtn.
2,483 ft.

WOODBURY MOUNTAINS

Wolcott

Fisher Covered
Railway Bridge

Worcester

To Montpelier

Lamoille River

15A

Morrisville

Elmore Mtn.
2,608 ft.

ELMORE STATE PARK

12

Mt. Worcester
2,900 ft.

100

15

To Stowe

N

0   2   4 Miles

0   2   4 Kilometers

Rivers. **St. Johnsbury,** affectionately nicknamed "St. J" by locals, is a surprisingly elegant and cultured town in Vermont's mostly rustic Northeast Kingdom. Built along the riverbanks and terraces, the town retains its industrial roots and prosperity shown by Victorian mansions along Main Street, stately stone and brick buildings (including a fine museum and the St. Johnsbury Athenaeum), and a bustling downtown.

St. Johnsbury

The area was first settled in 1786 after Jonathan Arnold and a group of fellow Rhode Islanders received a town charter. They named their farming community for French consul Michel Guillame Jean de Crevecoeur, a friend of Vermont Revolutionary War hero Ethan Allen who wrote under the pen name of J. Hector Saint John. Beginning as a farming center, St. J flourished in the 19th century as a railway hub and industrial center. The Fairbanks family, early settlers and inventors, fueled the town's growth and provided an industrial and philanthropic legacy that remains.

Thaddeus and Erastus Fairbanks established an iron foundry here in 1823. Thaddeus, the family inventor, patented a cast-iron plow and later came up with the idea of a platform scale using a system of levers to reduce the weight needed to counterbalance a load of local hemp, which was sold to make rope. His ingenious idea became the Fairbanks Scale in 1830, and the family fortunes soon swelled as precision industrial scales were shipped around the world for measuring everything from doses of medicine to railroad cars. The scale factory still exists in St. Johnsbury. After the conglomerate ownership threatened to relocate the factory elsewhere in the 1960s, townspeople banded together and raised the funds to build a new plant.

The influence that the Fairbanks family and industry had on St. Johnsbury goes far beyond the factory. The Fairbanks brothers and their progeny became a 19th-century dynasty that produced not only a thriving business but two Vermont governors. The **Fairbanks Museum and Planetarium,** founded by Franklin Fairbanks in 1889, occupies a red sandstone building on Main Street. The museum's collection includes a natural history section with fossils; stuffed bears, moose, and 300 hummingbird species; Indian artifacts and stone tools; a Civil War exhibit; Fairbanks Scales; a Vermont wild plants exhibit in summer; a hands-on kids' nature center; one of the nation's oldest weather stations; and a 50-seat planetarium.

The **St. Johnsbury Athenaeum,** built in 1871 by Governor Horace Fairbanks, is another Fairbanks legacy. It houses the town library and a fine art museum with a superb selection of American 19th-century landscapes. The collection centerpiece is Albert Bierstadt's grand *Domes of the Yosemite,* a huge 116-inch by 180-inch painting hung below a skylight on the gallery's back wall. Other notable town buildings are the Gothic-style North Congregational Church with red granite pillars, the Neoclassical, white-clapboard South Congregational Church, the 1856 Caledonia County Courthouse, and the 1883 Canadian Pacific Railroad Depot.

Make sure to visit **Maple Grove Farm** just east of St. Johnsbury on US 2. The farm, a popular Vermont tourist attraction, is the world's largest maple candy maker. Owned by the Cary Maple Sugar Company, Maple Grove and the Sugar House Museum offers informative exhibits that detail the maple sugar to syrup process. The candy factory produces maple candy and associated products such as maple salad dressing. Visitors can sample some of the delights, as well as purchase almost any maple product imaginable in the gift shop.

St. Johnsbury to Hardwick

After visiting St. Johnsbury and its attractions, head west to the junction of I-91 and US 2 just west of town. The drive follows a two-lane, paved highway that runs northwest along the Sleepers

River in rolling forested hills broken by occasional farms and fields. After a couple of miles, the highway bends southwest away from the river up a shallow valley, and after 6 miles it reaches a high plateau. A pullout on the south side of the highway yields an excellent view of the Vermont hills above the Connecticut River Valley stretching southeast to the looming White Mountains in northern New Hampshire. Snow crowns the high peaks much of the year. On clear days their white summits glisten in the sun like alabaster towers.

Past the overlook, the road dips through a vale and climbs into Danville after 7 miles. A pretty village spread across a rounded hilltop, **Danville** was northeastern Vermont's largest town some 200 years ago when it had a population of 1,500. The state legislature even met here in 1805. But St. Johnsbury eclipsed it in size and population, and in 1855 the Caledonia County seat was transferred from Danville to St. J. The town, built around an attractive, tree-shaded green, was first settled in 1784 and named for French Admiral d'Anville. Much of the village was destroyed by fires in the 1880s, and from the ashes rose the library in 1890 and the imposing town hall in 1925. The Caledonia Bank, one of the state's safest banks, was last held up in 1935—such a rare occurrence in Vermont that it warranted national publicity. One of Danville's most famed citizens was Thaddeus Stevens, a grim, bitter abolitionist and congressman who served as chairman of the powerful House Ways and Means Committee. He opposed the post–Civil War reconstructionist policies of President Andrew Johnson, arguing for sterner measures to punish slave owners and secessionists.

Danville is home to the 2,500-member **American Society of Dowsers.** A dowser is a valued New England resident, since he or she uses a forked stick (called a water witch or wand) or a pendulum to divine subterranean water. The society holds its colorful annual convention in Lyndonville in mid-June every year. The **Dowser's Hall** offers informative displays and dowsing artifacts, and has a library of eclectic books and magazines and

The old Hardwick Inn, part of the Downtown Hardwick Village Historic District, was renovated into shops and offices.

what Nathan Platt with the association calls "argueably the largest collection of dowsing resources on the planet." Practitioners can purchase dowsing equipment, and beginners can learn to dowse just by coming into the headquarters.

The drive route continues west on US 2 across the high plateau, with more views of the upland hills and New Hampshire's White Mountains. Drivers reach **West Danville** after 3 miles. Its main point of interest is **Hastings Store,** a genuine, old-fashioned general store that appears unchanged since the 1850s. The drive turns north here at the junction of US 2 and VT 15; turn north (right) on VT 15.

The road swings around the north shore of **Joe's Pond,** an L-shaped lake named for Indian Joe. This Indian guide and Revolutionary War scout is remembered with the lake that bears his name and a small memorial in West Danville. Joe's Pond, an old summer resort with a public beach, drains south to the Connecticut River and Long Island Sound, while neighboring Molly's Pond, named for Joe's wife, empties north into the St. Lawrence River.

The drive bends north past the pond and follows a wooded valley alongside Joe's Brook for 4 miles to **Walden.** This rural hamlet was originally built around a military blockhouse on the **Bayley–Hazen Military Road** and named for its commander. The 55-mile road, authorized by George Washington, was begun in 1776 for launching possible attacks on British Canada. After a month builder Colonel Jacob Bayley decided that the road would also make an ideal passage for British troops to march south into New England and suspended construction until 1779. After the Revolution the road opened northern Vermont to settlement. The road stretched from Newbury on the Connecticut River to Hazen's Notch at Westfield. Almost two-thirds of the route remains in use today.

The highway turns west and climbs into thickly forested hills, passing hayfields and farms. Good views of the Green and Worcester ranges to the southwest may be glimpsed through the trees. After a few miles the road descends through a gentle valley to South Walden, a small village with a handful of houses. The highway continues down the narrowing valley beside winding Haynesville Brook and reaches its junction with VT 16 and the Lamoille River after 20 miles. Continue west along the river a few miles more to Hardwick.

A good-sized industrial town of 3,200, **Hardwick** is spread along the banks of the Lamoille River in a shallow valley. The town was first settled by Captain John Bridgam in 1797 as an agricultural center. It grew, along with neighboring Woodbury to the south, into one of the nation's leading granite centers after Henry Mack's 1868 granite discovery. As many as 14 quarries cut mammoth blocks of Vermont granite and shipped it to Hardwick via the Hardwick & Woodbury Railroad. The railroad boasted the most hairpin turns and steepest grades of any eastern line until its abandonment in 1940. Skilled European stonecutters milled the

Buffalo Mountain looms over South Main Street in Hardwick.

stone, which was then shipped all over the world. The busy, prosperous town, nicknamed "Little Chicago," boasted five churches, numerous saloons, a couple of elegant hotels, and three creameries. Hardwick's fortunes and population ebbed after the 1920s, leaving the town a shell of its glorious past.

Along the Lamoille River

Continue through Hardwick on VT 15 past its junction with VT 14. Follow the placid Lamoille River northwest out of town. The river, rising northeast of here at Horse Pond, is one of three Vermont rivers that flow east to west through the Green Mountains to Lake Champlain. The three rivers—the Lamoille, Missisquoi, and Winooski—are "antecedent" rivers in geologic terms, following courses established before the Green Mountains began uplifting some 430 million years ago.

A couple of miles past Hardwick, the highway bends west and crosses to the river's west bank. Just upstream of this crossing sits the 103-foot-long **Fisher Covered Railway Bridge,** a unique bridge spanning the river's slow currents, on the south side of the drive. The wooden bridge, built in 1908 and reinforced with steel beams in 1968, is the last covered railway bridge in Vermont. It is no longer in service. The weathered bridge features a full-length cupola that provided an escape for locomotive smoke. A pullout with restrooms allows travelers to stop and view the bridge.

After crossing the river the highway runs alongside the river before recrossing and bending through **Wolcott,** a tiny hamlet founded in 1789 and named for General Oliver Wolcott, a signer of the Declaration of Independence. The drive continues down the broad valley, past wooded hills and occasional farms. A sign on a barn with a steep metal roof close to the road warns drivers to watch for sliding snow from the roof.

The Fisher Covered Railway Bridge, spanning the placid
Lamoille River, is the last of its kind left in Vermont.

A cemetery in Wolcott, which was named for General Oliver Wolcott, one of the signers of the Declaration of Independence in 1776.

Farther west the road passes a private campground. Views of the Green Mountains unfold to the west, including the prominent escarpment of 3,715-foot White Face Mountain on the north end of the Mount Mansfield massif. The long, humpbacked ridge of 2,608-foot **Elmore Mountain** looms to the south. **Elmore State Park,** 4.2 miles southeast of Morrisville on VT 12, straddles the mountain's slopes and offers hiking, camping, and picnicking. A superb hike with great views of the Worcester Range, Green Mountains, and Lamoille Valley climbs 1,528 feet in a few miles from the park's parking area to the Elmore Fire Tower perched atop the mountain summit.

The drive ends at the junction of VT 15 and VT 15A. VT 15 continues west along the twisting Lamoille River to Jeffersonville and Cambridge before turning southward. VT 15A bends south, crosses the river, and enters **Morrisville,** a lumber and dairy town spread across a gravel terrace south of the river.

8 Lake Willoughby

General description: A 35-mile drive in Vermont's Northeast Kingdom between Lyndonville and Derby Center.

Special attractions: Lake Willoughby, Willoughby State Forest, Great Falls of the Clyde River, scenic views, hiking, fishing, boating, ice and rock climbing.

Location: Northern Vermont.

Drive route numbers: US 5, VT 5A, and VT 105.

Travel season: Year-round. Winters are snowy and icy.

Camping: No public campgrounds are found along the drive. There are a couple of private ones near Lake Willoughby, including White Caps Campground.

Services: All services in St. Johnsbury, Lyndonville, and Derby Center. Limited or seasonal services in other towns along the highways.

Nearby attractions: St. Johnsbury attractions, Connecticut River, Smugglers Notch State Park, Mount Mansfield State Forest, Stowe, Chester A. Arthur birthplace, Franconia Notch (NH), Crawford Notch (NH), White Mountain National Forest (NH), Mount Washington (NH), Dixville Notch (NH).

The Route

The Lake Willoughby drive traverses a scenic and hauntingly beautiful section of northeastern Vermont, crossing 35 miles of the remote upland area nicknamed the "Northeast Kingdom." The drive, following US 5, VT 5A, and VT 105, begins in Lyndonville just north of St. Johnsbury and ends in Derby Center 5 miles from the border between the United States and Canada. Along the drive is fjordlike Lake Willoughby, a long finger lake bounded by mountains, which is one of Vermont's most spectacular natural wonders.

Lake Willoughby

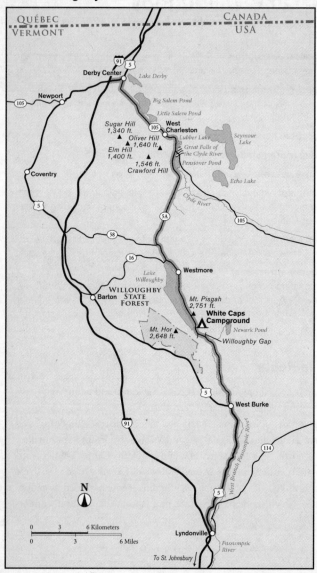

Lyndonville & West Burke

Following paved roads and open year-round, the drive begins in Lyndonville just north of St. Johnsbury. To find the beginning of the drive, take exit 23 from I-91 north of St. Johnsbury and follow US 5 north through bustling **Lyndonville.** The town was chartered to Jonathon Arnold in 1780, who named it for his son Josias Lyndon Arnold, but not settled until 1788. Spreading across the east bank of the Passumpsic River, Lyndonville prospered as a railroad hub, headquarters for the Passumpsic Division of the Boston & Maine Railroad in the late 19th century. Today the town, site of the Caledonia County Fair since 1846, serves as a supply center for smaller villages and farms in northeast Vermont as well as a bedroom community for larger St. Johnsbury.

From the town green, head north on US 5, cross a wooden bridge over the river, and strike northward up the West Branch of the **Passumpsic River.** The highway runs up the broad, glacier-carved valley, following the west branch of the **Passumpsic Valley esker,** one of New England's longest. An esker is a long ridge of sand and gravel that was deposited along the course of a river or stream that tunneled through a melting glacier. This sinuous esker begins on the west side of the river just south of St. Johnsbury and snakes alongside the river and highway to Lyndonville, where it splits into east and west branches along the river's two valleys. The esker's total length from start to end on the longer east branch is 24 miles. The esker is quarried in places for its clean mix of gravel and sand, used in construction work.

Rolling hills blanketed with spruce and pine line US 5 as it heads up the broad valley. Farms with cornfields and pastures break the forest and offer pastoral views. A roadside rest area with picnic tables shaded by white pines sits 3 miles up the highway. Farther along the road passes a Christmas tree farm before entering the hamlet of **West Burke.** This small village offers visitor services, including gas, groceries, and bed-and-breakfasts. A spired church sits off the town center. At the center, continue straight on

VT 5A; US 5 takes leave here and heads west up the Sutton River to Barton.

Continue north up the valley of the West Branch of the Passumpsic River, now on the west side of the road as it meanders across a marshy bottomland. Thick woods hem in the valley and the road as it gently climbs to the river's headwaters. After a drive of almost 6 miles from West Burke, the highway crests **Willoughby Gap,** a high ridge with a roadside pullout. Stop here to marvel at the view.

Lake Willoughby

Lake Willoughby, flanked by precipitous cliffs on 2,751-foot Mount Pisgah to the east and 2,648-foot Mount Hor on the west, fills the glistening valley below. Much of the area is protected as the two-part, 7,682-acre **Willoughby State Forest.** The surprising and dramatic lake offers a startling view of a Vermont landscape that is not round and contoured as are most of the state's glacier-shaped features. The 5-mile-long lake itself, 308 feet deep, is one of New England's deepest. The area is also famed for its rare Arctic flora, relic plants from the last ice age that cling to the rocky cliffs and fallen boulders below. Some of these remnant plants, including yellow mountain saxifrage and green alder, are preserved in a state natural area on Mount Pisgah.

Lake Willoughby, like most of Vermont's natural features, was formed by glaciation. During the last ice age, a glacier followed a river valley along a fault line in the granite bedrock here. After encasing the surrounding land in a sheet of white, the glacier slowly chiseled the U-shaped valley deeper and smoothed the granite mountains on either side. After the ice retreated both the north and south drainages remained dammed with sand and gravel and formed today's lake.

A boat lies anchored off Westmore in northern Lake Willoughby; at 308 feet deep it's Vermont's deepest lake.

Wet with rain, the scenic highway twists alongside glacier-carved Lake Willoughby.

An excellent hike begins from an inconspicuous trailhead just north of the gap. The Mount Pisgah Trail goes only a few miles to its rocky summit. Numerous lookouts are found along the yellow-blazed trail, offering great views of the lake below. The poet Robert Frost referred to the rocky flanks of **Mount Pisgah** as "the Devil's den." The trail, as it reaches the airy cliff tops, is a great place to watch raptors. In fall, flocks of hawks and falcons catch rising air currents to drift over the mountains here. The area was also the last known nesting site in Vermont for the endangered peregrine falcon in the 1950s.

Lake Willoughby is popular with anglers, who come to cast for lake and rainbow trout and land-locked salmon. Sand beaches at both its north and south ends allow swimming, but a dip on all but the warmest summer days will quickly remind the bather of the lake's glacial origins.

A roadside waterfall cascades down polished metamorphic bedrock above Lake Willoughby.

The drive drops steeply from Willoughby Gap and reaches the lake's south shore in 0.5 mile. A small sand beach, a marina, houses, tourist cabins, and a private campground lie at the south end. The highway winds north along the lake's eastern edge, hemmed against the rocky shore by Mount Pisgah's abrupt flank of granite cliffs and slabs. This 1-mile shelf section offers spectacular views of the lake and cliffed Mount Hor to the west. Several pullouts give dramatic views of the choppy lake, the soaring cliffs, and cascading waterfalls.

Mount Pisgah's lakeside front above the highway is acclaimed as one of the nation's finest ice-climbing areas, with more than 25 ice floes on the cliff face during winter. Rick Wilcox, author of a New England ice-climbing guidebook, calls the ice climbs "unrivaled in sheer size, verticality and sustained difficulty." Since the mid-1970s the Lake Willoughby area has been a testing ground for those climbers who pursue the rigorous challenge of scaling frozen waterfalls. The first route here was established in 1974 at Twenty Below Zero Gully, named for the frigid conditions climbers encountered.

Past Mount Pisgah and the state forest, the highway passes a public boat ramp and enters an area of summer cottages, homes, and motels that reflect Willoughby's long-standing popularity as a summer resort. In the late 19th century, the area was filled with grand hotels, tearooms, and dance halls to entertain visitors. Today the activity is more subdued, with the small village of **Westmore** being the focal point for fishermen, snowmobilers, sailors, and windsurfers.

North to Derby Center

At the north end of the lake, VT 5A intersects VT 16. Continue north (straight) on VT 5A. The last 16 miles of the drive

The misty flanks of 2,751-foot Mount Pisgah rear above Lake Willoughby.

run north from here to Derby Center. VT 58 is reached after 1.5 miles. The drive runs over wooded hills broken by rolling farmland. Barns, silos, and farmhouses interrupt the brooding landscape. The road swings across the western edge of a broad valley. The slow **Clyde River,** named after the famed Scottish river, meanders through pastures and marshes on the valley floor. Upriver, the Clyde has such a low gradient that it sometimes reverses itself and flows backwards to its headwaters at Island Pond.

Pensioner Pond, a large lake surrounded by low hills, is 8 miles north of Willoughby. It received its name after a Revolutionary War soldier used his military pension to build a mill here. On the north end of this small lake, the highway meets Vermont Highway 105, which runs southeast through lovely country to Island Pond. VT 5A ends here. Continue north on VT 105. Just north of the highway intersection are the Great Falls of the **Clyde River.** Here the river narrows and plunges through a series of small falls and cataracts in a twisting gorge before emptying into Lubber Lake.

The road then curves through **West Charleston,** a small village that thrived before the local lumber-milling industry closed down, and continues northwest along the Clyde River past pastures and dairy farms. Big and Little Salem Ponds lie alongside the road and offer good salmon, bass, and northern pike fishing. The highway winds slowly downhill, dips to cross the river on an old bridge, and climbs into the town of **Derby Center.** Drive north past large white-clapboard homes and businesses along a wide green and, 0.5 mile later, reach US 5. Turn left here and drive a mile west to the drive's northern terminus at I-91, which you can take south to Lyndonville and St. Johnsbury. Québec lies a scant 5 miles north.

APPENDIX:
SOURCES OF MORE
INFORMATION

For more information on lands and events, please contact the following agencies and organizations.

Addison County Chamber of Commerce
2 Court St.
Middlebury, VT 05753
(802) 388-7951, (800) SEE-VERMONT
midvermont.com

Bennington Chamber of Commerce
100 Veterans Memorial Dr.
Bennington, VT 05201
(802) 447-3311, (800) 229-0252
bennington.com

Brattleboro Chamber of Commerce
180 Main St.
Brattleboro, VT 05301
(802) 254-4565, (877) 254-4565
brattleborochamber.org

Central Vermont Chamber of Commerce
PO Box 336
33 Stewart Rd.
Barre, VT 05641
(802) 229-4619
central-vt.com/chamber

Green Mountain National Forest
231 N. Main St.
Rutland, VT 05701
(802) 747-6700
fs.usda.gov

Lamoille Valley Chamber of Commerce
34 Pleasant St., Unit 1
Morrisville, VT 05661
(802) 888-7607
lamoillechamber.com

Manchester and the Mountains Chamber of Commerce
5046 Main St.
Manchester Center, VT 05255
(800) 362-4144
manchestervermont.net

Northeast Kingdom Chamber of Commerce
51 Depot Sq., Ste. 3
St. Johnsbury, VT 05819
(802) 748-3678, (800) 639-6379
nekchamber.com

Quechee State Park
5800 Woodstock Rd.
Hartford, VT 05047
(802) 295-2990
vtstateparks.com

Smugglers Notch Area Chamber of Commerce
1073 Junction Hill
Jeffersonville, VT 05464
(802) 644-8232
smugnotch.com

Smugglers Notch State Park
6443 Mountain Rd.
Stowe, VT 05672
(802) 253-4014
vtstateparks.com

Stowe Area Association
Main Street
PO Box 1320
Stowe, VT 05672
(802) 253-7321, (877) GO-STOWE
gostowe.com

Vermont Department of Tourism and Marketing
1 National Life Dr., 6th Floor
Montpelier, VT 05620
(802) 828-3237, (800) VERMONT
travel-vermont.com

INDEX

Stewart M. Green, living in Colorado Springs, Colorado, is a contract writer and photographer for FalconGuides/Globe Pequot. He's written over 30 travel and climbing books for Globe Pequot, including *Scenic Routes & Byways Colorado, Scenic Driving New Hampshire, Scenic Routes & Byways California's Pacific Coast, KNACK Rock Climbing, Rock Climbing Colorado, Rock Climbing Europe, Rock Climbing Utah, Rock Climbing Arizona, Rock Climbing New England, Best Climbs Moab, Best Climbs Denver and Boulder,* and *Best Climbs Rocky Mountain National Park.* He's also a professional climbing guide with Front Range Climbing Company in Colorado and is the About.com Expert on Climbing. Visit him at green1109.wix.com/stewartmgreenphoto for more about his writing and photography.

ABOUT THE AUTHOR

Stewart M. Green, living in Colorado Springs, Colorado, is a contract writer and photographer for FalconGuides/Globe Pequot. He's written over 30 travel and climbing books for Globe Pequot, including *Scenic Routes & Byways Colorado, Scenic Driving New Hampshire, Scenic Routes & Byways California's Pacific Coast, KNACK Rock Climbing, Rock Climbing Colorado, Rock Climbing Europe, Rock Climbing Utah, Rock Climbing Arizona, Rock Climbing New England, Best Climbs Moab, Best Climbs Denver and Boulder,* and *Best Climbs Rocky Mountain National Park.* He's also a professional climbing guide with Front Range Climbing Company in Colorado and is the About.com Expert on Climbing. Visit him at green1109.wix.com/stewartmgreenphoto for more about his writing and photography.